Science,
Physiology,
and Nutrition

For the Nonscientist

Judi S. Morrill, Ph.D.

Illustrations: Ann Reisenauer, Lorenzo Ramos
Technical Support: Jean Shiota
Glossary. Sheri Cimino Bakun
Cartoons: Nick Downes, John Chase
Printer: Prodigy Press - Palo Alto, CA

Orange Grove Publishing
www.orangegrovepub.com
contact@orangegrovepub.com

ISBN 978-0-9657951-3-5

To my students—my challenge and my joy

Preface

Narrowing the communication gap between scientists and the general public takes a concentrated effort on both sides. This book aims to reach across that gap, to the general public and to students who aren't science majors. Many students who are apprehensive about taking science classes do so only to fulfill a core requirement. Some students are "against science," but most are simply intimidated by the technical terms and the flood of details.

This book had its start more than 20 years ago (1988) and was written specifically for a course that fulfills a general education requirement in science. Our course requires a textbook that blends nutrition, physiology, biochemistry, genetics, evolution, and chemistry; is organized by body systems (nutrition textbooks are typically organized by nutrients); includes the scientific method and issues of diversity; encourages critical thinking—and is compact enough to cover in a semester.

The challenge has been to select and present the required information in a timely and interesting—but not superficial—way. My hope is that readers of this book will come to appreciate, if not share, the excitement that scientists have about their work. The book has been revised continually, reflecting what students teach me in conversation—and in their answers on exams. I've tried to make the presentation as informal and with as few technical terms as possible while retaining a depth of coverage.

In the brief "lifetime" of this book, there have been astonishing advances in the life sciences. The biggest biology project ever—the Human Genome Project—was completed in 2000 and took us deep into the genetics of our being and into new ethical dilemmas. Today, the sequencing and identification of genes are commonplace in animal and plant species of all kinds and their application in many fields, such as medicine, anthropology, and agriculture, continues to expand rapidly. Much of what separates those who are excited by such advances and those who are frightened by them is a basic knowledge of the life sciences. We need that common language.

Judi Sakimoto Morrill

Content

1. **Behind the Soundbite 1**
Communication Gap in Science 1
History of Nutrition Science 3
   Scurvy, Beriberi, Pellagra 3-4
Science and Nutrition Today 5
Behind the Sound Bite 7

2. **Scientific Method 9**
Forming a Hypothesis 9
Observation vs. Intervention 10
Retrospective vs. Prospective 10
Cross-Sectional vs. Longitudinal 10
Sampling 11
Controlling Variables 12
Research Animals 14
Clinical Trials 17
Evaluating Data 18
Reporting, Verifying Scientific Studies 19
   Claim of Cold Fusion 20
Buyer Beware 20
Alternative Medicine 22
Summary 23

3. **Chemistry 25**
Atoms 25
   Nuclear Fusion 26
   Atomic Weight 29
Molecules 29
   Molecular Formulas 31
      Calculating the Amount of a Mineral
      in a Supplement 32
Chemical Bonds 32
   Ions and Ionic Bonds 33
   Covalent Bonds 34
Chemical Reactions 34
Acids and Bases 35
Energy 36
   Caloric Value of Food 37
      Practical Applications of Calculating
      Food Calories 38
Summary 39

4. **Dietary Requirements and Recommendations 41**
Essential Nutrients 41
   Water 41
   Energy-Providing Nutrients 43
   Vitamins 43
   Minerals 44
Determining Amounts Needed 44
Recommendations 45
   Recommended Dietary Allowances
      (RDAs) 46
   Daily Values 47
   ChooseMyPlate.gov Eating Guide 48
   Dietary Guidelines for Americans 48
Practical Application of Dietary Guides 51
Dietary Supplements 54
Summary 55

5. **Energy-Providing Nutrients 55**
Carbohydrate 55
   Sugar 55
   Complex Carbohydrate 57
      Starch, Glycogen 57
   Fiber 58
   Alcohol 59
Fat 59
   Concentrated Sources of Calories 59
   Functions of Fat 61
   Triglycerides, Fatty Acids 64
      Saturated vs. Unsaturated Fatty
      Acids 64
      Hydrogenated Fat 64
      Trans Fatty Acids 65
   Oxidation of Double Bonds 65
   Omega Double Bond 65
   Fatty Acids Essential in the Diet 66
   Lecithin 66
   Cholesterol 67
Protein 68
Summary 71

6. Digestive Tract 73
Mouth 75
    Taste, Sweetness 75
    Tooth Decay 76
        Mouth Bacteria 76
        Saliva 77
        Sites of Decay 78
        Fluoride, Feeding the Bacteria 79
Esophagus 80
Stomach 80
    Acid, Intrinsic Factor 81
    Stomach Cancer 81
Small Intestine 82
    Duodenal Ulcers 85
    Lactose Intolerance 85
Colon 86
    Gas 86
    Diarrhea, Constipation 87
    Diverticulosis 87
    Colon Cancer 88
Summary 89

7. Circulatory System 91
Heart 91
Blood Vessels, Blood Pressure 93
Blood 95
    Red Blood Cells 95
        Hemoglobin 95
        Athletic Competition 95
    Anemia 96
        Iron-Deficiency Anemia 96
            Iron in Foods 97
            Iron Supplements 98
            Iron Toxicity 98
        Folate-Deficiency Anemia 99
        Pernicious Anemia 100
    White Blood Cells, Platelets 101
    Plasma Proteins 102
        Antibodies 102
        Albumin, Clotting Factors 103
        Lipoproteins 104
Summary 105

8. Atherosclerosis 107
Premature Death 108
Risk Factors 110
    High LDL-Cholesterol 110
    Genetic Predisposition 110
    Smoking, High Blood Pressure 111
    Male Gender 111
    High Blood-Homocysteine 112
Treatment 112
Prevention 113
    Smoking 113
    Blood Pressure 113
        Sodium, Alcohol 114
    Blood Cholesterol 119
        Saturatedand Trans Fat 115
        Fiber 115
        Dietary Cholesterol 116
        HDL-Cholesterol 116
    Omega-3 Fatty Acids 118
    Medication 118
Summary 119

9. Cells and Metabolism 121
Cell Structure 123
    Cell Membrane 123
Metabolism 123
    Enzymes, Coenzymes 123
    B-vitamins 124
        Niacin-Tryptophan-Pellagra 124
    Energy-Releasing Reactions 124
        Anaerobic Energy Production 124
        Aerobic Energy Production 126
        Athletic Performance 127
            Types of Muscle Cells 127
            Oxygen Delivery 128
            Glucose Supply 128
    Energy-Requiring Reactions 129
        Protein Synthesis 129
Storing Excess Calories 129
Maintaining Blood Glucose 130
    Carbohydrate-Free Diets 130
    Blood Glucose 131
    Diabetes 132
    Hypoglycemia 133
Summary 133

10. Genes, Proteins, and Viruses 135
Genes and DNA 135
How a Cell Makes Protein 136
  Copying and Delivering the Recipe 136
  Making the Protein 137
DNA Analysis 138
  Human Genome Project 138
  DNA Fingerprinting 138
Viruses 143
  AIDS Virus (HIV) 144
Biotechnology 145
  Making Human Protein 145
  Gene Therapy 146
  Cloning 147
  Plant Genetics 148
Mutations 149
  Sickle-cell Anemia 149
  Spontaneous Mutations 150
  Ames Test 151
Summary 152

11. Dietary Protein 153
Evaluating Dietary Protein 153
  Protein Quality 154
    Amino Acid Content 154
    Limiting Amino Acid 154
    Complementing Proteins 155
  Amount of Dietary Protein 156
Protein Requirements 153
  Effect of Inadequate Calories 157
  Effect of Dietary Source of Protein 157
  Recommended Dietary Allowance
    (RDA) 157
  Protein Requirements of Athletes 158
Protein Deficiency 159
Excess Dietary Protein 159
Moderation in Protein Intake 160
Vegetarian Diets 161
Summary 163

12. Cancer 165
Trends in Cancer Rates 165
  Current Cancer Statistics 167
    Death Rates, Diagnosis Rates 167
Biology of Cancer 168
Assessing Risk 170
  Direct Contact: Breathing, Eating,
    Drinking, Chewing 171
  Cancer at Remote Sites 173
    Bladder Cancer 173
    Liver Cancer 174
    Breast Cancer 175
    Prostate, Testicular Cancer 176
Treatment 177
  Survival Rates 177
Prevention 178
  Diet and Cancer 179
    Carotenes/Carotenoids 179
    Carcinogens 181
Summary 181

13. Energy Requirements 183
Basal Metabolism 184
  Age 184
  Hormones 186
    Thyroid Hormone 187
      Iodine, Goiter 187
      Goitrogens 188
      Excessive Thyroid Hormone 188
    Miscellaneous Factors 188
Physical Activity 190
Energy Expended Upon Eating 191
Adaptations for Survival 192
Obesity 193
  The Urge to Eat 193
    Hunger, Appetite, Satiety 193
  Genes vs. Environment 196
Summary 197

14. Musculoskeletal System 199

Muscle 199
    Exercise, Anabolic Steroids 200
    Growth Hormone 201
    Aging, Muscle Contraction 202
Bone 203
    Bone Nutrients 204
        Vitamin D 204
        Calcium 206
        Vitamin C 207
        Phosphorus 208
    Osteoporosis 208
        Risk Factors 209
        Prevention 210
Periodontal Disease 211
Summary 213

15. Nervous System 215

Neurons 216
Transmission of Nerve Impulses 216
    Neurotransmitters 217
        Nerve-Muscle Junction 219
    Stimulants 220
        Caffeine 220
    Inhibitors 220
        Alcohol 222
            Withdrawal, Wernicke-Korsakoff
                Syndrome 222
            Fetal Alcohol Effects 223
Diet and the Brain 223
    The Developing Brain 224
        Lead 224
    Food and Mood—
        The Tryptophan Connection 227
        Tryptophan Transport into the Brain
        227
        Tryptophan Supplements 227
    Nutrients and Brain Dysfunction 229
        Alzheimer's Disease 230
Diet and Behavior 230
Summary 231

16. Food Safety 233

Natural Chemicals in Plants 233
    Natural toxins 234
Food Additives 235
    Safety Legislation 236
        GRAS List 236
    Assessing Risk 236
    "Macro-Additives" 238
Pesticides Applied to Food Crops 239
    Integrated Pest Management 240
Environmental Contaminants 240
Microbial Hazards 240
    Keep Them Out 241
    Keep Them From Growing 241
    Kill Them 243
    Botulism 244
        Infant Botulism 244
    E. Coli O158:H7 245
    Tracking Microbial Contamination 246
Hazard Analysis Critical Control Points
(HACCP) 247
Consumer Confusion 247
Summary 249

Appendix 251

A-1: Measurement Conversion Factors
    251
A-2: Periodic Table of Elements 252
A-3: Elements 254
A-4: Adult Recommended Intakes,
    Daily Values, Upper Limits 255
A-5: Vitamins and Minerals 256
A-6: Readings, References,
    Study Questions 258
A-7: Glossary 266

Index 275

Chapter 1

Behind the Soundbite

*The rate of communication is accelerating.
Busy people wage a desperate battle
each day to plow through as much
information as possible.*

From *Future Shock* (1970) by Alvin Toffler

Ah, the soundbite—that media-produced tidbit that catches our attention. Put it there with the bottom lines of business reports, the abstracts of articles in science journals, and the reviews of books we don't have time to read.

Fiber doesn't prevent colon cancer? Throw out my breakfast cereal. But wait, I heard it prevents heart disease! The media constantly bombard us with soundbites about recent findings, and this makes us anxious. *Does everything cause cancer?*

A basic knowledge of science gives us some stability in the flood of scientific and not-so-scientific information. It helps us separate fact from fiction, and fads and nonsense from the scientific and truthful. It makes us less vulnerable to the many charlatans, quack cures, and easy fixes that are constantly offered in one guise or another.

We also need to understand how scientific information is gathered and reported. Otherwise, we become impatient and find it frustrating that scientists often say *however* or *perhaps*, and rarely say *always* or *never*. We like solid bottom-line advice. *However,* there aren't many simple explanations in today's complex world. We should be suspicious of easy answers. An old joke is that

legislators, in seeking expert testimony, want scientists with only one arm—they're fed up with scientists who answer simple questions with, *"On one hand..., on the other hand ..."* Nonscientists can seem more credible when talking to the public about science because they typically don't hedge their answers as scientists do.

Communication Gap in Science

Cholestyramine lowered the level of circulating low-density-lipoprotein apoprotein by doubling (P < 0.01) its fractional clearance via the receptor path. Sentences like this are perfectly clear and fascinating to scientists. Nonscientists react differently but can't escape the jargon. Even the morning toast is spread with margarine described as cholesterol-free, polyunsaturated, and partially hydrogenated.

There's a growing need for scientists to communicate their knowledge to the public. But nonscientists are often uneasy about science and technology. The uneasiness is perhaps like that felt in the past with "unnatural" achievements— traveling by air, vaccinations, splitting atoms— but is probably greater with today's wider gap between science's high level of achievements and

"In layman's terms?
I don't think I know any layman terms."

the public's low level of scientific literacy. When the Wright brothers took off from the ground, most people could reasonably assess the bright and dark sides of this achievement. With today's gene therapy, the situation is far different.

Nonscientists need some basic knowledge as a starting point. A best-selling book on diet and health claims that improperly combined foods (e.g., meat and bread) aren't properly digested and thereby produce toxic wastes that contribute to obesity. Anyone with a basic knowledge of how the body works recognizes this as nonsense. Meat and bread are well digested, whether eaten together or separately. Excess calories—not "toxic wastes"—cause obesity.

Scientists can't easily counter such nonsense if listeners don't know the basics of how the body works. Imagine a scientist sitting beside the exuberant best-selling author and saying, "Let me first take an hour to explain the physiology of digestion and how the body turns food into fat." A basic knowledge of science is the best defense against being misled and misinformed.

One would think that science would best be taught by scientists.

But most scientists have a hard time teaching general audiences. The same qualities that make them good scientists—a compulsion to be exact, the ease with which they understand science, concern with detail, and unbridled enthusiasm—can cause them to lose their audiences with floods of information presented in technical terms.

For example, linoleic acid is a fat and an essential nutrient. Speaking to a general audience, the term *essential fat* is a friendly substitute for *linoleic acid.* It's hard for scientists to make this substitution because *essential fat* is ambiguous, whereas *linoleic acid* isn't. It's hard for scientists to communicate what they know to the public. When scientists can't be lengthy and exact, they tend to simplify to such an extent that the information isn't very useful. It's hard to strike a balance between overwhelming detail and oversimplification.

Understanding today's science isn't easy. You need to know some physics to understand chemistry, some chemistry to understand physiology, and so on. Nonscientists, recalling their own stress with science and math classes, know that when you don't learn the early stuff, it's nearly impossible to understand the more complex stuff that follows. An upper-division course in biochemistry has

"I think I'm beginning to grasp the concept of infinity".

more prerequisites than an upper-division course in history, sociology, or English.

Presenting science and physiology in the context of nutrition makes the science more palatable (pardon the pun). Nutrition as a scientific discipline overlaps many fields in which we may already have an interest, such as child development, anthropology, psychology, agriculture, history, economics, or marketing. Many of us are interested in nutrition simply because we want the best diet for our own health and fitness. Let's start with a bit of nutrition history.

History of Nutrition Science

Most of what's known about nutrition was discovered in the past century. In 1900, only four nutrients were known—carbohydrate, protein, fat, and ash (minerals). But when these were purified from milk and then recombined and fed to mice, the mice didn't survive. Something else in milk—vitamins—was required for life and was missing.

Before the discovery of vitamins, it wasn't generally accepted that the lack of something in food could cause disease. It seems incredible that for centuries people suffered from severe nutritional deficiency diseases, such as scurvy, beriberi, and pellagra, that had such simple cures.

Scurvy

A severe vitamin C deficiency causes scurvy. A dramatic degeneration of many body tissues causes muscular weakness and pain, bleeding gums, mental depression, and ultimately, death. Scurvy was described in 1500 B.C. and has been a part of many historical events. It was rampant among crusaders, explorers, soldiers, and sailors who went on long journeys where fresh food wasn't available.

Sailors left on long voyages knowing that many of them would die of scurvy (this didn't speak well for life at home). In 1498, Vasco da Gama completed his historical voyage around the Cape of Good Hope. About half of his original crew of 140 men died of scurvy. In 1535, when the crew of the explorer Cartier had to stay in Canada for a winter, many crewmen with scurvy were cured by a local Indian remedy—the juice from tree leaves (probably white cedar, which we now know has vitamin C).

In 1747, James Lind, a Scottish surgeon with the British navy, did a classic experiment. On a ship, he took 12 sailors with scurvy and divided them into 6 pairs. Each of the pairs was given either sea water, vinegar, sulfuric acid, hard apple cider, a medicinal paste, or oranges and lemons. Only those who were given oranges and lemons were cured.

On Captain James Cook's historic voyage of 1772-1775, the captain and crew avoided scurvy by restocking the ship with fresh fruits and vegetables at ports along the way. In 1796, daily supplements of lemon or lime juice became standard issue in the British navy, and the sailors were nicknamed *limeys*. Preventing scurvy with citrus juice and fresh fruits and vegetables is thought to have contributed to the superiority of the British navy at that time. It wasn't until 1932 that vitamin C was identified as the substance that prevented and cured scurvy, and named ascorbic acid [*ascorbic* = *ascorbutic* (without scurvy)].

Beriberi

Beriberi, caused by a deficiency of the B-vitamin thiamin, was described in the Chinese medical literature more than 3,000 years ago. But its cause wasn't known to be related to diet until late in the 19th century. Symptoms include difficulty in walking with subsequent paralysis of the legs, malfunctions of the heart, and mental confusion.

In the late 19th century, beriberi was common wherever the diet was mainly white rice, produced in newly developed "polishing machines" that removed the thiamin-rich outer coat (bran). In Indonesia, then a Dutch colony, beriberi became common amongst Indonesians because their diet was mainly rice. But the Dutch in Indonesia did not suffer from beriberi because their diet was more varied—other foods provided what the white rice lacked.

Timeline of Some Discoveries in Nutrition Science	
1750	Oranges and lemons can cure scurvy
1800	Animals use oxygen to burn fuel, emitting heat and carbon dioxide
1850	Cod liver oil used successfully to treat rickets
	Four nutrients known carbohydrate, fat, protein, "ash" (minerals)
1900	Beriberi is a dietary deficiency disease. *vita B thiamin*
	Discovery of "5th nutrient" (vital amines/vitamins)
	First vitamin discovered (thiamin)
	Liver-rich diet cures pernicious anemia
	Vitamin A plays a role in vision
1950	Last vitamin discovered (vitamin B_{12})
	Dietary fat related to heart disease
	High-fat diet associated with certain cancers
	Heavy alcohol intake associated with high blood pressure
	Leptin hormone helps regulate appetite and metabolism
2000	Ghrelin hormone stimulates appetite
	Obestatin hormone lessens appetite

In 1890, Dutch physician Christiaan Eijkman, assigned to a military hospital in Indonesia, saw chickens developing a similar disease. He found that they were being fed day-old cooked rice discarded from the hospital. When they were fed brown rice, with the bran still attached, they remained healthy. He did more experiments and, in 1929, received a Nobel prize for his pioneer work on the existence of vitamins.

In 1926, thiamin was purified from rice polishings—the first time that a vitamin in pure form was extracted from food. By 1936, thiamin could be made in the lab (rather than tedious extraction and purification of tiny amounts of a vitamin from huge amounts of food), providing an inexpensive way to obtain large amounts of a vitamin in pure form—a forerunner of our vitamin pills.

Availability of purified food components enabled their individual effects to be studied. From experiments using pure vitamin C, for example, we know that it—and not the other substances in vitamin C-rich food—is what prevents scurvy.

Using newly-available synthetic thiamin to enrich white rice, an experiment took place in the Philippines, where beriberi was common. On the Bataan Peninsula, a mountain range geographically divided the population into two groups. One group was given thiamin-enriched white rice (the experimental group). The other group (the control group) continued to eat unenriched white rice. After 9 months of eating thiamin-enriched rice, 90% of those who earlier had symptoms of beriberi got better, and the death rate from beriberi in the experimental group was a third of the control group's. After 2 years, there were no deaths from beriberi among those eating the enriched rice.

Pellagra

Pellagra, caused by a niacin deficiency, is characterized by what's known as the *3 Ds*—diarrhea, dermatitis (skin inflammation), and dementia (mental impairment). Its name comes from the Italian *pelle agra*, which means painful skin.

In the early 1900s, there were about 200,000 cases of pellagra in the U.S. Many people in mental institutions were there because of pellagra dementia. In 1914, Joseph Goldberger, a U.S. Public Health Service physician, was sent to the South to investigate the cause of pellagra, which was epidemic among the poor. His observations led him to believe that it was caused by a dietary deficiency.

The diet was mostly cornmeal, molasses, fatback (fat from a hog's back) and some greens, but very little meat, eggs, or milk. The prevailing theory

Figure 1-1: Age-adjusted Increase in Obesity

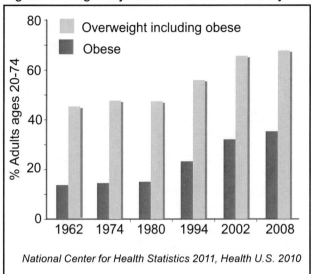

National Center for Health Statistics 2011, Health U.S. 2010

was that pellagra was an infectious disease since it "spread easily" in the unsanitary and cramped quarters of the poor and the institutionalized. Although Goldberger clearly demonstrated that he could prevent and cure pellagra in orphanages and jails simply by providing foods like milk and eggs, many skeptics still weren't convinced.

To demonstrate that pellagra wasn't infectious, Goldberger recruited 14 healthy volunteers, mostly physicians. He, his wife, and the volunteers were "infected" with various secretions taken from 17 people with pellagra. Nasal secretions from pellagra patients were applied to the nasal linings of the volunteers; skin scrapings, urine, and feces were ingested by mixing these with flour to make pills; and blood from pellagra patients was injected into the volunteers' muscles. None of the volunteers developed pellagra. This was convincing evidence that pellagra wasn't infectious.

Niacin was identified in 1937 as the substance that prevents pellagra. But well before then, pellagra was less common because of education to improve diets, more income to buy nutritious foods, etc. The Red Cross even loaned milk cows to needy families. Pellagra virtually disappeared in the U.S. in the early 1940s when we began enriching refined corn and wheat flour with niacin, iron, thiamin, and riboflavin.

Science and Nutrition Today

The early 1900s marked the golden age of nutrition research, generating great excitement among scientists—much like the excitement in today's golden age of biotechnology and neurobiology. For their discoveries relating to vitamins, scientists won a cluster of Nobel prizes in 1928, 1929, 1934, 1937, 1938, and 1943. The era of rapid progress in identifying vitamins and nutritional deficiency diseases was essentially complete by 1948 when vitamin B_{12} was discovered (it was the last vitamin discovered).

Despite the discoveries of "simple cures" for nutritional deficiencies, these diseases are still widespread throughout the world. The news brings us vivid pictures and stories of people dying from starvation (lack of calories). Fewer of us are aware that serious nutritional deficiency diseases such as beriberi are still common in many parts of the world, or that vitamin A deficiency is still a major cause of blindness in children. Barriers such as poverty and politics still lie between what is scientifically possible and what has been achieved in preventing these diseases.

In the U.S., the major nutrition problem is no longer dietary deficiencies, but an "exercise deficiency" combined with excesses in eating. This situation is an anomaly in human history. We evolved mostly during the nearly 500,000 years that make up the Stone Age.

Life was hard. People didn't grow crops or raise livestock; they hunted and gathered their

Figure 1-2: Age-adjusted Increase in Diabetes

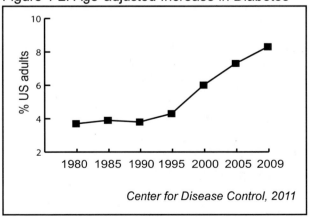

Center for Disease Control, 2011

food. Famines were common, and hard physical labor was required for survival.

The harsh environment selected for those who stored fat efficiently and relinquished it sparingly, preferred fatty foods (concentrated sources of calories) and salty foods (salt was scarce). Even with ample body fat, feeling hungry every few hours drove the continual hunting and gathering that was essential for survival. These same traits now work against us with our constant and abundant supply of food and little need to exercise, leading to a higher risk of obesity, diabetes, heart disease, osteoporosis, and the like (Fig. 1-1, 1-2).

Much of nutrition research now focuses on obesity, obesity-related diabetes, and the effects of diet on chronic diseases like heart disease, cancer, and osteoporosis. Heart disease is the leading cause of death in this country, cancer is the second, and osteoporosis is a common cause of disability in the aged. Scientific progress is relatively slow due to the complexity of these diseases. In stark contrast to an acute disease like scurvy, chronic diseases develop over many years, involve many genetic and environmental factors, and aren't easy to cure.

Many chronic diseases have common risk factors, thus simplifying health advice. Smoking, for example, not only raises the risk of lung cancer, but also that of heart disease, chronic bronchitis, emphysema, and cancer of the esophagus, bladder, and pancreas. Diet plays an important role in many diseases, such as heart disease, chronic liver disease, and some cancers. The American Heart Association, American Cancer Society, and other agencies that evaluate the scientific evidence relating to diet and health all give similar advice.

Scientific information is now disseminated quickly—a far cry from the communication of what Cartier and Lind learned about scurvy. *The New England Journal of Medicine* has subscribers worldwide, is published weekly, and is only one of thousands of scientific research journals—many of them available online. Online journals can include videos.

Scientific information is transmitted faster than ever. Physicians often hear about a journal

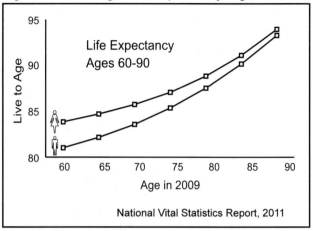

Figure 1-3: Average Life Expectancy, Ages 60-90

Life Expectancy Ages 60-90

Live to Age

Age in 2009

National Vital Statistics Report, 2011

article in the news before they get a chance to read the article themselves. Of course, misinformation also is transmitted faster. Much nutrition nonsense and quack cures for all sorts of diseases, real and imagined, are on the Internet.

The Internet also has fanned the already huge interest in dietary supplements. Food and medicine now overlap, with *functional foods* like Benecol (a margarine used to lower blood cholesterol) and *nutraceuticals* (nutrients used as pharmaceuticals/medicine).

Dietary supplements include a wide array of substances, from vitamin pills to herbs to hormones, so it's hard to make generalizations. But one important generalization to keep in mind is that, unlike drugs, dietary supplements don't have to be proved safe and effective before being sold. Testing for safety, effectiveness, purity, etc., is extremely expensive and time consuming. Thus, there's a huge economic advantage to calling something a dietary supplement rather than a drug, though it can be hard to tell which is which. For example, pills of thyroid hormone (made by the thyroid gland) are sold as a drug, yet pills of the hormone melatonin (made by the pineal gland) are sold as a dietary supplement.

Sellers of dietary supplements often provide a distorted view of their products. The more objective information from scientific studies often comes in soundbites that can inadvertently push the products. You hear in the news that a study found that people with higher blood levels of beta-carotene (usually from eating a lot of fruits and vegetables) have a lower risk of cancer. You're not sure what beta-carotene is, worry if you get enough, so you run out to buy a bottle. There's a lot behind soundbites that we should know before acting on them.

Behind the Soundbite

Television and radio give us health information as soundbites—a catchy sentence or two (scary ones work best). News online or in newspapers tell us more, but many of us only read the headlines (*news soundbites*). Here's a soundbite that alarms an 80-year-old man: *Life expectancy in the U.S. has risen to 75.* He feels he's due to die any minute. What didn't fit into the soundbite was that men his age live to an average of 88 (Fig. 1-3). If he lives to 85, the average age of death goes up to 91 because those who died between 80 and 85 drop out of the average. (The biggest gains in life expectancy come from saving the lives of infants, just as an average test score of 70% gets the biggest boost when those scoring near zero do a lot better.)

Here's a soundbite that scared women: *Women in the San Francisco Bay Area have the highest rate of breast cancer.* Unsaid was that they didn't have the highest *death* rate from breast cancer, but the highest *diagnosis* rate (and not by much), which was fully explained by more screening and known risk factors (e.g., having children at an older age, hormone replacement therapy after menopause). Also, as will be discussed in Chapter 12, diagnosis rates are tracked only in 11 geographical regions, representing about 10-15% of the U.S. population. The San Francisco Bay Area is one of those regions, so *highest* here means that it's the highest among the 11 regions only.

In the past few years, the age-adjusted death rate has been falling faster for heart disease than cancer (Fig. 1-4). So here's a possible future soundbite that would scare us all: Cancer is now our leading cause of death. This wouldn't be cause for alarm if cancer became #1 by default due to a faster drop in death rate from heart disease, but this added information would dilute the soundbite's impact.

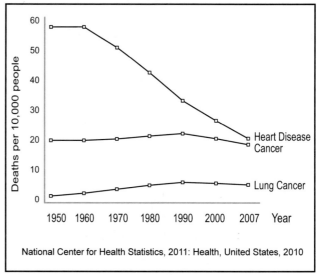

Figure 1-4: Age-Adjusted Death Rates for Heart Disease and Cancer (1950-2007)

National Center for Health Statistics, 2011: Health, United States, 2010

Most of us hear about the latest scientific findings via soundbites. This can cause confusion and anxiety, especially when the soundbites conflict. Soundbites put studies on equal footing although, as will be discussed in the next chapter, studies differ a lot in research design, validity, and in how the results relate to us personally.

Scientists critically examine the details behind the soundbites. Even when a study passes muster, it's just a small addition to a big picture—the normal way scientific information is gathered. Nonscientists, too, can assess new information more objectively if they know the criteria for good experimental design and valid conclusions. Also, we can assess new information more calmly, knowing that scientific knowledge comes in bits and pieces, some of which are discarded as results of new studies trickle in.

We're bombarded with nutrition and health information from diverse sources, such as advertisements, food labels, health books, and magazine articles, not all of which are based on scientific evidence. Often, the information is tied in with marketing, not only of food products and dietary supplements, but of newsletters and magazines wanting subscribers and of organizations seeking donations. These—together with a steady stream of soundbites that sometimes seem to conflict—often leave us bewildered.

Figure 1-5: "Rectangularizing" the Survival Curve

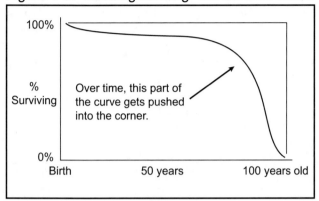

The chapters that follow explain the basics of how scientific information is gathered and how the body works. This knowledge will make us better equipped to sort out scientifically based advice and use it to improve our health. Even small changes in dietary and living habits can dramatically prevent or delay our most common diseases. Heart attacks, for example, usually result from narrowing and blockage of arteries that supply blood to the heart. Because the narrowing occurs gradually over many years, taking measures to slow this process, even slightly, can delay or prevent a heart attack.

Scientists speak of *the rectangularization of the survival curve,* in which case we'd all survive to old age (Fig. 1-5). They speak of *pushing a disease out of the life span*—delaying the disease until after age 100 or so. Scientists also speak of *compressing the period of morbidity*—shortening the time we're ill before we die. In layman's terms, we want to live life to its full measure in good health.

Chapter 2

Scientific Method

What is a scientist after all? It is a curious [person] looking through a keyhole, the keyhole of nature, trying to know what's going on.

Jacques Cousteau (1910-1997), oceanographer

The Scientific Method is the process whereby scientific knowledge is acquired. It's a logical, objective, and orderly way to formulate and test theories. Scientists state their hypothesis, do experiments to test it, then publish the results that are then evaluated by others. If and when the results are consistently confirmed by other scientists, the findings become accepted scientific knowledge.

This method sounds formal, but we use it in our daily lives. Suppose every time Tom bakes a chocolate cake, his children devour it within 24 hours. Tom decides to sneak in some grated carrots. His hypothesis is that they'll still like the cake. The children complain that the cake tastes weird, and don't eat it. Tom is puzzled. He hadn't changed the frosting, and the carrots didn't change the cake's appearance or sweetness (he controlled these variables).

Tom tells his mom (he reports his findings). She says he didn't grate the carrots fine enough (she evaluates the experiment). She makes the cake with very finely grated carrots; the kids don't complain *(be nice to grandma),* but the cake remains uneaten. Mom confirmed Tom's finding that the kids don't like carrots in the cake. If they were scientists, they'd say, "Some children

between the ages of 5 and 9 years do not readily consume a cake when grated carrots are added." As Albert Einstein said, *"The whole of science is nothing more than a refinement of everyday thinking."*

Forming a Hypothesis

Most hypotheses stem from earlier studies and observations. The hypothesis that a high-fat diet raises the risk of colon cancer is based on the observation that populations with a high-fat diet have more colon cancer. This is reasonable, based on what's known about dietary fat and physiology. Populations with a lot of television sets also

"The whole of science is nothing more than a refinement of everyday thinking."
Albert Einstein

have more colon cancer—there is a link—but it's unreasonable to hypothesize that television causes colon cancer.

Observation vs. Intervention

Observational studies range from case reports (e.g., one person's unusual response to a drug), to studies encompassing the world's population (e.g., countries whose native diets are rich in fruits and vegetables have less cancer). The value of these observations lies with their scientific rigor.

In case reports, it isn't enough to say someone had advanced cancer and was cured of it by a certain therapy (as done in testimonials). Details such as documentation that the person actually had cancer and was cured of it must be included in the report.

Suppose Dr. Jones claims that his research shows that vitamin pills make people healthier. He questioned hundreds of people about their health and use of vitamins. But despite all his data, his finding had little scientific value. Perhaps those who took vitamins also didn't smoke, ate a better diet, and got more exercise. Or maybe they were healthier simply because they were younger. He didn't control for these variables. He showed only that taking vitamins was associated with *(linked to)* better health. He didn't show a cause-and-effect *(causal)* relationship that his subjects were healthier *because* they took vitamins.

Interventional studies look to document causal relationships by intervening, e.g., giving a drug to one group and comparing the outcome to that of a group not given the drug. Intervention isn't necessarily better than observation. Many factors determine a study's scientific value.

Interventional studies can have serendipitous findings. Viagra was meant to be a drug for high blood pressure, but when tested in an interventional study, its unusual side-effect was discovered and it became the blockbuster drug for erectile dysfunction. A drug for glaucoma had an unexpected side-effect of lengthening eye lashes, and is formulated as Latisse for this cosmetic use.

Retrospective vs. Prospective

We get clues to the causes of disease by grouping and comparing people with different diseases, dietary habits, etc. In retrospective *(looking back)* studies, people with a disease are compared to those without it. For instance, comparing people with bladder or pancreatic cancer to people of similar age, ethnicity, socioeconomic group, drinking habits, etc., shows that a history of smoking is more common in the cancer patients. This suggests (but doesn't prove) that smoking increases the risk of pancreatic and bladder cancer.

A prospective *(looking forward)* study would group healthy people into smokers and non-smokers to see if smokers subsequently develop more pancreatic and bladder cancer. Prospective studies are better controlled but are costly, and it can be decades before enough members of a healthy population develop the disease.

Most studies of the effect of diet on chronic disease are retrospective. Comparisons are based on people's recollection of their diets, sometimes clear back to childhood. Recollections are subject not only to bias but also to differences in memory.

Cross-Sectional vs. Longitudinal

To come up with ways to prevent diseases like heart disease and osteoporosis, scientists need to know how the diseases develop over the life span. The quickest and least costly way to study this is to make one-time measurements in people of various ages and deduce the pattern of changes that occur over the years. This is called a cross-sectional study because a cross section of the present population is studied.

Cross-sectional studies of changes in bone mass over the life span make one-time measurements of bone density in people of different ages. From such studies, it appears that bone mass peaks at about age 25 and declines steadily after about age 40. This kind of study has obvious pitfalls. Today's 75-year-olds had, at age 20, different diets, exercise habits, diseases, etc., than today's 20-year-olds, so we can't really say that today's 20-year-olds will be, at age 75, like today's 75-year-olds. In a more whimsical example, many young people in Miami are immigrants from Cuba, and many elderly Jews go to Miami to retire. So a cross-sectional study of the Miami population to look at changes that occur over the years would show, incorrectly of course, that people in Miami are born Cuban and die Jewish!

In a longitudinal study, the same people are studied as they age (e.g., measure someone at age 10, and again at ages 20, etc.). This gives better information but is slow, tedious, and expensive. One such study is of the population of Framingham, Massachusetts. This longitudinal— and prospective—study began in the mid-1950s, is still in progress, and has provided key information about risk factors and the development of chronic diseases throughout the life span.

Sampling

Ideally, one would select a **representative sample** of the target population for study. Pollsters are quite accurate in predicting the outcome of presidential elections because they are good at getting a representative sample of voters.

Representative samples can be hard to get. In 1987, the extent of HIV (Human Immunodeficiency Virus) infection in the U.S. was to be estimated by randomly and anonymously testing 50,000 people. But a preliminary survey showed that 30% of the population would refuse to participate, and there was no way to know if the infection rate in this 30% was the same as in the other 70%. Similarly, the nation's infection rate can't be accurately estimated based on select groups like blood donors and Armed Forces applicants. It's easy to see why estimates of HIV infection can vary from one news report to the next.

Sometimes, it's impractical to use representative samples. Most human studies of drugs and nutrients use very select samples, eliminating people who are unreliable or are more vulnerable to harm. The subjects of a highly publicized study that showed that aspirin helped prevent heart attacks were selected from a group of male physicians (see below)—hardly a representative sample of the U.S. population.

The **size of the sample** also is important. The smallest number of subjects needed to test a hypothesis is based mainly on how dramatic an outcome is expected. To test a powerful insecticide, you only need a few insects. It's enough to show that 8 of 8 treated insects die, compared to 0 of 8 untreated controls.

How many are needed to test the hypothesis that a low-fat diet lowers the risk of breast cancer? To get enough breast cancers for comparison, 10,000 women would have to follow a low-fat diet for 10 years, and 22,000 more would be needed as controls, according to one proposal in 1988. The study wasn't funded, in part because of concern that the low-fat group might not stick to a low-fat diet for 10 years, and the control group might lower their fat intake on their own. The study

261,248 male physicians ages 40-84 contacted by mail.

112,528 responded.

59,285 willing to participate.

26,062 eliminated because of liver or kidney disease, peptic ulcer, gout, cancer, previous heart attack or stroke, currently using aspirin or similar drug, etc.

33,223 given a 18-week trial run with aspirin and placebo.

11,152 eliminated because of adverse effects, didn't do as told, dropped out, etc.

22,071 randomized into double-blind study; 11,037 given aspirin, 11,034 given placebo.

In next 6 years, 104 heart attacks in aspirin group, 189 in placebo group.

was proposed again as part of the $625 million study of 63,000 postmenopausal women called the Women's Health Initiative (which includes many objectives and has expanded in cost and size); recruitment of subjects began in 1993.* It was reported in 2006 that the group assigned to a lower-fat diet did not have a significantly lower risk of invasive breast cancer than the group on their usual diet after an average follow-up of 8 years.

When expected differences between groups are small, or there's a lot of variation in response, huge samples are needed to provide the statistical power to document differences. A single study can involve subjects and scientists from medical centers throughout the world.

In some cases, the needed numbers are achieved by combining the subjects and results from several smaller studies and then statistically analyzing the combined data, a process called meta-analysis. Say there are 25 published studies of whether a high-fat diet raises the risk of prostate cancer, but none shows statistically significant differences, although 12 show a slightly higher risk with a high-fat diet, 5 show no difference, and 8 show a lower risk. By combining the data, all subjects and prostate cancers can be simultaneously compared, possibly showing a slightly higher risk that reaches statistical significance.

There are drawbacks to meta-analysis, such as variation in the quality of the studies. Also, studies are less likely to be published if they show negative results (e.g., a study showing vitamin E doesn't lower the risk of heart disease), thereby skewing the combined data. This can especially be a problem when a study is privately funded. If you sell garlic pills and fund a study to see if your pills lower blood-cholesterol, you'd be quick to publish the results if your pills worked. But if your pills didn't work any better than the placebo...

Controlling Variables

Experimental and control groups should be as similar as possible except for the studied variable (e.g., diet pill). Subjects should be **randomly assigned**. Allowing them to choose their groups adds bias. Many people with advanced cancer desperately want to take part in studies of new treatments, but some will do so only if they're assured of being treated. But putting them into the treatment group, and those who "don't care" into the control group clouds the outcome. Did one group do better because of the treatment or because of uncontrolled differences in the groups? Sometimes, due to public pressure, patients are allowed access to the unproven treatment without participating in the study. But these same patients can get angry if the study finds that the treatment is ineffective or harmful, especially if the treatment was severe.

Placebos should be used whenever possible. A placebo is an inactive substance or sham procedure used for its psychological or peripheral effect (*placebo effect*). The placebo for a vitamin pill might be a sugar pill. If a drug dissolved in saline (salt water) is injected, an injection of saline alone would be the placebo; the injection process or the saline might have effects that would otherwise be falsely attributed to the drug. Placebos should look identical to the test substance (small red pills tend to "work better" than medium-sized green pills). Placebo effects can be powerful. Patients often get better—or worse—simply because they expect to, are less stressed about their situations, etc.

It's best if a study is **double-blind**—the subjects and investigators both (*double*) are *blind* to experimental groupings. If there are injections, neither the person getting the injection nor the person giving the injection knows whether it contains the drug or is a placebo.

*See www.nhlbi.nih.gov/whi Most such studies are funded by our tax dollars allocated by Congress to the National Institutes of Health (NIH) in Bethesda, Maryland. A lot of research is done at NIH, but NIH gives most of its money to scientists elsewhere (mainly at academic centers). Scientists submit their proposals to NIH. After extensive scientific review, the best proposals are approved for funding and given priority numbers. There isn't enough money for them all, so they're funded in order of priority number. Congress can instruct NIH to fund certain studies, even those with low priority numbers, sometimes on the basis of political considerations.

Double-blind studies control for bias and other psychological effects in the subjects and investigators. For example, many parents and teachers believe that sugar causes hyperactivity, and many children have been told this also. In studying the effect of sugar on hyperactivity, you can see why the children and the parents and teachers evaluating them shouldn't know whether the children have been given sugar.

In a study of a cancer drug, pathologists evaluating cancer in tissue samples may have to decide between two grades of severity when the pathology is intermediate. Investigators and subjects alike hope the drug is effective. If it's ineffective or only marginally effective, bias can be enough to tilt the outcome.

Double-blind studies typically have an oversight committee that knows the groupings and monitors the results so the study can be stopped if a clear benefit or hazard appears. In the double-blind study of aspirin in preventing heart attacks, the oversight committee advised ending the study early because far fewer heart attacks occurred in the group taking aspirin. It was deemed unethical to continue the study because this would withhold the benefit of aspirin from the placebo group. In the Women's Health Initiative, it became shockingly clear that the women given a combination of estrogen and progestin had an increased risk of breast cancer, and this part of the study was stopped early.

In some studies, psychological or peripheral effects can't be neutralized. One can't do a double-blind study comparing coronary bypass surgery to drugs for preventing a second heart attack. To control for a placebo effect of surgery itself, the surgeon needs to open the chest of those in the medication group without doing a bypass (*sham surgery*). This usually isn't done, but a possibility of peripheral effects should be kept in mind when assessing such studies.*

This point is well illustrated by a study reported in 1959. Earlier studies of patients with heart disease showed that tying off arteries to the mammary (breast) glands relieved angina (pain from not enough oxygen to the heart muscle), and the procedure was popularized by an enthusiastic article in *Reader's Digest.* There was no physiological explanation for why it worked; a placebo effect was suspected.

To test this hypothesis, 17 patients with severe, disabling angina were told only that they were participating in an evaluation of this simple surgical procedure done under local anesthesia. All subjects thought that their mammary arteries were going to be tied off, but were randomly assigned to either the control or experimental group. In both groups, the same incisions were made and the mammary arteries located, but the arteries were tied off only in the experimental group (8 patients). All subjects were followed for 3 to 15 months, and exercise tolerance (minutes on treadmill without angina), number of nitroglycerin pills self-administered for pain relief, etc., were compared with the same measurements before surgery.

---

*Cost-containment pressures have brought back the controversial use of sham surgery to test new surgical procedures for certain diseases. People with Parkinson's disease, for example, have good days and bad days in muscular debilitation. A positive outlook can help, perhaps by patients being more active and thereby improving muscle function. Sham surgery for implanting fetal cells into the brains of Parkinson patients would mean at least drilling the requisite holes in the skull. Brain surgery that just "seems to work" isn't very good evidence for a procedure that in itself is risky and expensive.

Both groups improved, not only in the patients' own subjective evaluations, but also in exercise tolerance and number of nitroglycerin pills taken per week (average 37 pills pre-surgery; 21 post-surgery). In fact, the control group improved more than the experimental group. The report says, *"...improvement in some cases was extraordinary. One patient* [in the control group] *who had been unable to work because of his heart disease, was almost immediately rehabilitated and was able to return to his former occupation. He reported a 100% improvement at 6 months and 75% improvement after a year."* Controlled studies are crucial to discovering the scientific truth.

Research Animals

Many studies in biology and medicine use animals (95% are rats and mice). We're biologically similar to these animals. Our hearts, lungs, kidneys, eyes, and livers, function similarly. Protein, fat, and carbohydrate in our food undergo similar chemical reactions in our bodies. Even the required vitamins and minerals are similar. Using animals to study new vaccines, implants for arthritic joints, etc., gives us an idea of how they might work in humans, though this impression can be incorrect.

Animals mirror even such human tendencies as overeating when given appealing food. Rats overeat when offered a variety of human foods (such as cookies) instead of their usual fare of nutritionally adequate, greenish-brown pellets and water. Similarly, studies show that over-weight people eat much less on a liquid diet. They'd probably eat even less on rat pellets and water!

Lab rats and mice are bred to be genetically similar, and their environment is controlled precisely. Animal quarters are kept at a comfortable temperature with heat and air conditioning; even light and dark periods are regulated. The best researchers can do with human subjects is to confine them away from home, but who's to know if someone slips in a prohibited candy bar hidden under the mattress and eaten at midnight?

People can be undependable in doing what they're told and inaccurate in reporting what they do—problems you don't have with animal studies. Objective measurements are much more reliable, e.g., measuring cotinine (a nicotine metabolite) in the urine to determine how much a person smokes, rather than relying on what he or she tells you.

There are even bottle caps with electronic chips that record when medicine bottles are uncapped, as a check on when people say they've taken their pills. If you compare the caloric value of people's reported physical activity (overestimated) with the calories in the food they say they eat (underestimated), the U.S. population should be losing—not gaining—weight!

Humans vary a lot in genetic make-up, so genetic effects are hard to separate from environmental effects—the old nature-versus-nurture question. Environment is hard to control in human experiments—especially when diet is involved.

"All he thinks about is that stupid ball."

It's hard to pinpoint causes of diseases like breast cancer because there are so many variables. Breast cancer is much less common in Asia than in the U.S. Is it genetics? Fat intake is much less in Asia. Is this a factor? Women of Japanese ancestry who live in the U.S. have more breast cancer than women in Japan. Is this because their diets have changed, or does it reflect another change?

Animal studies help answer such questions. Results of animal studies may not apply to humans, but can provide supporting evidence. Some animal studies show an increase in breast cancer with a high-fat diet. Had scientists not shown this, the hypothesis relating dietary fat to breast cancer in humans might not have been pursued so vigorously.

Animals can be bred to have specific genetic characteristics. For example, some strains are more susceptible to high blood pressure or obesity. The human population also includes sub-populations that may be comparable to such animal strains. For example, a drug for high blood pressure could be first tested on rats with high blood pressure, not only to test its effectiveness, but also to look for side effects. If the drug causes kidney damage in rats, it isn't likely to be tested in humans.

The shorter life span of animals is used to study the long-term effects of diet on chronic diseases. It's virtually impossible to control the variables in human studies of how diet in childhood affects development of chronic diseases later in life. Besides, researchers usually like to complete their studies in their lifetime.

Much of the progress in biology and medicine comes from animal studies. A major step toward conquering many human diseases is finding an animal model. A strain of mice that spontaneously develops breast cancer is used not only to study how breast cancer develops, but also to evaluate drugs for treatment and strategies for prevention. Advances in biotechnology and discoveries of disease-causing genes enable breeding of animal models with the exact same disease-causing genes. A mouse model developed for multiple sclerosis will certainly help in finding a cure.

The effect of specific genes can be studied by inactivating an individual gene in a mouse, creating a "knockout mouse."* It's like not knowing the function of the specific part of your car engine, and finding out by taking it out to see how it affects the engine.

The use of animals in research becomes more important as the use of human subjects is more restricted. Human experiments are much harder to get approved these days. During World War II, conscientious objectors participated in starvation studies, providing data that are still useful. The subjects fully recovered from the starvation regimen, but such studies wouldn't be approved in the U.S. today. Studies on U.S. federal prisoners are no longer allowed. Participation was voluntary, but the fact that the volunteers are prisoners can interject a subtle form of coercion to participate.

Because strict guidelines exist for human studies and lawsuits can result from adverse

---

*The first knockout mouse was created in 1989 by Mario Capecchi, Martin Evans, and Oliver Smithies, who were awarded a Nobel Prize in 2007.

effects, scientists in the U.S. rely more on animal research. Sometimes, people in other countries are used to follow up animal studies. Polio vaccine was first tested on people in the former Soviet Union, even though the vaccine was developed here. A chicken pox vaccine was tested on people in Japan before being tested in our population.

The experiments mentioned in Chapter 1 that tested the effects of supplemental thiamin on beriberi and that tested the infectivity of pellagra wouldn't be allowed in the U.S. if such studies were proposed today. In the beriberi study, it would be deemed unethical to withhold thiamin-supplemented rice from the control population when there was ample evidence that thiamin prevents beriberi. In the pellagra study, it would be deemed unethical to "infect" healthy people with what was thought to be an infectious agent.

It goes without saying that research animals should be treated humanely and used only when necessary. Federal, state, local, and institutional guidelines and regulations address this concern. Organizations such as the American Veterinary Medical Association have long-standing guidelines for the humane care and use of research animals.

Scientists are as appalled as anyone else by abuse of animals. Animal abuse shouldn't be tolerated, but isolated instances of abuse shouldn't implicate all animal research. Lab animals often are referred to as a single group although they're used for purposes other than biomedical research

"Relax, folks. You've treated me pretty good."

(e.g., testing cosmetics and household products).

The animal rights movement has had a big impact on scientific research and includes a range of opinions. Some people don't object to animal research as such, but seek laws that ban the use of animals obtained from pounds.* Others aggressively advocate a total ban of animal research to the point of raiding laboratories and threatening scientists and their families. According to the Association of American Medical Colleges, medical schools spend about $6 million yearly for security and for repairing damage stemming from animal rights activities.

Many animal rights groups focus on the use of larger animals, such as dogs and monkeys, although most research animals are rats and mice. It's expensive to use animals in research, especially big ones. Scientists don't use big ones when they can use small ones, and they don't use animals at all unless they need to. For example,

---

*Several states and communities now restrict the use of pound animals for research. (Over 10 million dogs and cats are killed in the U.S. each year in pounds and shelters.) In Massachusetts, for example, dogs and cats used for research must have been bred specifically for research, at a cost of several hundred dollars each.

dogs often are used when human-sized organs are needed. Research using larger animals is used to develop such surgical procedures as organ transplants, correction of heart defects in newborns, and coronary bypass operations.

Animal research can benefit animals as well. Animal studies investigating leukemia are useful in understanding both human and feline (cat) leukemia. Animal research has led to immunizations against distemper, rabies, infectious hepatitis, anthrax, and tetanus; orthopedic surgery in dogs and horses; cancer treatment in dogs; prevention of brucellosis and tuberculosis in cattle; and improved nutrition for pets.

Ironically, animal-rights activists burned a lab under construction, causing about $3 million in damages to the School of Veterinary Medicine of the University of California at Davis, one of the leading veterinary schools in the country. Its scientists and its graduates have made major contributions to improving the health and welfare of animals.

Clinical Trials

Results of test-tube and animal studies can be applicable to humans but, at some point, people must be tested. Such studies are usually major undertakings, very expensive, and take place only after the product or procedure has been tested for safety and effectiveness in test-tube experiments and animal studies.

When heart disease was *linked* to high blood-cholesterol, research focused on two questions: (1) Can high blood-cholesterol *cause* heart disease? (2) If healthy people lower their blood-cholesterol, will they lower their risk of heart disease? Solid evidence now shows that high blood-cholesterol can directly cause heart disease.

The question of whether heart disease could be prevented by lowering blood-cholesterol was harder to answer because it required clinical trials—also called intervention trials because researchers intervene to lower blood-cholesterol by diet, drugs, etc. Many clinical trials have shown that middle-aged people with high blood-cholesterol lower their risk of heart disease by lowering their blood-cholesterol. A nationwide effort is underway to improve our diet and to identify and treat people with high blood-cholesterol *before* they show signs of heart disease.

Before a drug is submitted for approval, the Food and Drug Administration requires that clinical trials be undertaken in phases. In Phase I, the drug is tested for safety in a small group of people. In Phase II, the drug is tested for effectiveness in a larger group. In Phase III, the drug is tested for safety *and* effectiveness in a much larger group. Stock prices of drug companies often reflect how upcoming drugs are progressing in clinical trials. Information about current clinical trials can be found at www.clinicaltrials.gov.

Some drugs that appear safe in clinical trials are later withdrawn because of unanticipated side effects. As in the aspirin study, drugs typically are tested on a very select group of subjects. When a drug is used in the general population, it's used by many more people who vary much more in their state of health, reliability, etc. In "real life," people forget to take a pill and take a double dose the next time, or take it with a variety of other pills and supplements. Also, the much larger group provides the statistical power to detect side effects that were undetectable in the smaller clinical trials.

One clinical trial with a completely unexpected result was to see if beta-carotene pills lowered the risk of lung cancer in smokers. Beta-carotene was expected to protect against cancer. The Finnish trial included more than 29,000 male smokers. The group taking the beta-carotene got more lung cancer! This shocking result was first thought to be a "fluke," but a U.S. study published soon after of more than 18,000 male and female smokers, former smokers, or workers exposed to asbestors confirmed this finding. Getting beta-carotene in a pill isn't a shortcut for getting beta-carotene in the fruits and vegetables associated with lower cancer rates.

Evaluating Data

All of the information collected in a study is called data. Scientists scrutinize the data in assessing the conclusions of research by others. A favorite saying among scientists is, *In God we trust; everyone else has to show data.*

Scientific data typically are reported in metric units* and evaluated by statistical analysis. Suppose you measure the heights of girls attending a summer camp, and find that, on average, the girls from California are taller than the girls from Ohio. Is this difference "for real?" Scientists decide by using the variation in heights and number of girls to see if the difference is statistically significant *(probably not due to chance).* The greater the difference, the less the variation, and the larger the number of girls, the more likely the difference will be statistically significant.

Statistical analysis gives a measure of probability (*P*). The difference (e.g., in height) between study groups is said to be statistically significant when calculations show that the probability that the difference is due to chance is less than a 5% *(less than 5 in 100,* expressed as *P<0.05).* Conversely, if the probability of a chance finding is 5% or more, the difference is "not statistically significant." In other words, scientists can say that they found a difference between groups only if they're at least 95% sure (the odds are less than 5 out of 100 that the difference was a fluke).

The "scientific sentence" on page 1 says that the drug cholestyramine lowered the level of lipoproteins by doubling (P<0.01) its rate of removal from the blood. *P<0.01* means that the probability of getting this result purely by chance was less than 1 in 100 (<1%).

Many kinds of statistical analyses exist, including measuring the strength of a link between two factors (e.g., alcohol consumption and liver cancer). Factors that increase the risk of disease are called **risk factors**. The extent of risk often

is given as Relative Risk.† For example, a study of thousands of men working in the production of either beer or mineral water found that "excess" beer-drinking was linked to a higher risk of cancer of the liver and esophagus.

The study (1975-1978) took place in Denmark where workers producing beer belonged to the Danish Brewery Workers Union. The Union had a long-standing agreement with the breweries whereby each worker could drink up to 6 bottles (about 2 quarts) of free beer each day while working at the brewery. Workers producing mineral water weren't alloted free beer (or mineral water); they drank about as much beer as the general population. The brewery workers drank about 4 times more.

The Relative Risk of this excess beer was determined by tallying cancers in the brewery workers and a matched group not given this free beer.** The brewery workers had Relative Risks of 2.1 for esophageal cancer, 1.5 for liver cancer, and 1.1 for colon cancer. In other words, "excess beer" was linked to a 200% higher risk of esophageal cancer, a 50% higher risk of liver cancer, but the risk of colon cancer wasn't significantly higher.

Statistical analyses can be impressively complex, but no matter how fancy the measuring devices, how complex the statistics, or how precise the answers, the results are only as good as the data or sample selected *(garbage in, garbage out).* Fanciness can give an illusion of accuracy. A digital bathroom scale that displays the weight to three decimal points could be off by 2 pounds.

Be wary of how statistics are presented. Suppose you're told that the number of Americans dying of cancer has steadily increased. Before getting alarmed, ask if the size of our population has also gone up. If told that the cancer death rate (e.g., cancer deaths per 10,000 people) has steadily increased, ask if the population has changed in other ways; e.g., do older people make up a bigger portion of the population?

---

*See Appendix A-1 for conversion factors. United States, Myanmar (Burma), and Liberia are the only countries in the world that don't use the metric system in daily affairs, as in recipes, measuring height and weight, dispensing gasoline.

†Relative Risk RR = [number of (cancers) found] divided by [number of (cancers) expected].

**In this study, RR = [# of cancers in the brewery workers] / [# of cancers in the mineral-water workers].

Assessment of data, conclusions, and statistics must be objective. Statements such as, *this year 483,000 people will die of cancer—that's 1,323 people every day*, may elicit donations to cancer research, but don't provide much useful information.

Reporting and Verifying Scientific Studies

Research results are published in scientific journals, making them available to scientists and others throughout the world. Scientists scrutinize studies and refer to them in follow-up studies that verify or build on the results. When a finding is consistently verified by other scientists, it's accepted into the body of scientific knowledge (otherwise, it's discarded). Lavoisier's studies in the 1780s supported his hypothesis that animal life depended on oxygen. Others verified his findings that now are an accepted part of scientific knowledge.

The results of scientific research are usually reported in a standard format:

- **Introduction**: Includes the hypothesis and background information to orient the reader as to why the study was done.
- **Methods**: Describes in precise detail the materials (e.g., diet, animals) and methods used. Details are crucial; scientists in other labs must be able to duplicate and validate the results of the study.
- **Results**: Typically presented in tables and graphs that include statistical analyses.
- **Discussion and Conclusion**: Results interpreted and compared to other relevant studies.

Thousands of scientific journals are published throughout the world; they vary in subject matter, quality, and distribution. Many are specialty journals (vs. the more general, interdisciplinary ones). Some titles: *Sexually Transmitted Diseases, Lipid Research, Cell, Anesthesiology, Cancer, Aerospace Medicine and Biology, Clinical Chemistry, Blood, Gut* (not *Blood and Guts!*), *American Journal of Clinical Nutrition, Atherosclerosis, AIDS Research and Human Retroviruses*, and *Pediatrics*.

Among the most prestigious and widely read are two medical journals—*The New England Journal of Medicine* (www.nejm.org) and *The Lancet* (thelancet.com)—and two general science journals—*Science* (sciencemag.org) and *Nature* (nature.com). These four are all:

- **In English**, the most commonly used language in science. Journals in other languages often include English abstracts of their articles.
- **Widely read** throughout the world. Subscribers include many individuals, libraries, companies, college departments, etc.
- **Published weekly** (most journals are published monthly). Traditionally, credit for a discovery goes to whoever first publishes it in a scientific journal. As in the awarding of patents, this can be a very close and rewarding race. (Does anyone remember who applied for the patent for the telephone a few hours after Alexander Graham Bell? Not many have heard of Elisha Gray.)
- **Peer-reviewed**. Scientists submit their studies, which are reviewed critically by their peers—other scientists in the same field. The articles are then either rejected or accepted for publication. Even the accepted ones may be sent back to the authors for revision, e.g., to include discussion of a relevant study published earlier. The best journals are peer-reviewed. At the other extreme are journals that for a fee uncritically publish virtually any study; these don't generally attract high-quality research articles.
- **Very selective** in accepting only those articles considered the most timely and important. Getting an article into these journals is very competitive, so it's prestigious to get published in them—the journals' success breeds success.

Most of the breakthroughs in AIDS research were published in these four journals. In 1953, Watson and Crick published their discovery of the structure of DNA in *Nature* (they won the Nobel prize in 1962). In 1996, Richard Zare and his colleagues published in *Science* their evidence of microbial life 3.6 billion years ago on Mars.

In 2001, the two teams competing to complete the first draft of the Human Genome Project (see Chap. 10) published their results simultaneously: Francis Collins's group in the February 15th issue of *Nature*, and Craig Venter's group in the February 16th issue of *Science*.

Besides publishing in journals, scientists present their results at scientific meetings. For example, more than 10,000 scientists met in 2011 in Washington D.C. for the thousands of studies presented at the 95th annual Experimental Biology meeting. After the scientists present their studies, fellow scientists ask questions and make comments (peer review). The meeting provides an opportunity for dialogue among scientists. They even have dinner meetings based on their research interests—a Liver Dinner is not a dinner of liver!

Claim of Cold Fusion

The traditional way in which scientists report their findings is occasionally breached. The well-publicized claim in 1989 of chemists Stanley Pons and Martin Fleishmann that they produced energy by cold atomic fusion provides an insight into the practical importance of the scientific method for both scientists and nonscientists.

Their claim was astonishing because of what was already known about atomic fusion. Most of us know that what's too good to be true is usually untrue. As will be discussed in the next chapter, physicists have been working for decades on hot fusion—using extremely high pressure and temperature to fuse two hydrogen atoms to make one helium atom to get a virtually unlimited supply of energy.

The two chemists first reported their results at a press conference rather than at a scientific meeting or in a science journal. Because they didn't reveal the details of their experiments, other scientists couldn't evaluate their validity. Scientists traditionally withhold judgment until they can evaluate the data, so their public responses were subdued (*"I'd be very surprised if it were true"*). In sharp contrast was the exuberant response of many nonscientists who discussed the revolutionary consequences of cold fusion (e.g., solving the energy crisis and global warming) and put the two chemists on the cover of *Time*.

Other aspects of this episode shed some light on the Scientific Method and interactions among scientists:

- The day after their press conference, the chemists submitted a report of their study for publication in *Nature*. It was peer-reviewed, returned to the chemists for substantial revision (the report was lacking in essential details), and wasn't published in *Nature*. But another report they had submitted earlier to the *Journal of Electroanalytical Chemistry* was published shortly thereafter. Since then, many scientists have tried to duplicate their results, but generally without success.

- If Pons and Fleishmann had found an inexpensive way to produce energy by cold fusion, the commercial interest and the financial gain would have been substantial. This may help explain why they were reluctant to reveal the details of their experiments. Traditionally, scientists freely share their materials and data with other scientists. Ties between scientific and commercial interests can put a damper on this. Because of commercial interests and the increased scarcity of government funds, more university scientists (especially in biotechnology) are getting funds from industry.

- Nuclear fusion is more in the realm of physics than chemistry. Pons and Fleishmann are chemists. Because of the burgeoning knowledge in science, scientists have had to markedly narrow their research—scientists need to "know more and more about less and less" to make advances in their fields. It thus becomes less and less likely that chemists will make major discoveries in physics and vice versa—Pons' and Fleishmann's claims were much better received by their fellow chemists than by nuclear physicists.

It's increasingly hard for scientists to understand the intricacies of research in fields other than their own. There's the story of a chemist and a physicist who attended a lecture by a distinguished mathematician. Afterwards, the chemist said, "I lost the thread of the lecture about two minutes from the end." The physicist replied, "That's amazing; I didn't understand any of the lecture at all." The chemist replied, "Well, I didn't say which end I was referring to!"

Buyer Beware

As discussed in Chapter 1, research results are disseminated very fast, not only to scientists but to the public as well. The public gets selective information (reporting that drinking water is safe doesn't sell newspapers) and in soundbites—the bottom line without the details. But without the details, one "finding" is given the same weight as another, even when one is flimsy and the other is backed by solid evidence. Scientists approach research findings with "healthy" skepticism. You should too.

If you hear that a study shows that people who take vitamins have fewer cancers (a link), this doesn't mean that the study showed that taking vitamins lowers the risk of cancer (cause-and-effect). Finding links between what people do and their diseases are jumping off points for further studies. Sometimes the links turn out to be cause-and-effect linkages, sometimes not.

Many links are hard to separate out for study, because health habits, socioeconomic status, etc., are all interlinked. One of the strongest links to poor health is poverty. Poor people in this country are less likely to see a physician when ill, smoke more, have more stress, eat poorer diets, take fewer vacations, subscribe to fewer magazines, live in more crowded conditions, take fewer vitamins, are less educated, have fewer teeth, have older cars, have more cancer and heart disease, and die younger. So, all of these factors are linked. You can say that people who eat poorer diets have more heart disease. Or people who take fewer vacations have fewer teeth. Or people who don't take vitamins have more cancer. Or people who don't subscribe to magazines die younger.

In many cases, statistical adjustments are made to try and separate out a link. If people who drink more coffee are found to have more heart attacks (a link), adjustments for other factors such as smoking have to be made to see if coffee is a separate link. (Smoking increases the risk of a heart attack, and smokers drink more coffee than nonsmokers.) You can adjust for well-established risk factors, but others may be equivocal or unknown. Seventh-Day Adventists are used in some studies of the health benefits of vegetarian diets. Adjustments are made for their abstention from alcohol and tobacco, but other ways in which they differ from comparison groups also may affect health.

Even if a study shows that taking a certain substance improves health, this doesn't mean that it will improve your health. A study of a rural population in China showed that those given a supplement of carotene, selenium, and vitamin E had less cancer (a supplement of vitamin A and zinc, or riboflavin and niacin, or vitamin C and molybdenum had no effect). The study was well-publicized in the U.S., including a television segment on *PrimeTime Live*. In fact, so many viewers inquired about the exact doses taken in the study, the doses were announced again on the program.

"Ignore him"

The rural Chinese in the study had a poor diet, with a chronically low intake of several nutrients. They also have one of the world's highest cancer rates; more than 85% of their cancers are of the esophagus and stomach. Their diet also was unusually deficient in selenium. The local soil is one of the world's lowest in this essential mineral, and most of what they ate was grown locally. Of course they were healthier when given nutrients they lacked! The required vitamins and minerals are, by definition, essential for good health. If you're already getting enough, taking more won't make you healthier.

The study mentioned earlier, that aspirin lowered the risk of heart attacks, also got a lot of publicity. Aspirin hampers the formation of blood clots (see Chap. 7), so it would be expected to lower the risk of heart attacks (usually from a blood clot blocking an artery that feeds the heart). The study was done on older male physicians in this country. Those who shouldn't take aspirin (e.g., those with an ulcer or those with risk factors for a hemorrhagic stroke) were excluded as subjects.

For young men who wonder if they should take aspirin to lower their risk of a heart attack: Your risk of a heart attack is much lower than your risk of bodily injury (see Fig. 8-2)—auto accident, gunshot wound, etc.—in which case you want your blood to clot full speed ahead!

Healthy skepticism also means: don't go to the other extreme and dismiss studies just because they aren't perfectly controlled. Suppose you hear that breast-fed babies are found to be healthier and smarter than bottle-fed babies. Look at the details (e.g., who and how many were studied, how health was measured, whether other relevant variables such as I.Q. of parents were taken into consideration), but don't disregard the study just because it wasn't randomized or double blind and only showed a link rather than a cause-and-effect relationship. In many such studies, it's the best one can do given the circumstances and funding. In time, such studies accumulate to give a *preponderance of evidence* of a cause-and-effect relationship—as with smoking and lung cancer.

One can see that huge variations exist in the particulars of a study. It's no wonder that different studies can come to different conclusions. Some studies "simply" observe thousands of people for years to look for statistically significant links in health habits. Others study a few people intensively in controlled settings. Then there's the *definitive clinical trial*, where huge numbers of people are randomized into an elaborately controlled double-blind study.

Alternative Medicine

Alternative medicine is that which generally lies outside of what's traditionally taught in U.S. medical schools. It includes methods such as aromatherapy, therapeutic touch, homeopathy, and herbal medicine. It evokes a soft and caring image, versus the impersonal, high-tech image of conventional medicine. Many people are frustrated with the failures of conventional medicine.

What upsets many scientists is that much of what distinguishes alternative from conventional medicine is that conventional medicine relies on scientific evidence of efficacy, whereas much of alternative medicine does not. Certainly some alternative medicine therapies will prove their worth in controlled studies. When they do, they become a part of conventional medicine.

Many controlled studies of alternative medicine are in progress, particularly in the field of herbal medicine. Herbal extracts used in these studies are standardized so that a consistent product is used. In the marketplace, it's hard if not impossible for consumers to tell exactly what they're getting. Potencies and contaminants vary widely, and one can't rely on label information. However, if an herbal extract proves effective in controlled studies, most consumers will seek the specified and standardized product tested.

Herbal medicine is classed as a dietary supplement, so is only loosely regulated. The Dietary Supplement Health and Education Act of 1994 allows supplement manufacturers to sell products without showing safety or effectiveness, but only allows claims related to bodily structure or function. Disease-related claims aren't allowed on the label. For example, it's okay to claim that a product *promotes bone health* (though it may not), but not okay to claim that it *prevents osteoporosis* (a disease). It's been ruled that aging, mild memory loss, pregnancy, morning sickness, menopause, premenstrual syndrome, and such, are not diseases, so claims can be made about these. Also, disease claims for supplements are often made in popular books (e.g., *"shark cartilage cures cancer"*)—freedom of speech.

Consumers should extend their healthy skepticism to alternative medicine. The key question is, how do you know that? Many claims have nothing but testimonials to support them. Ask for details. An advertisement for an herbal preparation that says, *"A clinical trial showed improvement in 75% of the subjects,"* can mean that it was given to four friends, and three of them said they felt better. Emphasis is on treatment. Diagnosis can be inaccurate, sketchy, or otherwise unreliable. In "conventional" studies, people must be verified to have cancer before claims can be made about their being cured.

Summary

The scientific method is a formal way to make scientific investigations. Scientists state their hypothesis, do controlled studies, then report their results and conclusions in scientific journals and meetings. Scientists throughout the world can then examine, discuss, and verify the bits and pieces of new information before adding it to the body of scientific knowledge. This process of verification is very important because each bit of new information serves as a stepping stone for further studies.

Comparison groups should be as similar as possible, except for the variable being tested. The "gold standard" in human studies is the prospective, randomized, double-blind, placebo-controlled study, e.g., the study of aspirin in the prevention of heart attacks:

Prospective: Heart attacks that occur after the start of the study are compared in those randomly assigned to the aspirin and placebo groups. (In a retrospective study, they would have been divided into those who have had a heart attack and those who haven't, and their past use of aspirin compared.)

Randomized: Assignment into groups is random so that the aspirin and the placebo groups start off as similar as possible. This makes it more likely that any differences between the two groups will be due to the aspirin. Significantly more heart attacks occurred in the placebo group, and it was concluded that aspirin helped prevent heart attacks.

Double-blind: Neither the subjects nor the investigators actively involved in the study know who's getting the aspirin and who's getting the placebo. A **placebo** is an "inert" substance or procedure used to control for psychological and peripheral effects. Not knowing who is in which group controls for unconscious bias in subjects and investigators alike. If there's a question of whether someone actually had a mild heart attack, unconscious bias could play a role in deciding.

It's important to note other features of a study. Although the aspirin study was prospective, randomized, double-blind, and placebo-controlled, the subjects—a selective sample of male physicians—certainly weren't representative of the entire U.S. population.

The rapid advances in medical research and treatment wouldn't have been possible without the use of laboratory animals. Rats and mice comprise about 95% of research animals. Their main advantages in research are that their environment can be precisely controlled, and they are physiologically similar to humans, can be bred to be genetically similar and with certain susceptibilities to diseases, have a short life span, and are relatively inexpensive.

When a substance (aspirin, vaccine, etc.) has been shown to be safe and effective in animal studies, it must be shown to be safe and effective in clinical trials (human studies) before it's approved for use in the general population. Phase I clinical trials test for safety in a small group of people. Phase II trials test for effectiveness in a larger group. Phase III trials test for both safety and effectiveness in a much larger group.

Once a study is completed, the data are evaluated statistically and by other scientists. A *significant* finding means that the likelihood that the finding was due to chance alone was calculated to be less than 5 in 100 (probability = <0.05).

When you hear about the results of various studies, especially if they sound a bit off-beat, question such details as whether the study controlled for bias, who the subjects were, and whether it showed a link or a cause-and-effect relationship.

Chapter 3

Chemistry

There are the rushing waves...mountains of molecules, each stupidly minding its own business...trillions apart...yet forming white surf in unison.

Ages on ages...before any eyes could see...year after year...thunderously pounding the shore as now. For whom, for what?...on a dead planet, with no life to entertain.

Never at rest...tortured by energy...wasted prodigiously by the sun...poured into space. A mite makes the sea roar.

Deep in the sea, all molecules repeat the patterns of one another till complex new ones are formed. They make others like themselves...and a new dance starts.

Growing in size and complexity...living things, masses of atoms, DNA, protein...dancing a pattern ever more intricate.

Out of the cradle onto the dry land...here it is standing...atoms with consciousness... matter with curiosity.

Stands at the sea...wonders at wondering...I...a universe of atoms...an atom in the universe.

Richard Feynman (1918-1988), Nobel laureate in physics

Chemistry is basic to life. Our mineral requirements are for certain kinds of atoms that the body needs. The body's use of food involves the breaking and forming of chemical bonds. Even the awesome creation of life occurs as a series of chemical reactions.

Everything around us, living and non-living, is a collection of atoms. Considering the seemingly infinite variety of things—sand, leaves, plastic, rubies, stars, air, human beings—one imagines that there are thousands, perhaps millions, of different kinds of atoms. But there aren't many more than 100, and only 14 make up almost all that's familiar (hydrogen, carbon, nitrogen, oxygen, sodium, magnesium, aluminum, silicon, phosphorus, sulfur, chlorine, potassium, calcium, iron). Living substances, from a leaf to the com-plex brain, are made mainly of only 4 kinds of atoms: carbon, hydrogen, oxygen, and nitrogen.

Atoms

An atom is a basic unit—it can't be subdivided without losing its unique characteristics. *Atom* means *uncut* in Greek. Atoms have **protons** that have a *positive charge,* **neutrons** that are **uncharged** (neutral), and **electrons** that have a **negative charge**.

Protons and neutrons are in the center (nucle-us) of atoms and have mass *(weight).* Electrons orbit the nucleus of the atom (the orbits are called electron shells). The weight (mass) of an electron is insignificant compared to that of a proton or neutron.

THE MORE MASS AN OBJECT
HAS, THE GREATER ITS FORCE
OF ATTRACTION. YOU ARE
EXTREMELY ATTRACTIVE.

Atoms are uncharged—each atom has an equal number of protons and electrons. The positive charge of each proton is offset by the negative charge of each electron (Fig. 3-1).

When speaking of specific atoms, the term *element* is often used. **The number of protons in an atom determines which element that atom is**. More than 100 protons can exist in an atom. Thus, there are more than 100 different elements, beginning with hydrogen with a single proton. The elements are listed by their numbers of protons (their *atomic numbers*) in the Periodic Table of Elements (Appendix A-2). Each element has a one- or two-letter symbol (Appendix A-3).

For example, the compound sodium chloride (table salt) = NaCl: One atom of sodium = Na (from its Latin name *natrium*), and one atom of chlorine = Cl.

Although the number of protons is unique for each element, the number of neutrons can vary. **Atoms that have the same number of protons but differ in the number of neutrons are called isotopes** (some, but not all, isotopes are radioactive). A carbon atom, for example, can have different numbers of neutrons, but it always has 6 protons. (It would be boron with 5 protons, nitrogen with 7 protons.)

Most carbon atoms (about 99%) have 6 neutrons and 6 protons (6+6 = carbon-12), but some have more neutrons. Carbon-13 (about 1% of all carbon atoms) is a nonradioactive isotope that has 7 neutrons and 6 protons.* Carbon-14 has 8 neutrons and 6 protons, and is radioactive. Its measurable radioactivity is used for such diverse purposes as determining the ages of ancient relics and following the fates of molecules in lab animals and cells.

Because the body can't change one element into another (i.e., the body can't change the number of protons in an atom), each element the body needs must be taken in as food or in the air we breathe. For example, potassium (19 protons) and calcium (20 protons) are needed in the diet. The number of protons differs by only one, yet potassium and calcium are very different in their physical characteristics and functions in the body. One can't substitute for the other, nor can one be made from the other. The same principle applies in chemistry as it does in biology. Recall how alchemists in the Middle Ages tried (unsuccessfully, of course) to turn lead (82 protons) into gold (79 protons).

Nuclear Fusion

Extraordinary circumstances, such as the high temperature and pressure found in the sun and stars, are needed to change one element into another. In fact, nearly all of the elements were originally hydrogen atoms (1 proton) that fused

---

*Natural diamonds are 99% carbon-12 and 1% carbon-13. In 1990, scientists at General Electric made a diamond of only carbon-12. This was exciting because the occasional carbon-13 causes slight imperfections in the crystal. Diamonds are used as components of high-tech devices because they're transparent, hard, and the best known heat conductor. Compared to ordinary diamonds, 100% carbon-12 diamonds conduct heat 50% better and withstand 10 times the intensity of laser radiation. Using these "super-diamonds" in laser devices and miniaturized components (e.g., microchips) has immense practical value, e.g., enhanced heat conductivity in a microchip means that their components can be packed closer together, enabling computers to be smaller and work faster without overheating.

Figure 3-1: Diagram of some Atoms and Covalent and Ionic Bonds

Atoms have equal numbers of protons (+) and electrons (•). The number of neutrons varies and aren't shown. The circles represent the spherical electron shells.

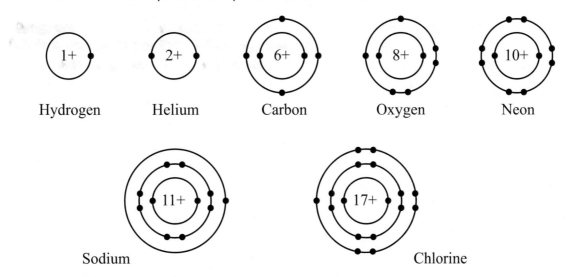

Covalent Bonds are formed when atoms share electrons to complete their outer electron shells (the 1st shell needs 2 electrons to be complete; the 2nd shell needs 8).

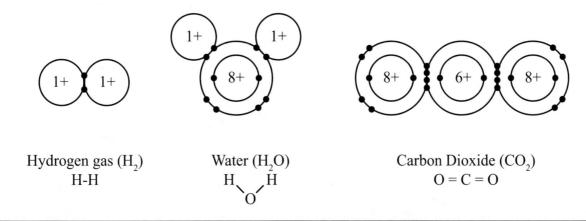

Ionic Bonds are formed by the attraction of oppositely charged ions. When atoms give up or take on extra electrons (negative charges), they become positively or negatively charged and are called ions. As shown below, a sodium ion is positively charged because it has given up an electron, so now has 10 electrons (negative charges) and 11 protons (positive charges).

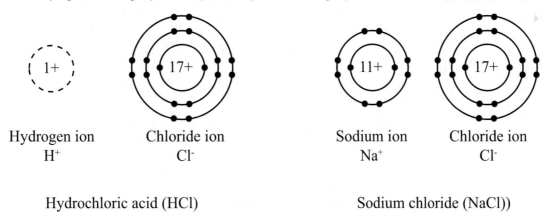

to form atoms with more than one proton (all the other elements).

The nuclei of atoms must come very close together before they can fuse. Nuclear fusion is extremely difficult because the nuclei are positively charged, and similarly charged particles strongly repel each other.

Extremely high temperature and pressure in the sun and stars cause atoms to move and collide such that their nuclei come close enough to fuse and become the heavier elements. In the sun (about 15 million °C), about 657 million tons of hydrogen atoms (1 proton each) fuse to make about 653 million tons of helium atoms (2 protons each) per second:

2 Hydrogen atoms (1 proton each)

Nuclear Fusion
→

1 Helium atom (2 protons) + Energy

The atomic weight of a helium atom is slightly less than that of two hydrogen atoms. The "missing mass" of 4 million tons is converted into the heat and energy that sustains life on earth. Mass is converted to energy according to Einstein's famous equation: $E = mc^2$ (E = energy, m = mass, c = the speed of light.) This conversion of mass to energy is what keeps the sun shining, a discovery that led to a 1967 Nobel prize for Hans Bethe. Yes, the sun will eventually burn itself out, but not for billions of years.

All the heavy elements (carbon, oxygen, calcium, etc.) were—and still are—made by nuclear fusion in stars and in the extreme conditions that exist when stars explode. We are truly made in heaven—every atom in our bodies was once inside a star that exploded (a supernova explosion).

Hydrogen is the most abundant element on earth and a potential source of virtually unlimited energy. The hydrogen bomb, first exploded in 1952, works by uncontrolled **fusion** of hydrogen atoms (the atomic bomb dropped over Hiroshima in 1945 released energy by splitting very heavy atoms—nuclear **fission**). For decades, physicists have been trying to fuse hydrogen atoms in a controlled way to provide a sustained source of energy. They try to create conditions like those in the sun (*hot fusion)* using contraptions that are huge, complex, and expensive—quite unlike "cold fusion in a jar" (see Chap. 2).

Producing energy in a controlled manner by nuclear fusion would be revolutionary. Unlike the burning of fossil fuels (e.g., coal, gas), we'd have a virtually unlimited supply of energy, without climate-changing consequences. For example,

"I always get it confused. Was that an example of fusion or fission?"

the carbon dioxide produced when fossil fuels are burned contributes to the greenhouse effect* and isn't produced in fusion. And unlike today's nuclear fission power plants (which split big atoms like uranium), fusion plants wouldn't produce radioactive byproducts, or melt-down danger (radiation release from accidental melting of fuel rods).

An international effort to build a fusion reactor to test the viability of fusion as a major source of energy is in progress. The International Thermonuclear Experimental Reactor (ITER) is being built in France with the goal of being productive by 2019. The cost of this $22 billion project is shared by the project's partners: 45% by the European Union, and 9% each by China, India, Japan, South Korea, Russia, and the United States.

Atomic Weight

Protons and neutrons have weight (mass), whereas electrons, for all practical purposes, do not. Neutrons and protons weigh about the same. The numbers of neutrons and protons in an atom determine its atomic weight. The actual weights of atoms are infinitesimally small, so atomic weights are given as relative weights—relative to carbon having an atomic weight of 12 (6 protons plus 6 neutrons). Thus, hydrogen (1 proton, 0 neutrons) has an atomic weight of 1, oxygen (8 protons, 8 neutrons) an atomic weight of 16, etc. Some familiar elements along with their chemical symbols, atomic numbers, and atomic weights are listed in Appendix A-3.

Molecules

A molecule is a chemical combination of two or more atoms, and its characteristics are quite different from those of the atoms in it. A water molecule (H_2O)† is made of hydrogen and oxygen, which are gases (H_2 and O_2). A molecule's size ranges from the smallest—hydrogen gas (2 atoms of the smallest atom)—to molecules as big as human DNA (billions of atoms).

The infinite variety of substances comes mainly from the arrangement of atoms into various structures (if this seems incredible, think of the variety of music written with just a 12-tone scale on a piano). A striking example is the difference between a diamond and the graphite in pencils. Both are made entirely of carbon atoms, but differ in arrangement of those atoms.

In diamonds, the carbon atoms are linked closely in 3 dimensions, producing the hardest known substance. Diamonds are thus used in industry to cut other hard substances such as steel. In graphite, the carbons link in only 2 dimensions, producing layers that are only 1 atom thick. The layers easily slide past each other, making graphite soft and slippery and a superb dry lubricant (used to lubricate things from doorknobs to complicated machinery). When writing with a pencil, we slide layers of graphite onto paper. (Carbon atoms don't always come so neatly arranged—charcoal is a disorderly arrangement.)

To actually produce a sheet of carbons one-atom thick (graphene) wasn't easy. Complicated methods hadn't worked. In 2004, physicists Andre Geim and Konstantin Novoselov developed a method that started with their experimenting with scotch tape to peel off flakes from a chunk of graphite; they won a Nobel prize in 2010. Graphene is amazing—it conducts electricity, is transparent and flexible, yet is stronger than diamonds. It makes for many advances, especially in electronics. The South Korean company Samsung has already used it to make a touch screen.

At an extremely high temperature (2,000°C) and pressure (100,000 atmospheres), the carbons in graphite rearrange to form diamonds. (Natural

---

*This is the warming of the earth's surface and lower atmosphere due to the trapping of the sun's heat by more carbon dioxide (CO_2) and other greenhouse gases in the atmosphere. CO_2 made by animal life is normally offset by plant life using CO_2 (Fig. 3-2). This balance can be upset by making more CO_2 (e.g., burning of oil, gasoline, wood, coal) or absorbing less CO_2 from the atmosphere (e.g., by destroying forests).

†The numerical subscript following the chemical symbol tells the number of atoms of that kind in the molecule; no subscript indicates only one atom of that kind. A carbon dioxide molecule (CO_2) has 1 carbon atom, 2 oxygen atoms.

diamonds are made deep in the earth, where temperature and pressure are extremely high.) In 1954, scientists at General Electric used high temperature and pressure to make the first laboratory-made diamond. Most industrial diamonds are made this way.

Another arrangement is called a buckyball/ fullerene, because it resembles architect Buckminster Fuller's geodesic dome. The carbons form a sphere with their bonds in a geometric pattern like on soccer balls. At home, wanting to see if carbons could be arranged this way, chemist Richard Smalley's graduate student tried using candy gummy bears and toothpicks to represent carbons and their bonds. Drs. Smalley, Curl, and Kroto won a 1996 Nobel prize for discovering buckyballs, which have many novel and useful properties, e.g., they're much smaller than the carbon particles used in many printer cartridges— smaller carbon particles mean sharper copies (Xerox has patents on several such uses). The Epson Stylus C60 Ink Cartridge is filled with buckyballs (C60 = 60 carbons linked to form a sphere).

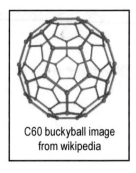

C60 buckyball image from wikipedia

Our cells rearrange atoms to convert one substance to another. Sugar is made of carbon, hydrogen, and oxygen. Our cells can break sugar down into carbon dioxide and water, or use the sugar's atoms to make more complex molecules like cholesterol. With minor structural changes, cholesterol can be made into the sex hormones estrogen and testosterone.

Rearranging atoms or making complex molecules from simpler ones requires energy. Sunlight provides energy to plants. Starch is made of thousands of carbon, hydrogen, and oxygen atoms linked together. Plants make it from carbon dioxide and water by using the energy in sunlight to link the atoms together, and oxygen is released as a byproduct (Fig. 3-2). This process is called *photosynthesis*, which means *[using] light to put together*.

Animals inhale the oxygen and eat the plants. The body breaks food down to carbon dioxide and water, and energy is released. This breakdown and release of energy from food is part of a process called *metabolism*, which means *to change* in Greek. Oxygen is used in this process. It could be said that we're solar powered— sunlight is the original source of the energy in our food (Fig. 3-2).

The body can make most of the molecules it needs. When it can't, the molecules must be consumed readymade. Vitamin C is a molecule that's required but that the body can't make. Most animals don't need vitamin C in their diet because they, unlike humans (and a few other species such as guinea pigs), can make it. In another example, the body needs 20 kinds of amino acids to make protein, but can make only 11 of the 20. The other 9 must come from the diet.

"It may be indistinguishable from a diamond chemically, Harry—but to me, charcoal is charcoal."

Figure 3-2: Energy, Carbon Dioxide, and Oxygen Cycle between Plants and Animals

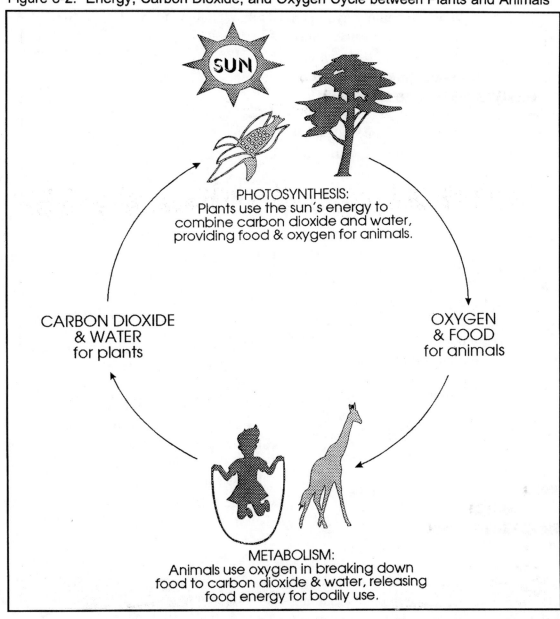

A molecule needed in the body isn't necessarily needed in the diet. In fact, one might expect that the body would make its <u>most</u> essential molecules rather than rely on dietary habits to get them. For example, cholesterol is a molecule that's essential in the body but not in the diet. It's an integral part of our cells and is used to make other essential substances like sex hormones. The body can make as much cholesterol as it needs.

When nutrients are absorbed from the intestine, the body recognizes their structures but not their sources. The body doesn't discriminate between the vitamin C you get in an orange, or that in an inexpensive vitamin pill made in a lab (*synthetic*) or that in an expensive pill with a bit of C extracted from rose hips added to lab-made C. Molecules of vitamin C are the same as far as the body is concerned. Don't pay more for pills advertised to give an illusion of being "more natural." If you want "natural," it makes more sense to get your C by eating oranges, strawberries, broccoli, cabbage, etc.

Molecular Formulas

Molecular formulas tell which—and how many—atoms are in a particular molecule. The composition of every molecule is exact. Even a small change in composition results in a very different molecule. For example, hydrogen peroxide (H_2O_2), which has just one more oxygen atom than water (H_2O), is a bleach and disinfectant. The molecular formula does not, however, tell how the atoms are arranged in the molecule. For example, table sugar (sucrose) and milk sugar (lactose) both have the same molecular formula ($C_{12}H_{22}O_{11}$), but their atoms are arranged differently.

Calculating the Amount of a Mineral in a Supplement

Mineral supplements like calcium or iron are ingested in combination with other elements because they don't occur in nature as calcium or iron alone. Calcium carbonate and calcium gluconate are common calcium supplements. Some people taking them don't realize that a 500 mg tablet of calcium carbonate has four times as much calcium as a 500 mg tablet of calcium gluconate.

To calculate the amount of calcium in a calcium supplement, one must know the:

- atoms that make up the supplement
- atomic weights of those atoms
- number of each atom in the molecule (molecular formula)

The molecular formula of calcium carbonate is $CaCO_3$, meaning it has one atom of calcium (Ca), one atom of carbon (C), and three atoms of oxygen (O). The atomic weight is 40 for calcium atom, 12 for carbon, and 16 for oxygen (refer to Appendix A-3 for atomic weights).

The molecular weight of calcium carbonate is the total of the atomic weights of all its atoms: $40+12+16+16+16 = 100$. Calcium accounts for 40 of that 100 (40%), so a 500 mg tablet of calcium carbonate contains 200 mg of calcium ($^{40}/_{100}$ x 500 mg = 200 mg).

In comparison, the molecular formula for calcium gluconate is $C_{12}H_{22}CaO_{14}$. The amount of calcium in a 500-mg tablet of calcium gluconate is calculated using the same method:

12 carbon atoms X 12 (atomic weight) = 144
22 hydrogen atoms X 1 (atomic weight) = 22
 1 calcium atom X 40 (atomic weight)   = 40
14 oxygen atoms X 16 (atomic weight) = 224
_____

Molecular weight (total) = 430

Calcium accounts for 40 of the total of 430 (9%), so a 500-mg tablet of calcium gluconate has only 47 mg of calcium ($^{40}/_{430}$ X 500 mg = 47 mg). This means that if you take 800 mg of calcium as a dietary supplement, you need to take seventeen 500-mg tablets of calcium gluconate— or four 500-mg tablets of calcium carbonate. Other calcium supplements include calcium lactate (13% calcium) and calcium citrate (21% calcium).

Chemical Bonds

The atoms in molecules are held together by chemical bonds such as covalent and ionic bonds. To understand these bonds, we need to return to the basic structure of the atom.

Electrons in an atom orbit the nucleus in pathways called electron shells (shown as circles in Fig. 3-1). Each shell can hold a limited number of electrons. Electrons fill the shells in an orderly fashion, starting with the shell nearest the nucleus. This innermost shell holds a maximum of 2 electrons. If there are more than 2 electrons, the electrons form another shell in an outward direction; this second shell holds a maximum of 8 electrons. After the second shell is filled, a third shell is formed, and so on. Recall that the number of electrons in an atom is different for each element—a unique number of electrons (negative charges) to balance the unique number of protons (positive charges) that characterizes each element (Fig. 3-1).

Atoms like helium and neon (Fig. 3-1) are stable—they don't combine with other atoms because their electron shells are completely full (only the outer shell can be unfilled; the inner shells always are full). Helium (used to fill balloons) and neon (in neon signs) are called noble gases— noble because they don't accept, donate, or share electrons with other atoms. In other words, they don't combine (form bonds) with other atoms, not even with another neon or helium atom; their outer electron shells are already full.

Most atoms don't have a filled outer electron shell, and fill it by accepting, donating, or sharing electrons with other atoms. In other words, these atoms readily combine/bond with other atoms to form molecules.

Ions and Ionic Bonds

Ions

When an atom fills its outer electron shell by accepting or donating electrons, it becomes an ion. Because electrons are negatively charged, atoms become negatively charged ions when they take on extra electrons (have more electrons than protons). Atoms become positively charged ions when they give up electrons (have fewer electrons than protons).

Atoms that have a nearly complete outer electron shell (see chlorine atom in Fig. 3-1) tend to get electrons from another atom. Atoms that have just a beginning of a new electron shell (see sodium atom in Fig. 3-1) tend to give up those electrons to another atom. Chlorine has 7 electrons in its outer shell, and needs only 1 more to fill it. Sodium has only 1 in its outer shell, so sodium readily gives up its single outer-shell electron to chlorine. Both sodium and chloride are now stable—each now has a complete outer electron shell.*

Sodium and chloride now have an electrical charge: sodium has given an electron (negative charge) to chloride.

Sodium, with 11 protons (positive charges), now has only 10 electrons (negative charges). It thus has a net positive charge of +1 and is called a sodium ion (Na^+). Chlorine, with 17 protons, now has 18 electrons. It thus has a net negative charge of -1 and is called a chloride ion (Cl^-).

Ionic Bonds

An ionic bond is formed by the attraction of a positively charged ion to a negatively charged ion (opposite charges attract). This is how a positively charged sodium ion is strongly attracted to a negatively charged chloride ion to form sodium chloride (table salt). An ionic bond is like a bond between a magnet and nails; the nails can be pulled away by another magnet. Ions held together by ionic bonds tend to separate when dissolved in water.†

"And now, for my next compound..."

---

*See bottom of Fig. 3-1 and compare it to sodium and chlorine atoms shown in the top section. Note also that sodium's electron shells are now the same—and as stable—as neon's.

†A water molecule, although overall neutral in charge, has a slight negative charge on one side and a slight positive charge on the other. This is because water's 2 hydrogen atoms (with their positive protons) are on one side of the water molecule (Fig. 3-1). Thus, when sodium chloride is dissolved in water, the charges on the water molecules tend to pull the sodium and chloride ions away from each other.

Figure 3-3: Phenylketonuria (PKU)—One Chemical Reaction Can't Occur

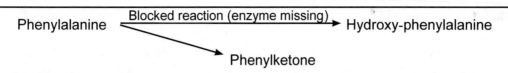

Some phenylalanine is used to make protein. Excess phenylalanine normally undergoes a set series of reactions. In PKU, the first reaction is blocked because the enzyme is missing or deficient. Phenylalanine then accumulates in the blood and damages the infant's developing brain. Accumulation of phenylalanine also causes an abnormal reaction that forms phenylketone, some of which spills over into the urine (phenylketonuria: *phenylketone in the urine).* Newborns are screened for this disease by looking for high phenylalanine in blood or phenylketone in urine. Prenatal diagnosis is also possible.

Salt (sodium chloride) separates into sodium ions and chloride ions when dissolved in the water in our bodily fluids. This separation into ions is very important in the body, e.g., the transmission of nerve impulses depends on sodium and potassium ions. (These ions are also called electrolytes because they conduct electricity.)

We'll see in upcoming chapters that calcium ions are needed for blood to clot, and a nerve cell can transmit nerve impulses because its cell membrane is polarized with positive ions lined up on one side and negative ions lined up on the other. We'll also see how the similarity of ions can fool the body. For example, calcium ions (required by the body) and lead ions (toxic to the body) each have two positive charges. Lead ions are toxic because they interfere with the essential jobs of calcium ions.

Covalent Bonds

Another way in which an atom can fill its outer electron shell is to share electrons with other atoms. This **sharing of electrons** between neighboring atoms creates a very strong and stable bond called a covalent bond *(covalent* in Latin means *strong together).** A water molecule (H_2O) has two hydrogen atoms that each form a covalent bond with oxygen. By sharing electrons, the two hydrogen atoms and the oxygen atom fill their outer electron shells (Fig. 3-1).

When 2 atoms share 1 pair of electrons (1 electron from each atom), it's called a single bond. When 2 atoms share 2 pairs of electrons, it's called a double bond. Scientists draw a single line between the symbols for atoms when the 2 atoms are linked by a single bond; a double line means a double bond. In Fig. 3-1, for example, a single bond between the 2 hydrogen (H) atoms in hydrogen gas is shown as H-H, and the double bonds are shown as O=C=O in carbon dioxide.

The structures of carbohydrates, fats, proteins, vitamins, and even genes are based on arrays of carbon atoms linked together by covalent bonds. It's no coincidence that carbon atoms make up the basic structure of the complex molecules that are unique to life. Carbon plays this central role because it has 4 electrons in its outer electron shell (Fig. 3-1). Since this shell needs 8 electrons to be complete, carbon forms 4 covalent bonds with other atoms (4 pairs of electrons = 8).

This ability to form 4 stable bonds with a wide variety of atoms gives carbon the versatility to form an immense variety of structures, from simple molecules such as carbon dioxide (CO_2) to complex molecules like cholesterol ($C_{27}H_{46}O$). Carbon atoms combine to form the basic structure of carbohydrates, proteins, fat, and even vitamins.

Carbon's versatility can be demonstrated with Tinkertoys, using rods as bonds and hubs as atoms—you can make a larger variety of structures with 4 rods per hub (e.g., carbon) than with only 1 (e.g., hydrogen), 2 (e.g., oxygen), or 3 (e.g., nitrogen) rods per hub. It's not surprising that life on earth is carbon-based.

---

*Covalent bonds are formed when atoms share electrons to become more stable, the electrons orbit the protons in both atoms. To simplify, this isn't shown for the covalent bonds in Fig. 3-1, e.g., hydrogen gas should show the 2 electrons in a single orbit around both protons.

Chemical Reactions

One substance is made from another by making and breaking covalent bonds in chemical reactions. Under ordinary conditions, molecules are rearranged, broken down, or made extremely slowly. The graphite in a pencil won't change to diamond no matter how long it sits on your desk. Laboratories and kitchens use heat, pressure, and changes in acidity to speed up chemical reactions. But in living things, severe changes in heat, pressure, and acidity are fatal.

Using catalysts is another way to speed up chemical reactions. **Enzymes are biological catalysts that accelerate chemical reactions that occur in living things**. Without enzymes, most reactions necessary for life would occur too slowly. Enzymes increase the speed of biochemical reactions by factors of about a million to ten billion. In other words, a reaction that would spontaneously occur once in 1000 years could occur in 1 second with the aid of an enzyme.

Enzymes are very specialized. Each chemical reaction is catalyzed by a specific enzyme. Thousands of enzymes catalyze the thousands of chemical reactions that occur in the human body.

We see the importance of even a single enzyme in the disease phenylketonuria (PKU), which occurs in about 1 of every 16,000 newborns in this country. It's one of many genetic diseases caused by a lack of a single enzyme, in this case a severe deficiency of an enzyme needed to make a simple change in the structure of the amino acid phenylalanine (Fig. 3-3). Lacking this enzyme, phenylalanine can't be processed normally. If the disease isn't diagnosed and treated immediately, this amino acid accumulates in large amounts, causing severe mental retardation.

Newborns in this country are routinely screened for PKU so that affected babies can be diagnosed and treated within the first few days of life. Before birth, the necessary enzyme is provided by the mother. Phenylalanine (found in all proteins) is an essential nutrient. Newborns found to have PKU are immediately taken off milk and put on a special infant formula that has minimal amounts of phenylalanine (barely enough for growth and development) to prevent the abnormal buildup that causes brain damage.

Some people with PKU stay on a low-phenylalanine diet throughout their life. NutraSweet (aspartame) contains phenylalanine; products sweetened with this artificial sweetener are labeled with a warning: *Phenylketonurics: contains phenylalanine.*

Acids and Bases

Whether a liquid is acidic or basic (alkaline) depends on the amount of hydrogen ions in it. Acidity and alkalinity are expressed as pH (pH literally means *hydrogen power* from the French *pouvoir hydrogene).* If a liquid has 0.01 gram (g) of hydrogen ions per liter (about a quart), its pH is 2 because the decimal point is 2 places to the left of 1.0 g of hydrogen ions. A liquid with 0.001 g hydrogen ions per liter has a pH of 3 (the decimal is 3 places to the left of 1.0 g).* When it has between 0.01 and 0.001 g hydrogen ions per liter, the pH is between 2 and 3.

Water-based liquids have a pH between 0 and 14. Pure water has a pH of 7.0 (0.0000001 g of hydrogen ions per liter) and is neutral in pH. **Liquids with a pH less than 7.0** (more hydrogen ions than pure water) **are acidic. Liquids with a pH higher than 7.0** (fewer hydrogen ions than pure water) **are basic**:

pH 0 ◄————— pH 7 ————► pH 14
very acid◄—acid ◄——neutral —►basic►very basic

Acids release hydrogen ions. An acid's strength depends on how easily the hydrogen ions are released. Hydrochloric acid (HCl, *stomach acid)* is strong because it easily separates into hydrogen and chloride ions (Fig. 3-1), thus releasing a lot of hydrogen ions. As a result, stomach fluid is about pH 2. Acetic acid, the acid found in vinegar, is

---

*In technical terms, pH is the negative log of the hydrogen ion concentration: A hydrogen ion concentration of 0.00000001 g per liter is 10-8 g per liter. The negative log of 10-8 is 8 (pH = 8).

"Come on in – the pH is fine."

weak because it doesn't easily release its hydrogen ions. Distilled vinegar is about pH 3.

Keep in mind that the difference between pH 2 and pH 3 is 10-fold (0.01 vs. 0.001 g hydrogen ions per liter). Battery acid has a pH near 0, lemon juice between 2 and 3, orange juice about 4, coffee about 5, and milk is slightly acid with a pH between 6 and 7. We're familiar with an acid taste, as in the tart taste of lemon or stomach acid backing up into the throat.

Bases remove hydrogen ions. Concentrated lye (NaOH, sodium hydroxide)—sometimes used to clear drains—is very basic (about pH 14). Sodium hydroxide easily separates into a sodium ion (Na^+) and a hydroxide ion (OH^-) when dissolved in water. The hydroxide ions (OH^-) combine with hydrogen ions (H^+) to form water (H_2O), thereby removing hydrogen ions. Household ammonia is about pH 11, and a solution of baking soda is about pH 9.

Strong alkaline solutions can break down organic material—like the grease in kitchen drains and the hair in shower drains. A cotton rag will "dissolve" in full-strength chloride laundry bleach (very alkaline). Rub some of this bleach between your fingers, and it feels slippery—it's

breaking down the surface of your skin.

Chemical reactions in the body take place in liquids and are affected by pH. The enzymes needed to catalyze the body's chemical reactions generally function within only a narrow range of pH.

The pH of blood and tissues is slightly basic and is between 7.35 and 7.45, the range at which their enzymes function optimally. The body has many safeguards to keep the pH within this narrow range. Certain blood proteins, for instance, act as buffers—substances that can take up and release hydrogen ions, making it harder to change the pH. The medical term for an abnormally low pH is acidosis; for an abnormally high pH, alkalosis. A blood pH below 7.0 or above 7.7 is fatal.

Energy

We use the word *energy* rather loosely. We say we're full of energy when we wake up in the morning feeling good, anxious to "hit the books" or go to work. In science, energy is a very specific term. It's defined as the capacity to do work (e.g., move or heat something). Scientifically speaking, we're full of energy when we're fat. The energy values of body fat and food and the energy the body uses are expressed as calories.*

The calories in food are measured in a bomb calorimeter, which has a small metal chamber surrounded by water (Fig. 3-4). A precise bit of food is put in the chamber, and the chamber is filled with oxygen. The food sample, ignited by an electric spark, burns in a flash. The heat (calories) generated by this burning is measured by the increased temperature of the surrounding water.

The calories that a person uses can be measured in an apparatus similar to a bomb calorimeter. In

---

*1 calorie = the heat (energy) needed to raise the temperature of 1 milliliter of water 1°C. A "food calorie" is actually 1000 calories—a kilocalorie—but consumers (and this book) call a kilocalorie a calorie.

this case, the chamber is a room, often big enough to even hold furniture. The measurements take much longer because the body doesn't burn its fuel (food) in a flash, but in a slow and controlled manner.

This apparatus for measuring energy expenditure is expensive and has obvious limitations. It certainly can't measure the calories we use playing tennis. But the calories used playing tennis can be measured indirectly by measuring the amount of oxygen used. Calories measured by either method (measuring heat produced or oxygen used) agree within a fraction of 1%.

Our bodies use much of the energy released from food to do work. For this, our cells make a chemical form of energy called **ATP** (adenosine triphosphate). It's made by capturing some of the energy that's released when our cells break apart fat molecules and other energy-providing nutrients (the covalent bonds that link the atoms together in molecules hold energy). ATP is used for energy-requiring activities like muscle contraction and synthesis of enzymes, hormones, and tissues.*

When we "burn" body fuel, the released energy isn't completely captured as ATP. More than half is "lost" as heat, just as we lose some fuel-energy as heat when we burn gasoline by driving a car. This heat can be useful (e.g., maintain normal body temperature) and is the reason we feel warm when we exercise.

In an endurance event, ATP is made and used quickly, and an athlete thinks of the energy lost as heat as wasteful and counterproductive to performance. In contrast, a person struggling to lose weight would like to "waste" more energy/calories as heat, rather than eat less or be more active.

Figure 3-4: Bomb Calorimeter

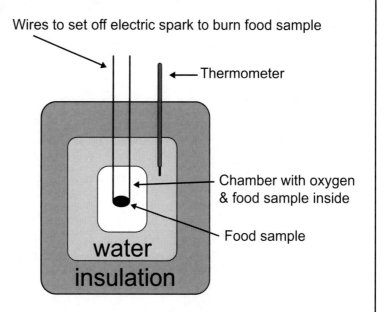

A bomb calorimeter (*calorie meter*) measures the calories in a food. The food is burned in a flash (*like a bomb*), heating the water around the chamber. The rise in temperature is an indirect measure of the food's calories.

Caloric Value of Food

When it's said that an apple has 80 calories, this isn't exactly correct. It's more accurate to say that an apple provides the body with about 80 calories. As measured in a bomb calorimeter, an apple has more calories than the 80 that the body can use. All of a food's calories can't be used if the body can't digest it or break it down to carbon dioxide and water.

The fiber in apples has calories as measured in a bomb calorimeter, but we don't have the enzymes to digest it. Thus, fiber doesn't provide the body with energy. Similarly, wood burns and gives off heat, but we don't get any calories from eating it.

Another example is saccharin, the non-caloric sweetener. It has calories as measured in a bomb calorimeter and is absorbed by the body, but we don't have the necessary enzymes to break it down (i.e., our body can't release any of its energy). We don't get any calories from it, and it's excreted

---

*The workings of key enzymes used to make and use ATP were discovered by Paul Boyer, John Walker, and Jens Skou, who were awarded the 1997 Nobel prize in chemistry.

unchanged in the urine. When it's said that fiber and saccharin don't have any calories, what's meant is that we can't use those calories. The caloric values we're familiar with are actually *physiological calories* (calories that the body *can* use).

Carbohydrate, protein, and fat are called energy-providing nutrients because the body gets energy from them. Conversely, vitamins, minerals, and substances like saccharin don't have calories because the body doesn't get energy from them. The caloric values of the energy-providing nutrients are:

> Carbohydrate* = 4 calories per gram
> Protein = 4 calories per gram
> Fat = 9 calories per gram
> Alcohol = 7 calories per gram

Practical Applications of Calculating Food Calories

Knowing the amounts of carbohydrate, protein, fat, and alcohol in a food, we can calculate its calories. For example, a cup of whole milk that has 11 grams (g) carbohydrate, 8 g protein, and 8 g fat has 148 calories (usually rounded to 150):

> 11 g carbohydrate X 4 calories/g = 44 calories
> 8 g protein X 4 calories/g   = 32 calories
> 8 g fat X 9 calories/g   = <u>72 calories</u>
>   **Total = 148 calories**

It's also useful to calculate how calories are distributed in a food, e.g., what percent of calories comes from fat. The 2010 Dietary Guidelines for Americans recommends that adults get 20-35% of their total calories from fat. To heed this advice, it's easier to compare foods when fat content is given as a percent of total calories, rather than as a percent of total weight. When given as a percent of total weight, comparisons are distorted by the amount of water in the food.

For example, whole milk has, by weight, about 3.5% fat, lower-fat milk 1-2% fat, and non-fat milk almost none. It isn't obvious that switching from whole milk to lower-fat milk would make much difference in % calories from fat. But milk is mostly water, so its fat content, by weight, is low and misleading.

Calculating % calories from fat, we see that about 50% of the calories comes from fat in whole milk, whereas it's 35% for reduced-fat (2% fat) milk, 15% for low-fat (1% fat) milk, and 5% for non-fat milk. Looking at milk's fat content this way, the advice to switch to a lower-fat milk is obviously a good way to lower fat intake.

For this calculation, you only need to know the grams of fat and the total calories in the food, numbers which are on food labels and in food composition tables:

1 cup **whole milk** (3.5% fat by weight): 8 g fat, 150 calories:
> $\dfrac{\text{8 g fat X 9 cal/g}}{\text{150 total calories}}$ X 100 = **48%** of total calories from fat

1 cup **reduced-fat milk** (2% fat by weight): 5 g fat, 125 cal
> $\dfrac{\text{5 g fat X 9 cal/g}}{\text{125 total calories}}$ X 100 = **36%** of total calories from fat

1 cup **low-fat milk** (1% fat by weight): 2 g fat, 120 calories:
> $\dfrac{\text{2 g fat X 9 cal/g}}{\text{120 total calories}}$ X 100 = **15%** of total calories from fat

1 cup of **nonfat milk** (0% fat by weight): 0.5 g fat, 90 cal
> $\dfrac{\text{0.5 g fat X 9 cal/g}}{\text{90 total calories}}$ X 100 = **5%** of total calories from fat

On a package of frankfurters, does *80% fat-free* mean that 80% of the fat was taken out, making them low in fat? Looking more carefully at the label, we find that one of these frankfurter has 100 calories and 8 grams of fat. This means that 72% of the calories comes from fat!

> $\dfrac{\text{8 g fat X 9 cal/g}}{\text{100 total calories}}$ X 100 = **72%** of total cal from fat

The label is misleading but technically correct because fat is given as a percent of total weight, and over half of the frankfurter is water. The label

---

*When talking about carbohydrate's calories or the carbohydrate content of foods, only digestible carbohydrates are considered. Indigestible carbohydrates—dietary fiber—are simply called fiber.

says that each frankfurter weighs 45 g and has 8 g of fat. This means that, by weight, the frankfurter is 18% fat [(8 g fat/45 g total weight) X 100 = 18% fat by weight]. The other 82% is fat-free! It would be more to the point to say, *more than 70% of the calories come from fat.* This, of course, would be disastrous for sales.

It was hard to compare brands of frankfurters when many didn't give nutrition information on their labels. U.S. government standards allow a maximum of 30% fat (by weight) in frankfurters. If it's less that 30%, we'd expect this to be emphasized on the label. A label stating *33% less fat* means that the frankfurters are 20% fat by weight (*80% fat-free!*) instead of the usual 30% (*70% fat-free!*). Fortunately, food labels are now required to give nutrition information, and claims are more tightly regulated. Unfortunately, the percent of calories from fat isn't given on the label (it can be calculated). Guess which food companies object to listing fat this way!

Summary

An atom is a fundamental unit—it can't be broken apart without losing its identity. If carbon and oxygen atoms are broken apart into their component protons, neutrons, and electrons, we can't tell which atoms they came from. Although there are more than 100 kinds of atoms, living substances are made mainly of only four—carbon, hydrogen, oxygen, and nitrogen.

An atom has protons and neutrons in its center (nucleus), and electrons that orbit the nucleus. Elements differ from each other by their number of protons—a different number of protons means a different element, e.g., magnesium has 12 protons; aluminum has 13 protons. Elements with the same numbers of protons but different numbers of neutrons are called isotopes.

Protons have a positive charge; electrons have a negative charge; and neutrons are neutral. An atom has the same number of protons (positive charges) as electrons (negative charges), making the atom itself neutral.

Protons and neutrons have "weight" (the weight of electrons is relatively trivial), and account for the atomic weight. Atomic weights are useful in calculating the amount of a mineral in a supplement, e.g., the amount of calcium in calcium carbonate.

Electrons orbit an atom's nucleus in electron shells. The number of electrons in an atom's outer shell is important in chemical reactions. An atom is stable only if its outer shell is completely filled with electrons. Helium and neon atoms are stable in this way and aren't chemically reactive.

Atoms with an incomplete outer electron shell "chemically react" to fill it and become stable. An atom does this by sharing electrons with other atoms (forming covalent bonds), or by losing or gaining electrons. When an atom loses or gains electrons, it becomes an ion. Because electrons are negatively charged, an atom becomes a positively charged ion when it loses electrons, or becomes a negatively charged ion when it gains electrons.

Molecules consist of two or more atoms held together by chemical bonds. In a covalent bond, atoms are held together by shared electrons. In an ionic bond, a positively charged ion bonds to a negatively charged ion by the attraction of their opposite charges. Water can cause the ions to separate. Ions play crucial roles in the watery fluids of our blood and tissues.

Covalent bonds are much stronger than ionic bonds. The body uses enzymes (biological catalysts) to break apart covalent bonds. In breaking apart bonds and forming new ones, one molecule is made from another. For example, digestive enzymes break apart starch into sugar (starch can't be absorbed from the intestine, but sugar can). In our cells, enzymes can break apart the sugar and join the fragments to make fat. Without enzymes, most of the reactions necessary for life can't proceed.

When talking about how acid a fluid is, we're technically referring to its content of hydrogen ions—the more hydrogen ions, the more acid the fluid. A fluid's acidity or alkalinity is expressed as pH, on a scale of 0 (most acid) to 14 (most basic). pH 7 is neutral, below pH 7 is acid, above pH 7 is basic.

Calories are a measure of energy. Energy in food is measured in a bomb calorimeter—we burn the food, measure the heat released, and give the measurement in calories. The energy-providing nutrients are fat (9 calories per gram), carbohydrate (4 cal/g), protein (4 cal/g), and alcohol (7 cal/g). These values can be used to calculate the amount of calories in a food and the percent of calories from fat, to make "fair" comparisons of the fat in foods.

We not only expend energy as heat, but use energy for work, such as the contractions of the heart muscle or the repair of a wound. For these activities, we use a chemical form of energy called ATP. Our cells make ATP only as needed. We don't store energy as ATP. We store energy (reserve source of calories) mostly as body fat.

We can measure the amount of energy we use for various activities by measuring the amount of heat we produce (ATP is used and heat is produced simultaneously). More commonly, we measure energy use by measuring the amount of oxygen the body uses, because we use oxygen in direct proportion to the amount of energy (calories) we use. Measuring by either method gives equivalent values.

Chapter 4

Dietary Recommendations

...the golden rule in life is moderation in all things.

from the play *The Lady of Andros* by Terence (190-159 B.C.)

Eat your vegetables!

Mom

The goal of a healthy diet is to get enough of the essential nutrients and follow a diet that lowers the risk of diseases like heart disease and cancer. For the essential nutrients, we want to know what they are and how to get enough (and not too much). Less is known about the effect of diet on chronic disease, but scientists know enough to offer dietary guidelines, which are continually updated to include new studies.

Essential Nutrients

To be classified as an essential nutrient, a substance must be shown to be needed in the diet for health and normal development and reproduction. This definition has been very useful, especially for including or excluding substances that have been proposed as essential nutrients, but it does present a few problems.

Vitamin D, for example, can be made in skin exposed to sunshine (ultraviolet light). Thus, many of us don't need D in our diet. But those who don't get enough sun do need D in their diet. As another example, most of us don't need

vitamin K in our diet because we get enough by absorbing the K made by intestinal bacteria. But we need K in our diet when not enough is made—as can happen if we take antibiotics for a long time (antibiotics can kill intestinal bacteria that make K).

We need energy (calories), protein, specific molecules that the body can't make (vitamins and certain amino acids and fatty acids), and certain elements (required minerals). These are listed in Table 4-1.

Water

Water isn't generally called a nutrient as such, but it's obviously essential. We can survive months without food, but only days without water. We feel the deficiency—dehydration—immediately. The body is over half water, and water is the bodily fluid in which chemical reactions take place and in which substances are transported. Water also plays a crucial role in keeping us from overheating—we are cooled as the water in perspiration evaporates from our skin.

Table 4-1: Essential Nutrients

Energy-providing nutrients
Carbohydrate
Fat: Essential fatty acids Linoleic acid (omega-6), Linolenic acid (omega-3)
Protein: Essential amino acids histidine, isoleucine, leucine, lysine, methionine, phenylalanine threonine, tryptophan, valine
Minerals
Major minerals: Calcium, Chloride, Magnesium, Phosphorus, Potassium, Sodium
Trace minerals: Chromium, Copper, Fluoride, Iodine, Iron, Manganese, Molybdenum, Selenium, Zinc
Vitamins (alternate names in parentheses).
Fat-soluble:
Vitamin A (retinol, retinal, retinoic acid)
Vitamin D (ergocalciferol, cholecalciferol)
Vitamin E (tocopherol, tocotrienol)
Vitamin K (phylloquinone, menaquinones, menadione)
Water-soluble:
Vitamin C (ascorbic acid, ascorbate)
B-vitamins:
Thiamin (vitamin B_1)
Riboflavin (vitamin B_2)
Niacin (nicotinic acid, nicotinamide, niacinamide)
Vitamin B_6 (pyridoxine, pyridoxal, pyridoxamine)
Folate (folic acid, folacin)
Vitamin B_{12} (cobalamin)
Biotin
Pantothenic acid

The amount of water we need depends on our activities, the weather, etc., but our body is adept in balancing the amount we use with the amount we take in. Under normal conditions, adults need about a quart to a quart-and-a-half of water per 1,000 calories used, e.g., 2-3 quarts/day for someone who uses 2,000 calories/day. This doesn't mean we have to drink this much water. We get a lot of water in food (note how much water is absorbed by rice as it cooks, or how much smaller a dried apricot is than a fresh one), and some as a byproduct of some chemical reactions in the body.

If we take in more than we need, we urinate more. If we use more than we take in, we get thirsty. But thirst isn't a reliable gauge when a lot of water is lost fast, as in severe diarrhea or vomiting, or in the profuse sweat loss from strenuous exercise in hot weather. Also, the thirst mechanism doesn't work as well in the elderly. In such situations, one should make a point of drinking enough water. Urine is normally light yellow, so a change to a deeper yellow typically indicates a need to drink more water.

It's very important for an athlete to drink plenty of water to prevent dehydration. Dehydration interferes with performance—and can lead to heat stroke. In hot weather, the sweat losses that occur in endurance events can be so large that athletes can't drink and absorb water fast enough to keep pace with their need. For events longer than a half-hour, athletes should drink plenty of water before, during, and after the event, even if they aren't thirsty. Cold water may be preferable because it's absorbed a little faster, and is itself cooling. But unchilled water is fine. A note of caution: don't overdo the water. Drinking water beyond what's necessary to replace water loss during an event can dilute the sodium in blood to dangerously low levels.

For most athletic endeavors of less than 90 minutes, plain water is all that's needed for optimal performance. Sports drinks don't give any performance advantage over plain water, except perhaps the psychological boost of believing they do. In endurance events of more than 90 minutes, beverages of 6 to 8% carbohydrate (glucose, sucrose, or glucose polymer), starting about 30 minutes before fatigue sets in, can enhance performance. Most commercial sports drinks have this amount.

One-third cup of table sugar (sucrose) per quart of water makes a sports drink of 7% carbohydrate.* You can add a bit of unsweetened Kool-Aid for flavor and color. A bit of sodium in the drink also seems to help by speeding up the absorption of the sugar and water. Adding 1/8 teaspoon of table salt (sodium chloride) per quart provides about 70 mg sodium per cup.

---

*Diluting some fruit juices with an equal part of water can also give you a 7% carbo drink. Undiluted apple juice, for example, is about 13% carbohydrate.

Taking sodium or other minerals isn't generally necessary. Loss of sodium and other minerals in sweat is small and doesn't compromise performance, except in extreme circumstances. (Add sodium to drinking water in endurance events of more than 4 hours; sweat loss is large and prolonged.) Furthermore, the body adapts to regular, heavy sweating. A trained athlete's sweat has less sodium and other electrolytes than sweat of an untrained person. Following the event, the lost minerals are readily replenished by a normal diet.

Other nutrients, such as amino acids and vitamins, taken right before or during an event don't help, and can even be detrimental to performance if taken in large amounts. Such excesses cause more urine to be made, hastening dehydration.

"Look—who cares what the nitrate level is?"

Energy-Providing Nutrients

The body gets energy from carbohydrate, fat, and protein (and alcohol). Besides water, these energy-providing nutrients—the topic of the next chapter—make up the bulk of the diet. They provide energy and also the basic molecular building blocks. For example, carbohydrate, fat, and protein can all be broken down to a 2-carbon molecule called acetate, the building block of some big molecules like cholesterol. Acetate is also the building block used to make the body fat that stores excess calories. This is why we can get fat whether the excess calories come from carbohydrate, protein, or fat.

Essential Amino Acids and Fatty Acids: Protein and fat also provide certain molecules that the body needs but can't make (Table 4-1).

Protein provides essential amino acids; fat provides essential fatty acids.

Vitamins

The other essential molecules that we need in our diet are called vitamins. There are 13 vitamins, grouped by whether they dissolve in fat or water. Vitamins A, D, E, and K are fat-soluble. Vitamin C and the eight B-vitamins (biotin, folate, niacin, pantothenic acid, riboflavin, thiamin, B_6, and B_{12}) are water-soluble.

Knowing whether they dissolve in fat or water has practical value. If you boil vegetables in water and discard the water, you lose some of the vegetable's water-soluble vitamins. Also, the body can rid itself of excess water-soluble vitamins in the urine; excess fat-soluble vitamins can't be excreted this way and are thus more likely to be toxic in big doses. (As with the disease PKU, discussed in the previous chapter, a familiar theme is that accumulating large amounts of even an essential substance can be harmful.) The vitamins are listed in Appendix A-5 along with some of their functions, food sources, and symptoms of deficiency and toxicity.

The hodgepodge of names given to vitamins is confusing. It began logically. In 1920, scientists thought there were three vitamins—A, B, and C. But vitamin B turned out to be eight vitamins, and some that were thought to be vitamins (e.g., B_{11}) didn't turn out to be. The naming was then in confusion, and vitamins were given alternate names, e.g., B_{12} is also called cobalamin because it contains cobalt. It also was found that vitamins can occur in several forms. Adding to the confusion, some substances can be converted to vitamins in the body, e.g., the amino acid tryptophan can be converted into the B-vitamin niacin.

Sometimes substances are promoted as vitamins when they really aren't. Pangamic acid has been called vitamin B_{15} and promoted for treating various ills. Laetrile has been called vitamin B_{17} and promoted for treating cancer. Neither are vitamins and have no known value in treating illnesses or maintaining health. But there's monetary value in naming substances vitamins—it helps make millions of dollars for their promoters.

Minerals

The human body is mostly carbon, hydrogen, oxygen, and nitrogen. These four elements make up about 99% of the atoms in the body. We get enough carbon, hydrogen, and oxygen by breathing and by meeting energy and water needs. We get nitrogen (and sulfur) as a part of the protein we eat. We need cobalt only because we need vitamin B_{12} (cobalt is a part of B_{12}). Thus, specific dietary requirements aren't given for these elements because we automatically get them by meeting other requirements.

Fifteen minerals are known to be essential in our diet (Table 4-1). Some are listed in Appendix A-5 along with some of their functions, foods sources, and symptoms of deficiency and toxicity.

The body protects itself from accumulating too much of a mineral by getting rid of excesses in the urine or by controlling the amount absorbed in the intestine in the first place. Sodium is easily absorbed, and excesses can be excreted in the urine. Water is needed to get rid of sodium, so we need more water if we ingest excess sodium. In other words, if we eat a lot of salty food (table salt is sodium chloride), we feel thirsty, drink more, and urinate more. Places that sell beer don't lose money on free bowls of salty nuts, pretzels, or tortilla chips!

In contrast, excess iron can be toxic and isn't excreted in the urine. So the intestine acts as a gatekeeper and doesn't let much in. But it can increase absorption a bit when a person's need goes up, e.g., during pregnancy.

Determining Amounts Needed

How much of these nutrients do we need? Scientist use methods that range from simply estimating the amounts consumed by normal, healthy populations, to using sophisticated lab equipment to determine precisely the nutrient requirements of individuals recruited for these special studies. As expected, individual requirements vary within a certain range, just as they vary in other measures like height and weight—normal variation (Fig. 4-1). Most adults are about 5 to $6\frac{1}{2}$ feet tall. Some are outside this range, but usually not by much. It's rare to see an adult 3 or 8 feet tall.

Nutrient needs of a specific person can't be determined without measuring that person individually. This is expensive, tedious, and usually requires long-term confinement. Estimates of averages and the range of variation of nutrient needs are derived from numerous studies, and generous recommendations are made to cover the needs of a population adequately.

To determine a level of intake that covers the range of individual needs, the average requirement and how widely the requirements vary are estimated. Individual requirements (as well as body weight, test scores, etc.) are generally

Figure 4-1: The Normal Curve

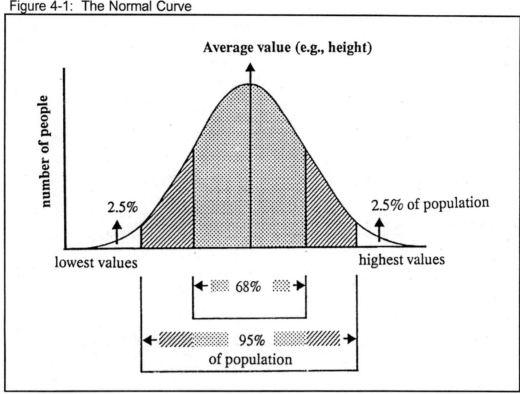

distributed in a bell-shaped distribution called a normal curve (Fig. 4-1). Most people are near the average. The further one moves away from the average, the fewer people there are.

This normal variation is taken into account in setting dietary recommendations. It's like deciding what the standard height for doorways should be. Everyone needn't be measured. Even without measuring anyone, you can make a good estimate by measuring old, existing doorways. A standard doorway is high enough for most people to pass through without having to duck (*the recommended intake meets most people's need*). Even people taller than the doorway need only duck, not crawl (*for the few with higher needs, it isn't higher by much*). What a specific person needs in doorway height (*the amount of a nutrient*) can be determined only by measuring that particular person.

Recommendations

Different countries have their own set of recommendations, as do organizations like the World Health Organization. Recommendations vary according to a country's population, native diet, and even the designated committee—different scientists with different opinions. For example, iron is more poorly absorbed from plants than it is from meat, so populations whose native diet is mainly vegetarian need more iron in their diet.

Setting standards isn't easy. For example, if a person doesn't get enough calories, the body uses protein for its calories rather than using it to meet protein needs. This makes it hard to set protein requirements in developing countries. Should the protein recommendation be higher, because calories are inadequate? Or should it be based on protein needs alone, as if people got enough calories (even if they don't)? This isn't a trivial question. When food policies are made, or when food aid is given, these dietary standards are used. It's much more expensive to provide protein than to provide calories. Using protein to provide calories is an inefficient use of resources.

In developing countries, the recommended levels of nutrients are usually lower than in developed countries—countries with a limited food supply can't afford the luxury of big margins over average requirements. The recommended intakes in different countries aren't identical, but it's reassuring and expected that they're similar.

As countries become more developed, dietary deficiencies become less common, and chronic diseases become more common. Heart disease, cancer, and diabetes are leading causes of death in developed countries. Thus, dietary guidelines in the U.S. focus more on the relation of diet to chronic diseases.

The Recommended Dietary Allowances and the Guide to Daily Food Choices make specific recommendations for meeting nutrient needs. The Dietary Guidelines for Americans and other such guidelines give more general advice, e.g., emphasizing the importance of moderation in the amount of fat and salt in the diet.

Recommended Dietary Allowances (RDAs)

During World War II, the U.S. government needed a guide for feeding the troops (many of the nutrients had just been identified in the previous decade). The Food and Nutrition Board of the National Academy of Sciences, made up of distinguished scientists with expertise in various areas of nutrition, was and is in charge of making this guide. The Board examines the scientific data, and then decides on the Recommended Dietary Allowances (RDAs)—amounts of nutrients in the diet that would be expected to meet the needs of virtually all healthy people in the United States (97.5% of a normal population; Fig. 4-1). RDAs don't quite cover those with the highest need (about 2.5% of the population). But even these people would be close to meeting their needs at RDA levels (Fig. 4-1).

The amounts recommended in the diet typically are higher than the amounts actually required by the body. Iron, for example, is poorly absorbed from the diet, so the RDA for iron is about ten times more than the body's requirement.

For some nutrients, the requirements aren't well established, and the RDAs are based mainly on customary intakes of healthy populations.

Our needs differ if we're growing, menstruating, pregnant, etc., so there are several sets of RDAs. The set for infants, for example, is used by manufacturers of infant formula. The sets of adult RDAs for some nutrients are given in Appendix A-4.

RDAs aren't daily requirements in the sense that you'll be deficient if you don't meet them every day. They're for daily averages because diets vary from day to day, and are generous; they aren't minimums. RDAs allow enough for normal stresses of daily life for adequate reserves in the body—even for water-soluble vitamins. Practically speaking, it's advised that nutrient intakes average the RDAs over several days. Dietary assessments are commonly done on 3-day diet records. (Disease can change dietary needs, and dietitians give special advice in such cases.)

RDAs are useful as applied to populations, but aren't as useful for individuals. You don't know what your exact requirements are (i.e., where you fall on the curve); you can use RDAs only to estimate the likelihood that you're getting enough. If your diet meets the RDAs, you can be quite sure you're meeting your needs. All that can be said beyond this is that the farther your intake falls below the RDAs, the greater the likelihood that you aren't getting enough.

RDAs are revised periodically to reflect new scientific knowledge. The 10th revision of the RDAs was published in 1989 as a single book by the National Academy of Sciences. The 11th and current revisions are published in several volumes (see Appendix A-6). The new values are called Dietary Reference Intakes (Fig. 4-2). They include the customary RDAs, and also include a Tolerable Upper Intake Level (UL—amount beyond which adverse effects have been known to occur, and an Estimated Average Requirement (EAR). Also, for the first time, the revisions are a joint effort with Canada.

Since World War II, the use of RDAs has expanded from its original use as a guide to plan and procure food for national defense. RDAs are now used for such purposes as evaluating diets of various groups in the U.S. population, establishing guidelines for food-assistance programs (e.g., school lunch programs) and food labels, and developing nutrition policy and nutrition education programs. This diverse use of the RDAs has complicated their revision; there are now economic and political issues.

Daily Values (DVs)

Daily Values are used for labeling food and dietary supplements. The Daily Value (DV) is a recommended amount, and a nutrient is given on the label as a percentage of this amount (% DV). This gives some perspective to the consumer. If told that there's 1 milligram of zinc in a food, we can't tell if this is a lot or a trivial amount, unless we have some idea of the recommended amount. It's much more useful to be told that the amount of zinc in a food is 5% of the recommended amount.

There are many sets of RDAs, so it's unwieldy to put the percentages of each set on a label. Thus, using the 1968 RDAs (the most current when DVs were created in 1973), one adult set of DVs (see Appendix A-4) was made by taking the highest RDA for each nutrient for those over age 4 (excluding pregnant or nursing women).* DVs

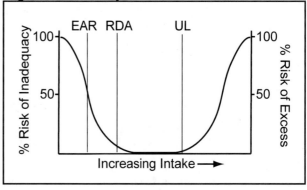

Figure 4-2: Dietary Reference Intakes

are set at 100%, and the nutrient content is labeled as % DV, e.g., a supplement with 6 mg of vitamin B_6 would be labeled as having 300% DV (the DV is 2 mg; 6 mg is 300% of 2 mg).

DVs are even more generous than RDAs. This means that you don't necessarily have to get 100% of a DV to get your RDA. For example, the DV for iron is 18 mg—the 1968 RDA for women of childbearing age (their current RDA is also 18 mg). The RDA for adult men is only 8 mg because they don't normally have blood losses (women lose iron in menstrual blood). A man getting 9 mg iron would be getting 50% DV for iron (9 mg is 50% of the 18 mg DV), but this is actually 112% of his RDA (9 mg is 112% of his 8 mg RDA).

DVs also include reference values for dietary components such as total fat, saturated fat, cholesterol, fiber, sodium. Values for some are based on the recommended amount in a 2,000-calorie diet. For example, it's advised that less than 10% of our calories come from saturated fat. On a 2,000 calorie diet, this means less than 22 grams of saturated fat (rounded to 20 gm on the label; see Fig. 4-3). So if a serving has 5 grams of saturated fat, its fat content is given as 25% DV (5 gm is 25% of 20 gm). This means, of course, that if you eat 2 servings, you'll have eaten 50% of your "allotment" for the day.

Nutrient deficiency diseases used to be our biggest nutritional problem, but now it's chronic diseases related to excess calories, solid fats, and sodium, and not enough fiber. So food labels

*There are 3 other sets of Daily Values: for infants up to 12 months old, children 1 to 4 years old, and pregnant women. These are used to label products intended specifically for these groups, e.g., the set for pregnant women is used for labeling prenatal supplements.

emphasize these. Regulations specify which health claims (e.g., *calcium may help prevent osteoporosis)* and terms (e.g., *low fat)* can be used on a label, and also define the descriptions (e.g., a food labeled *low-fat* can't have more than 3 grams of fat per serving).

Federal regulations require nutrition information on most food labels (Fig. 4-2, Table 4-2). It's voluntary for some foods. Grocery stores are expected to voluntarily provide nutrition information for meat and the most common fresh produce and seafood.*

ChooseMyPlate.gov Eating Guide

ChooseMyPlate.gov recommends a certain number of servings ("cups") per day from the grain, vegetable, fruit, dairy, and protein (meat/meat-substitute) groups (Table 4-3). Each group is particularly rich in certain nutrients, e.g., the dairy group is a rich source of calcium, riboflavin, and high-quality protein. The Guide is shown graphically in ChooseMyPlate.gov (Fig. 4-4) with vegetables, grains, and fruit groups filling most of the plate, with a smaller section for the protein group, and a "glass" for the dairy group. It replaces the Food Guide Pyramid graphic.

The serving sizes aren't always realistic; they're made to be somewhat equivalent in certain nutrients. One serving in the dairy group has about 300 mg calcium: 1 cup milk or 1½ oz cheddar cheese or 2 cups cottage cheese. Thus, ½ cup cottage cheese is ¼ only serving in the dairy group. Also, it's confusing that the serving size on a food label may be different than the serving size in this Guide. To try to lessen the confusion, we'll call a serving in a food group, a [nutrient] *portion* in Table 4-3.

The numbers of recommended portions for vegetable, fruit, and grain may seem high, but it isn't unusual to consume 1½ cup spaghetti (3 grain portions), 1½ cup orange juice (2 fruit portions), and bread two at a time in a sandwich or as two halves of a bagel or hot dog bun (2 grain portions).

Variety is important. We're assured of some variety by eating foods from each of the food groups, but we also should choose a variety within each group. The Guide steers us toward meeting nutrient needs. It's less helpful in steering us away from excesses.

Dietary Guidelines for Americans

The Dietary Guidelines Advisory Committee (made up of our top experts), established by the U.S. Dept. of Agriculture and U.S. Dept. of Health and Human Services, recommends a set of Dietary Guidelines for Americans ages 2 years and over. First published in 1980, they are revised every 5 years to reflect new scientific knowledge.

The 2010 Guidelines are very specific and detailed and underlie two broad concepts below. See www.dietaryguidelines.gov for details.

- **Maintain calorie balance over time to achieve and sustain a healthy weight** (Table 4-4). Focus on being physically active and consuming only enough calories to meet your needs at all stages of life, from childhood to old age.

  Balancing Calories: Enjoy your food, but eat less. Avoid oversized portions. Be physically active by picking activities that you like and start doing what you can for at least 10 minutes at a time.

- **Focus on consuming nutrient-dense foods and beverages.** The typical American diet is too high in calories, sodium, solid fat, added sugar, and refined grains. So the recommendation is to cut back on these and replace them with vegetables, fruits, whole grains (e.g., whole

---

*In order of popularity (in case you're curious): Fruit: banana, apple, watermelon, orange, cantaloupe, grape, grapefruit, strawberry, peach, pear, nectarine, honeydew, plum, avocado, lemon, pineapple, tangerine, cherry, kiwi, lime. Vegetable: potato, iceberg lettuce, tomato, onion, carrot, celery, corn, broccoli, cabbage, cucumber, bell pepper, cauliflower, leaf lettuce, sweet potato, mushroom, green onion, green bean, radish, summer squash, asparagus. Seafood: shrimp, cod, pollock, catfish, scallop, salmon, flounder, sole, oyster, orange roughy, mackerel, ocean perch, rockfish, whiting, clam, haddock, blue crab, rainbow trout, halibut, lobster.

Table 4-2: Nutrition Facts on Food Labels

Required*	Optional†
Calories per serving	
Calories from fat	Calories from saturated fat
Total fat	
Saturated fat	Polyunsaturated fat
Trans fat	Monounsaturated fat
Cholesterol	
Sodium	Potassium
Total carbohydrate	
Dietary fiber	Soluble fiber
	Insoluble fiber
Sugars	Sugar alcohol (e.g., sorbitol)
Protein	
Vitamin A	
Vitamin C	Other vitamins, minerals
Calcium	
Iron	

* Exceptions allowed in certain circumstances, e.g., soft-drink labels don't have to list cholesterol, fiber, etc.

† But required if they've been added, or if label makes claims about them; e.g., zinc's %DV required if zinc has been added to the food.

wheat, brown rice, oats, and whole grain corn), fat-free or low-fat milk or milk products, seafood, lean meats and poultry, eggs, beans and peas, and nuts and seeds.

- **Foods to Increase:** Make half your plate fruits and vegetables. These are rich in vitamins, minerals, fiber, and a variety of substances that lower the risk of heart disease and some cancers. They also tend to be low in fat.
- **Foods to Reduce:** Cut back on foods high in solid fats, added sugars, and salt, e.g., compare sodium in foods like soup, bread, and frozen meals—and choose the foods with lower numbers. Switch to nonfat or low-fat (1%) milk and milk products. Drink water instead of sugary drinks.
- **If you drink alcoholic beverages, do so in moderation.** Women who are pregnant or trying to conceive shouldn't drink any alcohol; alcohol can damage the unborn child.

Moderate drinking = no more than 1 drink per day for women; no more than 2 for men. One drink = about ½ oz pure alcohol, e.g., a 12-oz can or bottle of beer or wine cooler, 5 oz table wine, 1 jigger 1½ oz) vodka, rum, whisky, or gin.

Practical Application of Dietary Guides

Several organizations and government agencies give dietary advice, e.g., the American Heart Association (www.americanheart.org) and the American Cancer Society (www.cancer.org). Most of the dietary recommendations are covered by the Dietary Guidelines for Americans and ChooseMyPlate.gov. It's reassuring that experts from these various groups give similar advice.

Food groups focus on providing enough nutrients. Dietary guides help us select foods within food groups. Drinking non-fat or low-fat milk instead of whole milk, for example, means making a selection in the dairy group that is lower in saturated fat* and cholesterol. Also, non-fat and low-fat milk have fewer calories, so this choice can help sustain a healthy weight.

A major source of saturated fat is dairy fat (butterfat), as in cheese, ice cream, and whole milk. Fatty meat is another major source. To cut back, order a hamburger instead of a cheeseburger. How about pepperoni-mushroom pizza instead of pepperoni-sausage pizza; thick- instead of thin-crust pizza; ice milk, sherbet, or low-fat frozen yogurt instead of ice cream? Don't forget the possibility of just smaller portions of your favorite foods!

Make changes gradually. It's hard to switch abruptly from, say, whole milk to non-fat milk. Switch by combining whole milk and 2%-fat milk, gradually increasing the proportion of low-fat milk. Once you switch to the 2%, combine 2% and 1%-fat milk, and then 1 % and non-fat milk. Once you switch to non-fat milk, even low-fat milk may taste like cream and can then substitute

---

*The recommendation is to limit saturated fat intake to less than 10% of total calories: 10 g or less per 1,000 calories = 9% or less of calories from saturated fat (saturated fat is discussed in the next chapter).

Figure 4-3: Nutrition Facts on Food Labels

Serving sizes are stated in both household and metric measures.

The general goal is to choose foods that add up to 100% of the DV for total carbohydrate, fiber, vitamins, and minerals, and add up to less than 100% of the DV for fat, saturated fat, cholesterol, and sodium.

Many women, teenage girls, and less-active men use about 2,000 calories/day.

Nutrition Facts

Serving Size 1 cup (228g)
Servings Per Container 2

Amount Per Serving

Calories 250   Calories from Fat 110

	% Daily Value*
Total Fat 12g	**18%**
Saturated Fat 3g	**15%**
Trans Fat 1.5g	
Cholesterol 30mg	**10%**
Sodium 470mg	**20%**
Total Carbohydrate 31g	**10%**
Dietary Fiber 0g	**0%**
Sugars 5g	
Protein 5g	
Vitamin A	4%
Vitamin C	2%
Calcium	20%
Iron	4%

* Percent Daily Values are based on a 2,000 calorie diet. Your Daily Values may be higher or lower depending on your calorie needs:

	Calories:	2,000	2,500
Total Fat	Less than	65g	80g
Sat Fat	Less than	20g	25g
Cholesterol	Less than	300mg	300mg
Sodium	Less than	2,400mg	2,400mg
Total Carbohydrate		300g	375g
Dietary Fiber		25g	30g

% Daily Value (DV) shows how a food fits in your overall diet. Some DVs are upper levels (less than 20g saturated fat); some are recommended amounts (calcium: 1000 mg).

20% calcium means that 1 serving gives you 20% (200 mg) of what you need to get this recommended amount (1000 mg).

Many men, teenage boys, and very active women use about 2,500 calories/day.

for cream in coffee, etc. Dairy companies make the switch to lower fat milk easier by adding dry or condensed non-fat milk to give it more body.*

The dietary recommendations form the basis of a prudent diet—there are good reasons to believe that the advice is healthful, and there are few, if any, reasons to believe it's harmful. Most of us have a lot to gain from following the recommendations, whether we're overweight or underweight, athletes or couch potatoes.

Upcoming chapters explain in more detail how the dietary advice relates to health, and provide a basic knowledge of food composition so that we can make healthful choices. Some knowledge of how the body functions and the role of nutrients

in these bodily functions also is needed, not only to understand the basis of the various dietary guides, but also to make intelligent assessments of all dietary advice.

As a final note, keep in mind that it's the overall diet—not individual foods—that's *good* or *bad*. Think in terms of being able to eat anything you want—just make a habit of eating foods like candy, hot dogs, and potato chips in smaller amounts or not as often. People often think of healthy food as being bland and boring. Many cuisines tell us otherwise. What could be less boring, yet so in keeping with dietary guidelines, than a burrito topped with a hearty portion of a zesty salsa of red tomatoes, purple onions, bright

---

*Adding extra milk solids also adds more protein, calcium, etc. So it may say protein fortified on the carton. Vitamin A (fat-soluble) is removed when fat is removed, so A is usually added to low- and non-fat milk. Vitamin D is usually added to all milk (milk isn't naturally rich in D). D can be made in the skin with sun exposure, but it isn't a reliable source because not everyone gets enough sun. Children usually get their calcium from milk and need lots of calcium and D relative to their body size, so it's reasonable to use milk to provide D as well.

Figure 4-4: ChooseMyPlate.gov

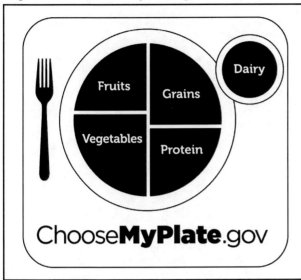

Make half your plate fruits and vegetables.

Eat red, orange, and dark-green vegetables, such as tomatoes, sweet potatoes, and broccoli, in main and side dishes.

Eat fruit, vegetables, or unsalted nuts as snacks—they are nature's original fast foods.

Switch to skim or 1% milk. They have the same amount of calcium and other essential nutrients as whole milk, but less fat and calories. Try calcium-fortified soy products as an alternative to dairy foods.

Make at least half your grains whole grains.

green cilantro, chili peppers, lime juice, and a dash of olive oil and salt?

Eating for health and eating for pleasure can be the same. Eating is more than ingesting a collection of nutrients. Good eating encompasses the social, cultural, and sensual aspects that we find so pleasurable.

Dietary Supplements

Many people don't meet all their RDAs (it's also true that people who take supplements tend to be those who need them the least). Not knowing whether our diet meets the RDAs, many of us take a multivitamin/mineral pill (the kind with 100% DV) *just in case.* This is reasonable, but still needs to be considered carefully, e.g., most men and postmenopausal women shouldn't take iron (see Chap. 7). Generally speaking, buy the least expensive pills, e.g., the body doesn't differentiate between vitamin C made in a lab and that extracted from rose hips—vitamin C is simply vitamin C.

Dietary supplements also include a wide variety of products—from protein powders to herbs—too wide a variety to discuss here. Be extra-cautious with these. Unlike drugs or food additives, dietary supplements don't have to be proven safe and effective (and may not even contain what they say) before being marketed.

You may already get a vitamin/mineral pill in your breakfast cereal (or energy bar), e.g., the label says, *has 100% DV of 13 vitamins and minerals!* Look at the label's ingredient list and Nutrition Facts section to see what and how much has been added. This is an expensive way to take a supplement. Buying an unfortified brand of the cereal and the vitamin/mineral pills separately saves money, and you're less likely to overdo it. Many cereals have a pill's worth sprayed on a serving (about a cup of flakes; about ½ cup of heavier cereal), and some people eat several bowls a day, e.g., college students looking for *fast food* in empty cupboards.

A pregnant woman who eats several servings of fortified cereal and energy bars in addition to vitamin pills can get several times her RDA of vitamin A—enough to risk a birth defect from excess A. Men who eat iron-fortified food and take iron-containing vitamin/mineral pills can get several times their RDA of iron—enough to worry about long-term accumulation of iron to toxic levels (see Chap. 7).

A few other caveats:
• A nutrient can cure what ails you only if the ailment stems from a deficiency of that nutrient. This seems obvious, but lots of supplements are sold by suggesting they're the answer to your lack of energy, bleeding gums, etc. Deficiencies can be at fault, but the usual causes are much

Table 4-3: Eating Guide for Ages 9 and older*

Grain Group: 5-8 portions† including 3-4 portions of **whole grains**.*

1 portion = 1 small pancake, regular slice of bread, small corn or flour tortilla; half a hamburger bun or hot dog bun or bagel or English muffin; 5 whole wheat crackers; 7 saltine crackers or round snack crackers; 4 square graham crackers; 1 oz. dry cereal (= 1 cup** cornflakes, ¼ cup Grape-Nuts); ½ cup cooked rice, pasta, cereal, grits.

Vegetable Group: 2-3 portions,† including dark-green, and red and yellow vegetables. See Fruit Group for portion sizes.

Fruit Group: 1½ - 2 portions†

1 fruit or vegetable portion = 1 medium fruit or vegetable (e.g., apple, carrot, banana, potato); 2 cups raw, leafy green vegetable (e.g., lettuce); 1 cup cooked or chopped fruit or vegetable (e.g., broccoli, applesauce, canned peaches, cooked spinach, cooked beans††, baby carrots); 1 cup (8 fl. oz) 100% vegetable or fruit juice (for fruit drinks, count only the amount of juice stated on the label, e.g., 1 cup fruit drink of 25% juice = ¼ cup juice).

Dairy Group: 3 portions

1 portion = 1 cup milk (or calcium-fortified soy milk), yogurt (regular or frozen), milk-based pudding, custard; 1½ cups ice cream, 2 cups cottage cheese; 1½ oz (1 oz = 1" cube) regular cheese (e.g., cheddar, swiss, monterey jack, mozzarella, parmesan); 2 oz processed cheese (e.g., Velveeta). [Cream cheese doesn't count; it's more like butter.]

Protein (Meat or Meat-substitute) Group: 2½ - 3 portions†

1 portion = 2 oz*** cooked poultry, fish, meat (including processed meats like frankfurters, bologna); 2 eggs; ½ cup cooked peas, beans, lentils or soybean curd (tofu); 1 oz. nuts or seeds, 2 Tablespoons peanut butter or almond butter, 4 Tablespoons hummus.

---

*Go to ChooseMyPlate.gov for ages 2-8 and for further details (e.g., list of whole grains, dark-green vegetables).
†Go to ChooseMyPlate.gov for specific number of portions by age and gender, within range for age 9 and older.
**1 cup = 16 Tablespoons = 8 fluid ounces (fl oz), a regular can of soda = 1½ cups = 12 fl oz
††1 cup cooked beans = 1 portion in the vegetable group or 2 portions in the protein group.
***The size of a deck of cards = ~ 1½ portions = 3 oz (ounces) cooked poultry, fish, meat; 16 oz = 1 lb..

---

more mundane (e.g., tired from not enough sleep, bleeding gums from poor dental hygiene) and aren't helped by supplements. Also, many ailments disappear on their own, e.g., an ache that comes and goes. If you get better after taking a supplement, the supplement often gets the credit, whether any credit is due.

- Nutrients at extremely high doses act as drugs rather than nutrients. Huge doses (1,000 to 9,000 mg) of the B-vitamin nicotinic acid (niacin) are used to treat high blood-cholesterol (see Chap. 8) and can have serious side-effects, e.g., liver damage, so should only be used under

a physician's care. The vitamin doesn't function here as a vitamin (the adult RDA is 14 to 16 mg).

- When you hear that a study showed a supplement helped prevent cancer, etc., look more closely at the study before running out to buy a bottle. For example, a study showing that selenium supplements lowered the incidence of cancer was widely publicized (see Chap. 2). The subjects were deficient in selenium because they lived in an area of rural China where the local soil was extremely low in selenium and their diet was almost exclusively locally grown

Table 4-4: A Healthy Weight*

BMI Categories for Adults

		Risk of Disease
Underweight	<18.5	
Normal weight	18.5-24.9	
Overweight	25.0-29.9	Increased
Obese (class 1)	30.0-34.9	High
Obese (class 2)	35.0-39.9	Very High
Extreme obese (class 3)	40.0+	Extremely High

Ht	Wt	Ht	Wt	Ht	Wt
4'10"	89-119	5'5"	111-150	6'0"	136-184
4'11"	92-123	5'6"	115-154	6'1"	140-189
5'0"	95-128	5'7"	118-159	6'2"	144-194
5'1"	98-132	5'8"	122-164	6'3"	148-199
5'2"	101-136	5'9"	125-169	6'4"	152-205
5'3"	104-141	5'10"	129-174	6'5"	156-210
5'4"	108-145	5'11"	133-179	6'6"	160-215

food. Hardly the situation here. Also, too much selenium is toxic, and high soil-selenium is a concern in some parts of the U.S.

• Many studies test supplements only at doses much higher than the RDA, and only focus on one outcome (e.g., cancer). If the supplemented group does better than the placebo group, the unanswered question is whether a smaller dose (the RDA or less)—an amount covered by a good diet—would have been as effective. Studies include people who are deficient in the nutrient and are helped by getting a bit more— again, an amount easily obtained by improved diet. Another unanswered question is whether the nutrient taken in high doses has untoward effects on other aspects of health that weren't examined.

Food is usually a much better source of nutrients than supplements, but it's very hard to get people to change their diet—as many of us know from personal experience. One solution has been to add nutrients to foods we already eat, e.g., iron and some B-vitamins added to white flour, vitamins A and D added to milk.

There are, of course, situations where vitamin/mineral supplements or fortified foods are well-advised. It's hard to meet RDAs on a very low calorie diet, so an inexpensive daily multivitamin/mineral pill is advised when dieting. An estimated 10-30% of those over age 50 have trouble absorbing vitamin B_{12} from food, so this age group is advised to get most of their B_{12} from fortified foods or a supplement.

Women capable of becoming pregnant are advised to get their B-vitamin folate RDA from fortified foods or a supplement. The folate RDA is much higher for pregnant women, and a deficiency in early pregnancy raises the risk of certain birth defects. (Folate deficiency also can raise the risk of heart disease.)

Staple grains like white flour are now fortified with folate (required as of 1998). Nutrition experts gave a lot of thought to this decision. The worry was that adding folate to a staple grain may present a risk to older people who may be deficient in vitamin B_{12}. Large amounts of folate can mask the anemia of B_{12} deficiency. This delays the diagnosis of B_{12} deficiency, which could lead to permanent nerve damage (see Chap. 6 and 7). Benefit versus risk is always a factor in deciding about fortifying foods or taking supplements.

An advantage of getting nutrients from food rather than supplements is that there are many healthful substances in food that aren't nutrients, per se, and many of these are yet to be identified. Also, you're not likely to make mistakes with dosages when you get nutrients from food. Be skeptical of advertisements—do you really believe that an advertised pill contains the equivalent of 2 stalks of broccoli?

---

*BMI (Body Mass Index) combines your weight and height into one number: BMI = your weight in kilograms divided by the square of your height in meters. A non-metric formula: BMI = your weight in pounds times 703 divided by the square of your height in inches. BMI is used to assess whether you are underweight, obese, etc., and your risk of diabetes, heart disease, etc. Excess abdominal fat is also a risk factor. For those with a BMI of 35 or less, a waist circumference of over 35 inches in women, and over 40 inches in men raises the risk of disease to the next category, e.g., a man with a BMI of 24.5 and a waist of 42 inches moves up to the Increased Risk of Disease category. The height-weight chart gives for each height, a "healthy" weight range.

Summary

An essential nutrient, by definition, is required in the diet for health and normal development. The body needs energy-providing nutrients (carbohydrate, fat, protein), certain amino acids, fatty acids, and vitamins and minerals. Water is also essential to life; it's the liquid wherein chemical reactions take place and in which substances are transported throughout the body. We lose water mostly through urine and perspiration. Maintaining hydration is important for optimal performance in athletic events. Except for endurance events of 1½ hours or longer, "sports drinks" aren't needed for optimal performance. Plain water is just fine.

Carbohydrate, fat, and protein, besides providing energy, are broken down into basic molecular building blocks used to make key substances in the body. The 9 amino acids and 2 fatty acids essential in the diet come from protein and fat, respectively.

The 13 vitamins are classified by whether they're soluble in fat or water. The 4 fat-soluble vitamins are stored in larger amounts, need to be consumed less often, and are more likely to be toxic in excess than the 9 water-soluble vitamins. There are 15 minerals required in the diet. To a certain extent, the body regulates its mineral content by controlling a mineral's absorption and/or excretion.

Exact nutrient requirements vary within a population, much as height and weight vary. But it's tedious, expensive, and hard to measure the exact amount of each nutrient needed by an individual. Instead, estimates are based on many studies. Normal diets of healthy populations also give a good indication of the amounts needed.

The main standard in the U.S. for assessing nutritional adequacy of a diet is the **RDAs (Recommended Dietary Allowances)**—the recommended amounts of nutrients in the daily diet. The amounts are generous, set to cover the needs of virtually all healthy people in the U.S. RDAs are not minimum requirements. And they don't need to be met every day (the body stores all nutrients to some extent). RDAs provide for maintaining reserves. Practically speaking, try to average the RDAs over several days. There are several sets of RDAs for different segments of the population, based mainly on age and gender.

RDAs are revised periodically to reflect new information. The 11th and current revisions have values called **Dietary Reference Intakes (DRIs)**, which not only include the RDAs but other reference values, such as Tolerable Upper Intake Levels (ULs) to address the issue of toxicity.

Daily Values (DVs) were put together for use in providing nutrient information on labels of food and dietary supplements. They're even more generous than RDAs. Most of the values for one adult set of DVs came from taking, for each nutrient, the highest 1968 RDA for people over age 4 (except for pregnant and lactating women). This set is the one used for most labels.

DVs are set at 100%, and each nutrient is given as % DV. In addition, dietary components for which there are no RDAs (e.g., fat and dietary fiber) have DVs to emphasize their importance to health. For these, the % DV is based on the recommended amount in a 2000-calorie diet. Regulations also spell out which health claims can be made on food labels, and give precise definitions for such terms as low fat.

ChooseMyPlate.gov (eating certain amounts of foods from the vegetable, fruit, grain, dairy, and meat/meat-substitute groups) and the Dietary Guidelines for Americans help us select a healthy diet. Such a diet needn't exclude any foods thought of as *bad* or *junk*. It's our overall diet—not individual foods themselves—that tends to be good or bad. Aim for a diet that's both healthy and pleasurable.

Chapter 5

Energy-Providing Nutrients

When we win, I'm so happy, I eat a lot.
When we lose, I'm so depressed, I eat a lot.
When we're rained out, I'm so disappointed, I eat a lot.

Tommy Lasorda, Dodgers baseball team manager 1976-1996

Carbohydrate, fat, and protein provide us with energy (calories). Carbohydrate and protein provide 4 calories per gram, and fat 9 cal/g. These calorie values are for dry weight (e.g., dry uncooked pasta). Alcohol, a fermentation product of carbohydrate, provides 7 cal/g.

Carbohydrate

Carbohydrate is made of carbon, hydrogen, and oxygen—*carbo*ns *hydrate*d (combined with) water [$C(H_2O)$]. The carbohydrate in our diet is mostly starch and sugar.

Sugar

Glucose, fructose, and galactose are the most common **single sugars** in food. All three are made up of the same number and kind of atoms—$C_6(H_2O)_6$—but the atoms are arranged differently (Fig. 5-1). **Glucose** is the most common and

is part of the double sugars sucrose, lactose, and maltose and is the repetitive unit in starch, glycogen ("animal starch"), and the fiber cellulose (Fig. 5-1).

Fructose, found in foods like honey and fruit, is about twice as sweet as glucose. **Galactose** is found mainly as a part of the "milk sugar" lactose (a double sugar) and isn't very sweet—about half as sweet as glucose. High-fructose corn syrup is a half-and-half mix of the single sugars glucose and fructose.

The most common **double sugars** (2 single sugars linked together) are sucrose, lactose, and maltose. **Sucrose (glucose+fructose)** is the sugar in the sugar bowl (*table sugar*). **Lactose (glucose + galactose)** is the sugar in milk and is the only carbohydrate of animal origin that we eat in significant (though tiny) amounts. **Maltose (glucose+ glucose)** is a breakdown product of starch and is the "malt" in malted milk and in the malted barley used to make beer.

Figure 5-1: Common Carbohydrates in Our Food

SINGLE SUGARS *Don't be intimidated by the molecular structures. Simply note that these sugars are made of the same number of carbon, hydrogen, and oxygen atoms, and differ only in how the atoms are arranged.*

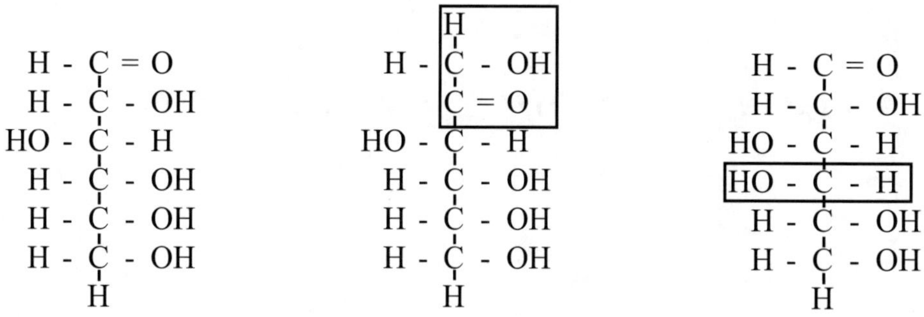

```
    H - C = O              H - |C - OH|           H - C = O
    H - C - OH                 |C = O |           H - C - OH
   HO - C - H             HO - C - H             HO - C - H
    H - C - OH             H - C - OH             |HO - C - H|
    H - C - OH             H - C - OH             H - C - OH
    H - C - OH             H - C - OH             H - C - OH
        H                      H                      H

     GLUCOSE               FRUCTOSE               GALACTOSE
```

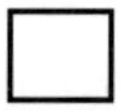

☐ = arrangement differs from glucose

DOUBLE SUGARS

Glucose - Fructose   Glucose - Galactose   Glucose - Glucose

SUCROSE   LACTOSE   MALTOSE

STARCH, CELLULOSE, and GLYCOGEN

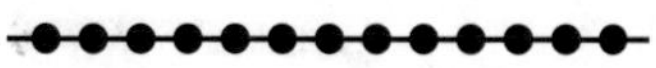

AMYLOSE (starch)   AMYLOPECTIN (starch)
CELLULOSE (fiber)   GLYCOGEN ("animal starch")

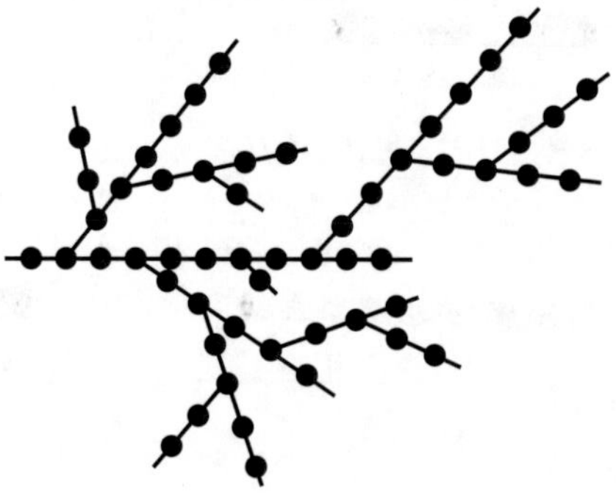

● = glucose

Table 5-1: Composition of Grains, Beans, and Tubers

	% of dry weight				% of cooked weight			
	water	carb.	protein	fat	water	carb.	protein	fat
Grains (wheat, corn, rice)	12	76	9	2	72	24	3	1
Beans (peas, lentils)	12	61	24	1	72	19	8	<1
soybeans	10	34	35	18	71	11	11	6
Tubers* (yams, potatoes)	80	12	7	<1	74	22	2	<1
cassava	12	84	3	<1	65	33	1	<1

*Dry weight for comparison purposes; tubers aren't usually dried.

Complex Carbohydrate

Starch

A complex carbohydrate is made of three or more sugars linked together—a complex of many sugars. Starch, found in plants, is the most common one. It's made of hundreds to thousands of glucoses linked together—a very complex carbohydrate!

The two forms of starch are amylose and amylopectin. In amylose, the glucoses are linked in a straight chain; the chain in amylopectin is highly branched (Fig. 5-1). Amylose is a better thickener than amylopectin; starches higher in amylose (e.g., cornstarch) are good in thickening gravy. Amylopectin is "stickier" than amylose. "Japanese rice" (rich in amylopectin) is stickier (and works better in sushi) than "Chinese rice."

Plants store energy as starch, so starch is found mostly in seeds (e.g., rice, beans) and tubers (e.g., potato), major sources of calories for people worldwide. Compositions of some staple foods are given in Table 5-1.

Grains (seeds) are about 75% starch (dry weight). Seeds are quite dry, so they store well. Refined grain (e.g., white rice) stores even better because most of the germ and outer coat, which are more susceptible to spoilage and more likely to be eaten by vermin, is removed. Rice is the staple food for about half the world's population. Wheat and corn (maize) are two other predominant staple grains.

Beans (also seeds) are about 60% starch and about 25% protein (more than twice the protein of grains). Beans (also called legumes) are an important source of protein for vegetarians. Lima beans, chick peas (garbanzo beans), lentils, and green peas are beans/legumes. Soybeans are also, but are higher in protein and fat and lower in carbohydrate.

Tubers such as potatoes, yams, and cassava also are rich in starch. The 20% starch content of potatoes doesn't sound very high, but it only seems low because the potato is 75% water. If it were dried to about the same water content as grains and beans, it would be about 80% starch. Cassava is a staple food in some countries where there's little else to eat. It's very low in protein, and protein deficiency is common in these countries.

Glycogen

Glycogen is the animal version of starch (*animal starch*); it's made entirely of glucose. Its structure resembles amylopectin in starch but with even more branches (Fig. 5-1). It's a negligible source of energy in food (trace amounts in meat), but an important source of energy within the body. Its concentration is low in tissues, but the body has a lot of tissue, so it has a sizable store of glucose and potential energy. We store about 300 grams (about 11 oz) of glycogen. Carbohydrate has 4 cal/g, so 300 g of glycogen provides 1200 calories.

We store glycogen in liver and muscle. In liver, glycogen is used to keep a steady level of glucose in the blood. In muscle, it's used to fuel muscle action. Knowing how glycogen is used in the body makes it clear why its highly branched structure is so important: Glucose is released at the end of the chains, and the branching gives many more ends from which glucose can be released, allowing a very fast release of glucose. If the chain were a long single strand, as in amylose, there'd be only two ends from which to release glucose.

Fiber

Fiber is a general term for the indigestible parts of plants. All plants have fiber (it isn't found in animal products). It's indigestible, so it isn't an energy-providing nutrient. Most fibers are made of many sugar or sugar-like molecules linked together. They're indigestible simply because our digestive tract lacks the enzymes to break the bonds that link the sugars. Fiber isn't necessarily fibrous, e.g., cellulose is fibrous whereas pectin isn't.

Cellulose gives plants structural support. Like amylose in starch, cellulose is a straight chain of many glucoses linked together (Fig. 5-1). But in cellulose, the connecting link is different. Our digestive enzymes can't break this link, though they can break the one that links glucoses in amylose. Enzymes are very specific.

Some animals can break down cellulose. Termites make a feast of wood (mostly cellulose). A ruminant (e.g., cow) can use the cellulose in grass and hay because bacteria living in its rumen break the links in cellulose, enabling a cow to absorb the resulting sugars.* In other words, grass

"This bread's been de-germinated, de-fibered, refined, processed, and bleached; on the other hand, it does have a picture of a farm on it."

has calories for cows but none for us.

Like starch, cellulose absorbs water. Hemicellulose, another fiber, is especially good at this. Thus, eating foods rich in these fibers adds bulk and softness to the stools, helpful in preventing constipation. Prunes, peanuts, and bran are good sources of cellulose and hemicellulose.

Pectin is a fiber made of galactose and other less-familiar sugars. Apples, oranges, and carrots are good sources. Unlike cellulose (which doesn't dissolve in water), pectin dissolves quite well. It gels, so is used to thicken jams and jelly. It can also bind to bile products in the intestine and carry them out in the stool (cellulose doesn't do this). Lignin, another fiber, is also effective this way. As will be discussed in Chapters 6 and 8, bile-binding substances such as pectin and lignin

---

*Ruminants are animals with several chambers in their stomach, one of which is called the rumen. Food in the rumen is regurgitated back into the mouth where it (the cud) is chewed a second time. This is why ruminating means thinking it over—to go over it again.

in food can help lower blood-cholesterol. Apples are a good source of pectin, so perhaps it's the pectin in *an apple a day [that] keeps the doctor away.*

Alcohol

Alcohol is a fermentation product of carbohydrate. Yeasts convert sugar to alcohol, using enzymes. In fact, the first enzymes were discovered in yeast; the word *enzyme* comes from Greek words meaning *in yeast*. Alcohol has about 200 calories per ounce (7 cal/g).

Yeasts use sugars—not starch—in fermentation. Thus, sweet liquids (e.g., fruit juice) are good starters. Starch must be first broken down to glucose or maltose (two glucoses linked together) before yeast can use it. One way to do this is called *malting*: Grain is allowed to germinate (sprout) for a few days. This produces enzymes that convert starch (the plant's stored form of energy) to maltose and glucose (fuel for the seedling).

An interesting way to convert starch to sugar for alcohol production was used in Peru in the 16th century. Peruvians chewed corn that had been ground and soaked in water, thereby mashing it further while mixing it with an enzyme in saliva that breaks starch into sugar. It then was spit into a pot, where the enzyme action continued. The pot was boiled for several hours, killing microbes and concentrating the sugars by evaporating the water. The mixture was then filtered, providing a clear sugar-rich liquid ready for fermentation.

In making wine, sugar in fruit juice (usually grape) is converted to alcohol. For beer, malted barley is the usual sugar source. Wine and beer have a bit of the nutrients of grapes and barley, and have a limited alcohol content (yeast can't grow once alcohol reaches about 15 to 20%). Wine is about 12% alcohol; beer about 4%.

To make high-alcohol drinks (*hard liquor*), alcohol is distilled (vaporized and condensed). Alcohol evaporates at a lower temperature than water. So when you heat a mixture of alcohol and water, alcohol vaporizes first, allowing alcohol to be separated and concentrated from liquids like fermented fruit (wine) and fermented grain (beer).

Doubling the percentage of alcohol in liquor gives its *proof*—a 100-proof liquor is 50% alcohol. Brandy (about 80 proof) is distilled from wine; whiskey (about 90 proof) from beer; and rum (about 90 proof) from fermented molasses.

Hard liquor is not only a concentrated source of calories because of its high alcohol content, but is essentially devoid of nutrients; even the small amount of nutrients in the original fermented product is left behind in the distillation process. Some people get more than half their calories from alcohol. Those who drink a lot are susceptible to both nutrient-deficiency diseases and the toxic effects of alcohol itself.

Fat

Fat doesn't dissolve in water. It's lighter than water, and rises to the top, as you see in bottles of oil-and-vinegar salad dressings: The oil (fat) forms a layer above the vinegar (water), and the dressing must be shaken and immediately poured on the salad before the oil rises again. This characteristic is useful in reducing the fat in some foods. If a fatty hot stew, broth, or spaghetti sauce isn't stirred, fat rises to the top, and can be scooped off.

Concentrated Source of Calories

Fat not only has more calories (9 cal/g) than carbohydrate or protein (4 cal/g), but it's an even more concentrated source of calories; unlike protein and carbohydrate, it doesn't take on the water that would dilute its calories. We eat fat "dry," and protein and carbohydrate "wet."

Salad oil is 100% fat, making it 9 cal/g (120 cal/Tablespoon). Butter, margarine, and mayonnaise are about 85% fat and have 7 cal/g (105 cal/T). The fat rises when butter is melted, leaving below the milky, watery portion. When this fat is drawn off the top, it's called drawn butter, clarified butter, or dehydrated butter. The water is gone, so drawn butter has the same amount of fat (100%) and calories (120 cal/T) as oil. Lobster and crab are often eaten dipped in drawn butter.

In contrast, carbohydrate and protein hold a lot of water. Note how much water is taken up by dry rice, pasta, and beans during cooking (Table 5-1). Also, note that when bread, cooked rice, oil and meat are left uncovered, the bread, rice, and meat dry out, but oil and the fat around the meat don't. Table 5-2 gives the fat, water, and calories in some foods to show how fat concentrates calories and how water dilutes them.* Many of us think of starchy foods, like bread, rice, pasta, and potatoes, as fattening. They get their reputation by association—we usually eat them with fat (e.g., buttered bread, french fries).

In their natural state (not dried), carbohydrate and protein hold about 3 times their weight in water. Potatoes, bananas, and the non-fat portion of meat are about 75% water and 25% carbohydrate or protein. So their calories have been diluted to only 1 calorie per gram:

$$4 \text{ cal}/(1 \text{ g carbohydrate or protein} + 3 \text{ g water}) = 4 \text{ cal}/4 \text{ g} = 1 \text{ cal/g}$$

Thus, as normally found in food (and in our own tissues), carbohydrate and protein have 1 cal/g, whereas fat has almost 10 times more (9 cal/g). This striking difference has important implications:

• If you add 1 Tablespoon of butter to ½ cup cooked rice, you double the calories, because each has about 100 calories (Table 5-2). This is why it's easier to consume excess calories on a high-fat diet.

In contrast, many people in developing countries don't get enough calories because foods rich in fat (e.g., meat, cheese, oil, butter) are scarce. This can make the diet too bulky for children to get enough calories. A 5-year-old child needs about 1800 calories per day. If there's only low-fat plant foods to eat, the child would have to eat the equivalent of about 26 cups of carrots or 17 bananas or 15 boiled potatoes or 8½ cups of rice to get those 1800 calories.

American children are stumped when asked, *when is chocolate candy nutritious?* They don't think of candy this way. A chocolate bar has about 150 calories/oz (600 calories per ¼ lb). Rich in fat (Table 5-2), it's a concentrated source of calories—very nutritious for a child suffering from a lack of calories. As our children dawdle over their vegetables, we sometimes tell them to think of starving children in other parts of the world. Our children would gladly send them the vegetables. But starving children are more in need of high-fat food—like the butter we put on our vegetables.

• *Simplesse*, the fat substitute used to make the imitation ice cream *Simple Pleasures*, is made of egg and milk protein shaped into tiny spheres. Protein is lower in calories and holds water, so it's a low-calorie (1 cal/g) substitute for fat (9 cal/g). The protein has been shaped to give the slippery "mouth-feel" of fat. *Simplesse* isn't used in products that must be heated (e.g., cookies and crackers) because heat alters its shape and thus its feel. (As will be discussed later in this chapter, heat alters protein's shape.)

• Fat makes hamburger juicy. How do you make a lean burger juicy? McDonalds' McLean Deluxe burger mixed lean beef with carrageenan, a soluble fiber from seaweed. The fiber holds water, making the hamburger "juicy." It also lacked the cheese and mayonnaise-type dressing. A McLean weighed about the same as a Big Mac and more than a Quarter Pounder, but had fewer calories (320) and less fat (10 grams) than either a Big Mac (530 cal, 28g fat) or a Quarter Pounder (430 cal, 21g fat). Due to poor sales, the McLean was phased out in 1996. In came the Arch Deluxe (570 cal, 31g fat) and the Arch Deluxe with bacon (610 cal, 34g fat) to compete with Wendy's big seller.

---

*Adding more water to "solid" food can help in weight-loss diets. We eat less when the same ingredients are made into a soup instead of a casserole—volume is a factor in how much we eat. It's been proposed that labels give caloric density of a food (e.g., how many calories per oz) so consumers aren't confused into thinking that low-fat cookies are low-calorie; they're high-calorie when dry and chock full of sugar.

Table 5-2: Fat, Water, and Caloric Content of Some Foods

	% Water*	%Fat*	Calories/gram
One Tablespoon† of:			
Salad oil = 120 calories**	0	100	9
Butter, margarine, mayonnaise = 105 calories	15	80	7
Table sugar (sucrose) = 45 calories	0	0	4
Honey = 60 calories	15	0	3
Jam, jelly = 55 calories	30	0	3
Sour cream = 25 calories	70	20	2
Catsup = 15 calories	70	0	1
Mustard = 10 calories	80	5	1
2 oz almonds = 355 calories	0	55	6
2 oz chocolate bar = 300 calories	0	35	5
1 saltine cracker = 15 calories	5	10	4
1 slice bread = 70 calories	35	5	3
½ cup cooked rice or I banana = 105 calories	75	0	1
1 orange = 65 calories	80	0	0.5
1 egg white = 15 calories	90	0	0.5
½ cup watermelon = 25 calories	95	0	0.3

* % Water by weight and % Fat by weight, rounded to the nearest 5%

† Tablespoons (T) of food differ in weight, e.g., 1 T sugar weighs less than 1 T honey or jam.

** Calories per portion

- Fat is a concentrated source of energy, storing lots of calories with minimal weight.* A 150-pound man of normal weight has about 15 pounds of stored fat that provides more than 60,000 calories.† This many calories worth of carbohydrate weighs about 120 pounds† and would certainly affect one's mobility!

Functions of Fat

Fat has other important functions besides serving as a concentrated energy source. Fat carries the fat-soluble vitamins in both food and the body, and insulates the body against cold and injury. Fat also provides longer satiety (*satisfaction of hunger*), carries fat-soluble flavors, and gives a smooth texture to foods.

When cookies are said to be so delicious that they melt in your mouth, it's the fat in the cookies that melts. Meat marbled with fat is more tender, juicy, and flavorful. Fat also makes other foods more tender, moist and flavorful—as in croissants baked with layers of butter. When food is deep-fried, it cooks quickly (*fast food*) as the fat browns, flavors, and crisps the outside—as in fried chicken and french fries.

The four types of fat that will be discussed here are: triglycerides, fatty acids, lecithin, and cholesterol (Fig. 5-2).

---

*Migrating birds accumulate fat for flight. If they stored energy as glycogen instead, they'd have trouble getting off the ground. They store the fat in their liver ("fatty liver"), a capacity used to produce the French delicacy foie gras by force-feeding duck or geese. Plants store energy mostly as carbohydrate (starch) because they're "grounded." But note that the plants' seeds are often rich in fat (e.g., sesame seeds). This makes seeds light (more mobile) and easier to disperse, and provides a compact source of the initial energy the seed needs to sprout.

†15 lb fat = 6,810 grams; 6,810 g x 9 cal/g = 61,290 calories. 1 g glycogen holds about 2.7 g water; 4 cal/g glycogen + 2.7g water = 4 cal/3.7g = 1.1 cal/g; 60,000 cal/1.1 cal/g = 54,545g = 120 lb

Triglycerides

When we speak of fatty foods or "getting fat," we're talking about triglycerides. Body fat is triglycerides, as is about 95% of fat in food. A triglyceride is made of three fatty acids attached to a backbone of glycerol (Fig. 5-2). *Saturated, monounsaturated*, and *polyunsaturated* describe the fatty acids in the triglycerides. Triglycerides from various foods don't have just one kind of fatty acid, but have a variety (Table 5-3).

Typically, fat from plants (*vegetable oil*) is rich in polyunsaturated fatty acids. But olive oil is rich in monounsaturated fatty acids, and coconut and palm oils (tropical oils) and cocoa butter are rich in saturated fatty acids. Most animal fats are rich in saturated fat. But fat from fish and poultry is rich in monounsaturated and polyunsaturated fatty acids.

Fatty Acids

A fatty acid is a chain of carbon atoms with an acid group at one end (the end with the oxygens in Fig. 5-2). Fatty acids differ in the numbers of carbons and double bonds in the chain. Those with 16 or 18 carbons are most common. Palmitic acid* [16:0 (16 carbons, 0 double bonds)], stearic acid (18:0), oleic acid (18:1), and linoleic acid (18:2) make up more than 90% of the fatty acids in the American diet (Table 5-3) and are mostly in triglycerides (Fig. 5-2). Only tiny amounts are "free" fatty acids.

Saturated vs. Unsaturated Fatty Acids

A saturated fatty acid doesn't have any double bonds in its carbon chain—it's saturated with hydrogen. No more hydrogen atoms can be added to the chain because there's no place for them to attach. Stearic acid (18:0) doesn't have any double bonds between any of its 18 carbons (Fig. 5-2). It's a saturated fatty acid.

A monounsaturated fatty acid has one double bond in its carbon chain—there's one (*mono*) place (*double bond*) where more hydrogen can be added. A polyunsaturated fatty acid has two or more (*poly*) double bonds in its chain.

The number of double bonds in the fatty acids affects whether a fat is solid or liquid. The more double bonds, the more liquid the fat. Because fat has a mix of fatty acids (Table 5-3), "majority rules." Beef fat is solid because it's mostly saturated fat. Corn oil is rich in polyunsaturated fatty acids (18:2), and olive oil is rich in monounsaturated fatty acids (18:1), and both are liquid at room temperature. If you refrigerate them, olive oil partially solidifies, whereas corn oil (with more double bonds) doesn't.

Fish have fatty acids with many double bonds; their tissues must be somewhat fluid (*soft*) in their cold environment (one such fatty acid has 5 double bonds). Fish that migrate to warmer or colder water can change the number of double bonds in their fatty acids to keep the same softness in their tissues. If fish had fatty acids like beef, they'd be too stiff to swim.

Fat from plants (e.g., olive or corn oil) is usually liquid because the fatty acids are mostly unsaturated. Tropical oil, e.g., coconut oil, is an exception. A more saturated fat is needed to keep the same fluidity in a tropical climate.

Hydrogenated Fat

Food manufacturers can change double bonds in fatty acids to single bonds by adding hydrogen, making fat more saturated and more solid. This is called hydrogenation (hydrogen gas, heat, pressure, and a catalyst are used). *Partially hydrogenated* corn oil means that some, but not all, of the double bonds in corn oil have had hydrogen added to them, converting them to single bonds.

Shortening (e.g., Crisco) is made by partially hydrogenating vegetable oil, which turns the

---

*Palmitic acid is often called palmitate; *-ate* replaces *-ic* when an acid is bound to something else. Vitamin A bound to palmitic acid is often added to food or supplements and is listed as vitamin A palmitate. Sodium bound to ascorbic acid (vitamin C) is sodium ascorbate. Monosodium glutamate (flavor enhancer MSG) is one (mono-) atom of sodium bound to glutamic acid (an amino acid)

Figure 5-2: Types of Fat

FATTY ACIDS   *Just note that these differ in the number of C=C double bonds.*

Stearic acid (18:0)
(a saturated fatty acid)

$$\begin{array}{c}\text{O} \quad \text{H} \; \text{H} \; \text{H} \; \text{H} \; \text{H} \; \text{H} \; \text{H} \; \text{H} \; \text{H} \; \text{H} \; \text{H} \; \text{H} \; \text{H} \; \text{H} \; \text{H} \; \text{H} \; \text{H}\\ \text{H-O-C-C-C-C-C-C-C-C-C-C-C-C-C-C-C-C-C-C-H}\\ \text{H} \; \text{H} \; \text{H} \; \text{H} \; \text{H} \; \text{H} \; \text{H} \; \text{H} \; \text{H} \; \text{H} \; \text{H} \; \text{H} \; \text{H} \; \text{H} \; \text{H} \; \text{H} \; \text{H}\end{array}$$

Linoleic acid
18:2/omega-6

$$\begin{array}{c}\text{O} \quad \text{H} \; \text{H} \; \text{H} \; \text{H} \; \text{H} \; \text{H} \; \text{H} \quad\quad \text{H} \quad\quad \text{H} \; \text{H} \; \text{H} \; \text{H}\\ \text{H-O-C-C-C-C-C-C-C-C-C=C-C-C=C-C-C-C-C-C-H}\\ \text{H} \; \text{H} \; \text{H} \; \text{H} \; \text{H} \; \text{H} \; \text{H} \; \text{H} \; \text{H} \; \text{H} \; \text{H} \; \text{H} \; \text{H} \; \text{H} \; \text{H}\end{array}$$

Linolenic acid
18:3/omega-3

$$\begin{array}{c}\text{O} \quad \text{H} \; \text{H} \; \text{H} \; \text{H} \; \text{H} \; \text{H} \quad\quad \text{H} \quad\quad \text{H} \quad\quad \text{H} \; \text{H}\\ \text{H-O-C-C-C-C-C-C-C-C=C-C-C=C-C-C=C-C-C-H}\\ \text{H} \; \text{H} \; \text{H} \; \text{H} \; \text{H} \; \text{H} \; \text{H} \; \text{H} \; \text{H} \; \text{H} \; \text{H} \; \text{H} \; \text{H} \; \text{H} \; \text{H}\end{array}$$

TRIGLYCERIDES   *3 fatty acids attached to glycerol*

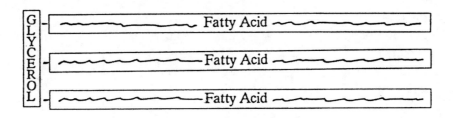

1 Glycerol + 3 Fatty Acids = 1 TRIGLYCERIDE

LECITHIN   *The choline-phosphate gives it emulsifying properties.*

$$\begin{array}{c}\text{H}_3\text{C} \quad \oplus \; \text{H} \; \text{H} \quad\quad \ominus\text{O}\\ \text{H}_3\text{C-N-C-C-O-P-O-}\\ \text{H}_3\text{C} \quad \text{H} \; \text{H} \quad\quad \text{O}\end{array}$$

1 Choline + 1 Phosphate + 1 Glycerol + 2 Fatty Acids = 1 LECITHIN

CHOLESTEROL
Just note the complexity of its structure.

$$\text{H-C-CH}_2\text{-CH}_2\text{-CH}_2\text{-C-CH}_3$$

Table 5-3: Common Fatty Acids in the U.S. Diet

Simply note that fats have a variety of fatty acids:

	Saturated		Monounsaturated		Polyunsaturated		
	<16:0	16:0*	18:0*	18:1	18:2*	18:3	>18:3
Plant Fat							
Safflower oil	0	6	2	12	74	0	0
Safflower oil**	0	5	1	75	14	0	0
Corn oil	0	11	2	24	58	1	0
Soybean oil	0	10	4	23	51	7	0
Peanut oil	0	10	2	45	32	0	0
Canola oil	0	4	2	56	20	9	0
Olive oil	0	16	2	72	8	1	0
Cocoa butter	0	25	33	33	3	0	0
Coconut oil	76	8	3	6	2	0	0
Palm oil	1	44	4	37	9	0	0
Animal Fat:							
Tallow (beef)	5	25	19	36	3	1	0
Tallow (mutton/lamb)	4	22	20	38	6	2	0
Lard (pork)	2	24	14	41	10	1	0
Butterfat	22	26	12	25	2	1	0
Chicken fat	1	22	6	37	20	1	0
Salmon oil	3	10	4	17	2	1	41
Sardine oil	7	17	4	15	2	1	28

* Fatty acids 16:0 (palmitic acid), 18:0 (stearic), 18:1 (oleic), and 18:2 (linoleic) make up >90% of the fatty acids in the U.S. diet. (18:3 = linolenic acid)

** Monounsaturated variety

USDA Nutrient Database

clear liquid into a white solid. Margarine is made the same way from vegetable oil, and carotene and vitamin A are added to simulate butter's color and vitamin content. Margarine cubes are more hydrogenated (harder) than margarine in containers.

Hydrogenating the oil in peanut butter solidifies it so it won't rise to the top. This makes the jar of peanut butter smooth and consistent from top to bottom. Sometimes, more hydrogenated oil is added—more peanut butter without more peanuts. "Old-fashioned" peanut butter isn't hydrogenated; the oil floats to the top, and must be stirred each time it's used.

When vegetable oils are hydrogenated, the fatty acids aren't the same as before, e.g., completely hydrogenated linoleic acid (18:2) becomes stearic acid (18:0) (Fig. 5-2). When you choose between margarines made from different oils (e.g., corn, safflower), choose by price, flavor, Nutrition Facts on label, etc.; margarines similar in softness are similar in how saturated they are.

Because oils can be hydrogenated to be physically similar (e.g., hard/soft, *melts in the mouth*), it's economical for food companies to buy whatever oil is least expensive at that time. The ingredient list will then say, *contains one or more of the following partially hydrogenated oils: soybean, cottonseed...* so that labels won't have to be changed when different oils are used. If one oil is more unsaturated than another, it can be hydrogenated more to get the same physical property desired in the food product.

Bacteria in the rumen of cows and sheep can hydrogenate fat; fat in beef and lamb is more saturated than fat from animals without a rumen

Figure 5-3: Cis and Trans Forms of Unsaturated Fatty Acids

Cis at the double bond:

$$-C-C-C-C-C-C-C \diagdown \diagup C-C-C-C-C-C-C-$$
$$C=C$$
$$H \qquad H$$

Trans at the double bond:

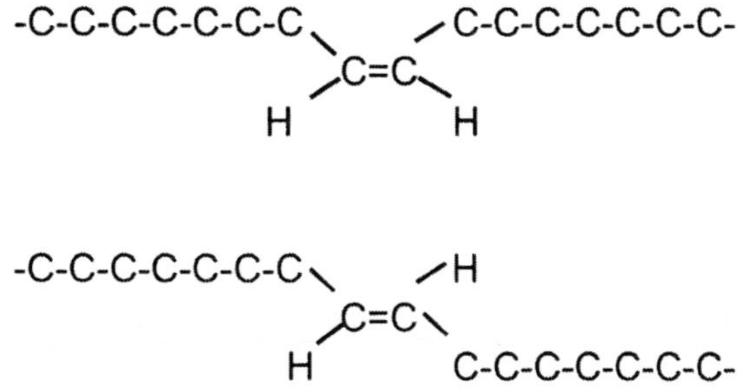

$$-C-C-C-C-C-C-C \diagdown \diagup H$$
$$C=C$$
$$H \qquad C-C-C-C-C-C-C-$$

In Tinkertoys, when 2 rods (*a double bond*) connect 2 hubs, you can't flip the hubs, as you can with only 1 rod (*a single bond*). It's this way next to the double bond in a fatty acid. The change from *cis* to *trans* makes the fat more solid.

(e.g., chickens). An animal's diet also affects fatty acid content of the animal fat.

Trans fatty acids: When fatty acids are partially hydrogenated—whether by food companies or in an animal's rumen—the arrangement of atoms around the remaining double bonds can change from *cis* (normal) to *trans* (Fig. 5-3). This makes the fat more solid (a fatty acid with one double bond is more solid in a trans arrangement than in a *cis* arrangement). In the body, *trans fat* also acts more like saturated fat in raising blood cholesterol (see Chap. 8).

Oxidation of Double Bonds

Fat's double bonds are fragile. Unlike single bonds, they can take on other atoms (as in hydrogenation). Double bonds are thus prone to oxidation (taking on oxygen), which breaks the fatty acid's carbon chain at that site (Fig. 5-4). This forms undesirable breakdown products—the fat has "gone bad" (*become rancid*). Fat in fish has so many double bonds, fish can develop an undesirable "fishy" odor and taste in a short time, especially if not kept at their normally cold temperature or colder.

Using partially hydrogenated fat, or coconut or palm oil (naturally rich in saturated fat) extends the shelf life of food products—there are fewer double bonds that can be oxidized. Antioxidants (e.g., BHT and BHA)* are often added to help prevent oxidation of the remaining double bonds. Vitamin E in food (and the body) is an antioxidant that protects the double bonds in plant oil (and body tissue).† Vitamin E is found in a wide variety of foods, such as salad oil, margarine, nuts, fish, olives, fruits, vegetables, eggs, muffins, beans—even chocolate—though it's richest in polyunsaturated oils.

Omega Double Bond

Besides differing in the number of double bonds, fatty acids also differ in the location of the double bonds. To describe this location, the carbons in the chain are numbered starting from the far end (the CH_3 end) of the fatty acid, called the omega end (omega is the last letter—the far end—of the Greek alphabet). **The omega number gives the location of the first double bond**. This site is important because the body can add double bonds (or more carbons) only beyond this point.

---

*BHT (butylated hydroxytoluene) and BHA (butylated hydroxyanisole) are then listed as preservatives.

†We need more vitamin E when our diet is rich in polyunsaturated fat, but foods rich in polyunsaturated fat naturally have more E (a fat-soluble vitamin). Vitamin E deficiencies are rarely seen, but symptoms (anemia and edema) have been seen in premature infants who are born with low levels of E and have difficulty absorbing fat (and thus fat-soluble vitamins).

Figure 5-4: Oxidation of Unsaturated Fatty Acids

-C-C-C=C-C-C- $\xrightarrow{\text{oxygen}}$ -C-C-C=O   O=C-C-C-

An unsaturated fatty acid can be broken by oxidation of its double bond.

The fatty acid linoleic acid has 18 carbons with 2 double bonds, with its first double bond between the 6th and 7th carbon (*omega-6*). It's abbreviated 18:2/omega-6 (Fig. 5-2). Whether a fatty acid has an omega-3 or an omega-6 double bond is important. The body makes different and important substances from these fatty acids.

Omega-3 fatty acids (first double bond between the 3rd and 4th carbon) have received popular attention because of evidence that they can protect against heart disease (Chap. 8). Omega-3 fatty acids include linolenic acid (18:3, Fig. 5-2) and the eicosapentaenoic acid (20:5) found in fish and human milk (the body can make it from linolenic acid).

Fatty Acids Essential in the Diet

Linoleic acid (18:2/omega-6) and linolenic acid (18:3/omega-3) are essential nutrients. Some of their functions and products are still being discovered. Some fatty acids made from linolenic acid are found in the brain and eye, but their exact functions aren't yet known. The body can use linoleic and linolenic acids to make substances called prostaglandins (so called because the first one was found in prostate gland secretions).*

Deficiencies of these two essential fatty acids are rare, having been seen only in patients with medical problems severely affecting fat intake or absorption. Infants and adults exclusively fed liquid formula diets with insufficient fat have become deficient.

Long-term hospital patients intravenously fed a fat-free formula developed a linoleic acid deficiency; symptoms include retarded growth in infants and appearance of scaly skin lesions. Symptoms of linolenic acid deficiency include blurred vision and numbness and pain in the legs.

Lecithin

Lecithin (a phospholipid—a phosphorus -containing fat) is structurally similar to triglycerides; the difference is that 1 of the 3 fatty acids in a triglyceride is replaced by a water-soluble phosphate-containing compound (Fig. 5-2). Fatty acids in lecithin vary, just as they do in triglycerides. Lecithin isn't needed in the diet; the body can make what it needs.

Because fat, by definition, doesn't dissolve in water, the fact that a portion of lecithin (the phosphate-containing part) does dissolve in water (*water-soluble*) gives lecithin a very useful property in both food and the body. In food, lecithin is useful as an emulsifier (emulsifiers suspend small particles of fat in a watery liquid). It allows fat and water to "mix" by acting as a bridge—the fat-soluble part of lecithin (the fatty acid part) connects with fat, and the water-soluble part connects with water.†

Lecithin in egg yolk is what suspends the oil in mayonnaise, usually made with salad oil, egg yolk, and a bit of lemon juice (or vinegar)—you mix the egg yolk and lemon juice vigorously while adding the oil slowly. The oil is thus finely

---

*Prostaglandins are potent hormone-like substances affecting such things as immunity, blood pressure, and inflammation. Aspirin hampers one of the enzymes needed to make (from linoleic acid) a prostaglandin involved in inflammation; aspirin lessens inflammation in arthritis.

†Monoglycerides and diglycerides (1 or 2 fatty acids attached to glycerol) also act as emulsifiers because they, too, have a fat-soluble (fatty acid) part and a water-soluble part (the part of the glycerol without fatty acids). (Only triglycerides have fatty acids attached at all 3 positions.) Monoglycerides and diglycerides are often used as emulsifiers in food products and are listed as ingredients on the label.

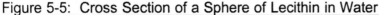

Figure 5-5: Cross Section of a Sphere of Lecithin in Water

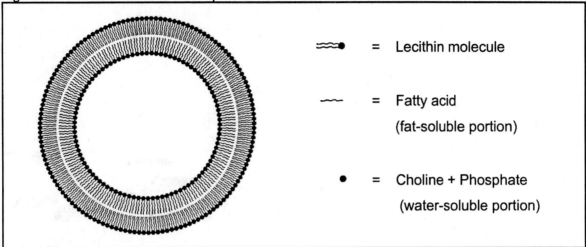

= Lecithin molecule

= Fatty acid
(fat-soluble portion)

= Choline + Phosphate
(water-soluble portion)

divided and kept suspended in this emulsion by the lecithin in egg yolk. Hollandaise sauce and béarnaise sauce are made similarly, except with butter instead of oil.

In the body, lecithin makes up the membranes of cells because of the same chemical property that makes it useful as an emulsifier. If you put lecithin in water, the water-soluble part turns toward water, and the fat-soluble part repulses water and is drawn to the fatty acids of other lecithin molecules. This causes the lecithins to automatically arrange into tiny spheres, much like globes filled with water (Fig. 5-5).* Body fluids are mainly water, so cell membranes are formed "naturally" from lecithin.

Lecithin forms an ideal cell membrane because it has a center layer of fat (Fig. 5-5). Many substances can't dissolve in fat (i.e., aren't fat-soluble) and thus can't easily cross the cell membrane because they can't get through the fatty acid "barrier." Cells can thus "choose" what they let in or out.

Glucose, for example, is dissolved in the water portion of blood and tissue fluid but can't pass through the fat-layer of cell membranes—glucose doesn't dissolve in fat. (You can demonstrate in a kitchen that sugar—and salt—dissolves in water but not in salad oil.) Glucose needs a special transport to enter a cell.

Another reason lecithin forms an ideal cell membrane is that the lecithins aren't physically connected. The membrane is simply an alignment of separate lecithin molecules (Fig. 5-5). This means that a cell can make proteins and insert them into its surrounding cell membrane. Cells do, in fact, do this. Cells make and insert a special protein called a glucose transporter (Fig. 6-2) that provides a special pathway for glucose to enter. Other proteins embedded in various cell membranes will be discussed later.

Cholesterol

Cholesterol (Fig. 5-2) is found in all cell membranes in the body and helps adjust the membranes' fluidity ("softness"). It's flat, so it fits easily between the lecithins aligned in the cell membrane (Fig. 9-1). Cholesterol also has other important functions, e.g., it's used to make sex hormones and the bile acids used in digestion.

Cholesterol is in cell membranes of all animals, so all animal tissues have cholesterol. **Plants don't have cholesterol.** Plants have cell walls made mainly of the fiber, giving plants structural support—we have skeletons for this! Table 5-4 gives the cholesterol content of some foods. Note that **cholesterol content is independent of total fat content** (e.g., shrimp is high in cholesterol, but

*These can be made in the lab for use in delivering various water-soluble medications (microscopic globes of fat filled with medication) that ordinarily have a hard time getting into cells.

Table 5-4: Cholesterol and Total Fat in Foods

	Cholesterol (mg*)	Fat (g*)
Egg: 1 egg or egg yolk	215	6
Meat:		
3 oz (ounces) fried liver	410	7
3 oz lean broiled hamburger patty	75	18
3 oz lean roasted leg of lamb	75	7
3 oz roasted chicken breast	75	3
3 oz (3 slices) bologna	45	24
3 oz canned ham, roasted	35	7
Fish:		
3 oz canned shrimp	130	1
3 oz baked salmon	60	5
3 oz baked sole or flounder	50	1
3 oz tuna, canned in water	50	1
Dairy products:		
1 cup whole milk	35	8
1 oz cheddar, American or cream cheese	30	9
½ cup ice cream	30	7
½ cup cottage cheese (4% fat)	15	5
½ cup low-fat cottage cheese (2% fat)	10	2
1 tablespoon butter	10	11
1 tablespoon sour cream	5	2

*1000 mg (milligrams) = 1 g (gram)

low in fat). When margarine, shortening, or salad oil is said to be *cholesterol-free*, don't be fooled into thinking that cholesterol was removed. These products come from plants, so there wasn't any cholesterol there to begin with.

Cholesterol isn't needed in the diet because the body can make all it needs. When you eat cholesterol, your body can respond by making less (but it won't completely shut down production). People respond differently to eating less cholesterol, ranging from a dramatic drop in blood-cholesterol to none at all.

Cholesterol is made entirely of carbon, hydrogen, and oxygen, but the body can't break it down to carbon dioxide and water as it does with triglycerides, etc.* Thus, when people eat or make excess cholesterol, the body can't readily dispose of it, and the excess can form plaques in the arteries and lead to heart disease (Chap. 8).

Protein

Protein is made of amino acids linked together. Amino acids have an amino part ($-NH_2$) and an acid part ($-COOH$). The amino part of one amino acid combines with the acid part of the adjoining amino acid to form the chain that makes up the protein (Fig. 5-6).

Like carbohydrate and fat, protein is made mostly of carbon, hydrogen, and oxygen. But protein differs in that it always has nitrogen (N) due to its amino part ($-NH_2$). Most of the nitrogen in the body (and food) is in protein. Protein has 4 calories per gram.

Twenty kinds of amino acids are needed to make protein; the body can make all but nine of these. These nine must come from the diet. Virtually all natural proteins have all of the 20 kinds of amino acids, although they have different amounts of each kind. Dietary protein is the topic of Chapter 11.

The amino acids are linked in a precise order to form a single chain. The number of amino acids in the chain can vary from just a few to more than a thousand. The sequence in which the amino acids are linked is unique for each protein.† The number of amino acids and the precise order in which they are linked are coded in our genes. There's a gene for each and every protein the

---

*The body's inability to break down cholesterol also means it's calorie-free, though the amount in the diet is tiny (milligrams) compared to the amount of total fat (grams; 1 g = 1000 mg). So its calorie-free status doesn't really change the 9 cal/g fat used to calculate a food's calories.

†Frederick Sanger in 1953 determined the amino acid sequence of a protein (insulin's 30 amino acids), showing for the first time that a protein's amino acids are linked in a precise order; he won a 1958 Nobel prize. Christian Anfinsen showed in 1960 that a protein's amino acid sequence determines its shape; he won a 1972 Nobel prize.

Figure 5-6: Protein is a Chain of Amino Acids

Glycine is the simplest amino acid, and the body can make it. Phenylalanine is needed in the diet; we can't make it. These are 2 of the 20 kinds of amino acids needed to make protein. All amino acids have an amino part and an acid part (shown boxed); the rest of the amino acid varies.

Phenylalanine

Glycine

$\boxed{\begin{array}{c} N-H \\ | \\ H \end{array}}$ = NH_2 = *amino* part $\boxed{\begin{array}{c} O \\ || \\ C-O-H \end{array}}$ = COOH = *acid* part

---

Amino acids are linked by the removal of water (H_2O): The -OH comes from the acid part of one amino acid; the -H comes from the amino part of the next amino acid in the chain. "Pulling out" water to form a bond (link) is common in body chemistry, as is adding water to break these same bonds (e.g., breaking proteins into amino acids).

Glycine

Water

Phenylalanine

---

20 kinds of amino acids are linked together to form a single chain, now called a protein. Each kind of protein is made up of a precise number of amino acids (aa), linked in a unique sequence.

- aa - aa - aa - aa - aa - aa - aa - aa - aa - aa - aa - aa - aa - aa - aa - aa - aa - aa - aa -

---

A chain of amino acids automatically folds into a shape determined by its sequence of amino acids, e.g., a chain tends to bend at the smallest amino acid glycine, and not bend at a bulky phenylalanine.

Two common ways of drawing a protein

body makes. (Likewise, every plant has a gene for each of its proteins.) Genes and protein synthesis are discussed in Chapter 10.

The chain of amino acids automatically folds upon itself to form a distinctive shape, based on the precise number and the unique order of amino acids in the chain. **A protein's shape determines its function**. The wide variety of proteins have a wide variety of uses, e.g., practically all of the enzymes that catalyze chemical reactions are proteins,* some hormones (e.g., insulin) are proteins, antibodies are proteins, and so are the ones in muscle that enable us to move.

Protein is said to be denatured when it's shape is altered permanently.† Cooks (and food companies) usually blanch (*heat quickly and briefly*) vegetables before freezing them. This denatures—and thereby inactivates—the vegetable's enzymes (proteins). Vegetables can be blanched by a short immersion into boiling water—long enough to denature the enzymes, but brief enough to minimize changes in the vegetable's flavor, texture, and nutrients. Putting these enzymes out of commission slows a vegetable's deterioration.

Corn loses its sweetness as it ages because its sugar turns to starch. This making of starch from sugar is catalyzed by enzymes. "Killing" these enzymes by blanching helps preserve the corn's sweetness.

If you add fresh pineapple to a gelatin concoction (e.g., Jell-O) it doesn't gel. You avoid this mishap with canned pineapple, because the pineapple was heated during processing. The heat kills, by denaturation, an enzyme in fresh pineapple that breaks down gelatin.

Cooks don't always have "killing" in mind when they denature protein by heating, beating,

etc. Egg white is protein and changes dramatically when denatured. Raw egg white is liquid and clear, but becomes white and fluffy when beaten/denatured to top a lemon meringue pie, and solid and white when heated/denatured to make a hard-boiled egg. The amino acids don't change when egg white protein is denatured by beating or boiling; only the protein's shape changes.

Protein is also denatured by acidifying the surrounding liquid. In the Latin American dish *ceviche*, raw seafood is marinated in seasoned lime juice and then served. It looks cooked because the acid in the lime juice denatures the seafood's protein.** We also see this acid effect when milk-protein curdles as milk "goes sour," or when we marinate beef in vinegar to make *sauerbraten*.

Proteins in the body can denature by changes in acidity as well. As discussed in Chapter 3, enzymes in blood and tissue work best only when the pH is 7.35 to 7.45 (slightly basic). This sensitivity is expected—a change in pH alters the shape of enzymes and thereby alters their function.

When athletes feel sudden fatigue (*hit the wall*) in endurance events, one explanation is that local acidity has impaired the function of muscle proteins (including muscle enzymes). Muscle fluids become more acid during intense and prolonged muscle action because lactic acid accumulates (Chap. 9).

Note that denaturation changes a protein's shape, not its amino acid content. So denaturing protein by cooking†† doesn't ordinarily lower its nutritional value. Cooking can, in fact, make a food more nutritious—particularly plant foods—by making it more digestible. Cooking improves the nutritional value of rice—uncooked rice is quite indigestible.

---

*All enzymes were thought to be proteins until Sidney Altman and Thomas Cech found that RNA (Chap. 10) can act as an enzyme; they won a 1989 Nobel prize.

†Prions are denatured proteins thought to cause the fatal brain disease "mad cow disease" in cows and Creutzfelt-Jacob disease in humans. Stanley Prusiner won a 1997 Nobel prize for discovering prions.

**"Cooking" this way, instead of using heat, can be a problem. Peru had a deadly epidemic of cholera in 1991 when cholera-contaminated sewage tainted the seafood. Ceviche is a popular "fast food" sold at stands along the Peruvian coast. Lime juice's mild acidity doesn't kill cholera organisms; thorough cooking does.

††Some amino acids can be altered by cooking, e.g., some combine with carbohydrate on the surface of foods like bread and cake when baked, making the surface brown

Making plants more digestible is especially important for people in developing countries; plants are their major source of both the calories and protein that are often deficient in their diet.

Summary

Except for people who consume a lot of alcohol and little food, we get most of our calories (energy) from carbohydrate, fat, and protein. Fat has the most concentrated calories at 9 calories per gram. Alcohol has 7 cal/g, carbohydrate 4 cal/g, and protein 4 cal/g.

Glucose is the basic unit of the most common carbohydrates found in food. Hundreds to thousands of glucoses are linked together in starch and glycogen. The most common sugars found in food are the single sugars glucose, fructose, and galactose, and the double sugars sucrose (glucose + fructose), lactose (glucose + galactose), and maltose (glucose + glucose). Sucrose is commonly known as table sugar.

With the exception of lactose in milk, virtually all of the carbohydrate in our diet comes from plant foods. Only trivial amounts of glycogen ("animal starch") and sugar are found in beef, fish, etc. Glycogen is the complex carbohydrate found in our bodies, two thirds in muscle, one third in liver.

Strictly speaking, some dietary fibers are carbohydrates, but in nutrition, carbohydrate refers to digestible ones, and fiber refers to the indigestible parts of plant foods, parts that are generally non-caloric. Thus, dietary fiber is found only in plant foods.

Fats include triglycerides, lecithin, and cholesterol. In common usage, fat refers to triglycerides, which make up most of the fat that we eat and the fat that we store in our bodies. A triglyceride is made of three fatty acids attached to a backbone of glycerol.

Triglycerides have a variety of fatty acids, making one triglyceride different from another. The most common fatty acids in our diet have a chain of 16 to 18 carbons. Two fatty acids are essential in the diet, linoleic acid (an omega-6 fatty acid) and linolenic acid (an omega-3 fatty acid). Omega-6 and omega-3 refer to the location of a key double bond in the carbon chain.

Hydrogen atoms are attached to these carbon chains. When the carbon chain has as many hydrogens as it can hold, it's a saturated fatty acid. If there's one place (a double bond) in the chain that can take on more hydrogen, it's monounsaturated. When there are two or more double bonds in the chain, it's polyunsaturated.

Food manufacturers often hydrogenate (add hydrogen to) some of the double bonds in vegetable oils to solidify the oils and to lengthen the shelf-life of their products. Hydrogenation creates a trans arrangement around some of the remaining double bonds; these are trans fatty acids. Trans fatty acids, though unsaturated, act like saturated fat—they're more solid and can raise blood-cholesterol levels.

Depending on which kinds of fatty acids predominate in the triglyceride, the fat is called saturated, monounsaturated, or polyunsaturated. Saturated fatty acids predominate in the triglycerides in beef, so beef fat is called a saturated fat. In olive oil, monounsaturated fatty acids predominate. In safflower oil, polyunsaturated fatty acids predominate. Saturated fat is solid at room temperature, whereas mono- or polyunsaturated fat is liquid.

Lecithin differs from a triglyceride: One of the three fatty acids in a triglyceride is replaced by a phosphorus-containing substance. Fatty acids in lecithin can differ, just as they can in triglycerides. In food, lecithin is useful as an emulsifier. In the body, lecithin forms the basic structure of cell membranes. Lecithin isn't required in our diet; the body makes it.

Unlike triglycerides and lecithin, cholesterol has no caloric value and is found only in animal foods. Cholesterol can't be broken down to carbon dioxide and water (unlike carbohydrate, protein, triglycerides, and lecithin). Thus, excess amounts in the diet can sometimes raise blood-cholesterol levels. Cholesterol is essential in the body as a component of cell membranes and as starting material to make sex hormones, bile acids for digestion, etc. Cholesterol isn't required in the diet; the body makes it.

Amino acids have nitrogen and are the basic units of protein. Amino acids can be broken down and used for energy, or can be used to make protein. Twenty different kinds of amino acids are used to make protein—the body can make 11, the other 9 are required in the diet.

Proteins have from a few to more than a thousand amino acids, linked together in a precise sequence, forming a single chain. The chain folds into a distinctive shape, according to the sequence of amino acids. A protein's shape is crucial to its function. A protein is said to be denatured when its shape changes permanently, altering its normal function.

Chapter 6

Digestive Tract

I think that I shall never see
A tract more alimentary.
A tube whose velvet villi sway
Absorbing food along the way.
Whose surface folded and striate
Does rapidly regenerate.
A magic carpet whose fuzzy nap
Minuscule molecules entrap.
Then, microvilli with enzymes replete
The last hydrolyses complete.

Small intestine described in *The Superbowel,* by George Fruhman, anatomy professor

In the simplest sense, the digestive tract is a long tube down the center of the body (Fig. 6-1). A child swallowing a marble demonstrates that this tube is continuous with the outside of the body—the marble goes in one end and out the other.

A more dramatic example is the use of the digestive tract to smuggle drugs packed in latex condoms or plastic bags. Diarrhea en route is a problem! One smuggler with really bad luck was on the Avianca flight from Colombia that crashed in New York in 1990. His contraband was found during abdominal surgery to treat his injuries. Many such smugglers have died of drug overdose when the condoms or bags broke or leaked—or when they made the mistake of using "natural" condoms made from digestible animal tissue.

Once something is swallowed, involuntary muscles move it downward. From the esophagus to the anus, circular muscles squeeze, and longitudinal muscles contract lengthwise. Coordinated muscle actions create "waves" of motion (peristalsis) that move the contents downward. Squeezing motions mix the food with digestive enzymes, and aid absorption by increasing contact with the absorptive lining of the digestive tract.

Digestion changes nutrients into a form that can be absorbed. Vitamins, minerals, cholesterol, and alcohol don't need digestion—they're absorbed "as is." Starch, double sugars, protein, and triglycerides must first be digested (broken down) by digestive enzymes into simpler components:

- Starch and double sugars are broken into single sugars.
- Proteins are broken down to amino acids.
- Triglycerides have at least two of their fatty acids removed.

Like other enzymes, each digestive enzyme works best within a narrow range of temperature and acidity, and each is usually named after the

Figure 6-1: The Digestive Tract

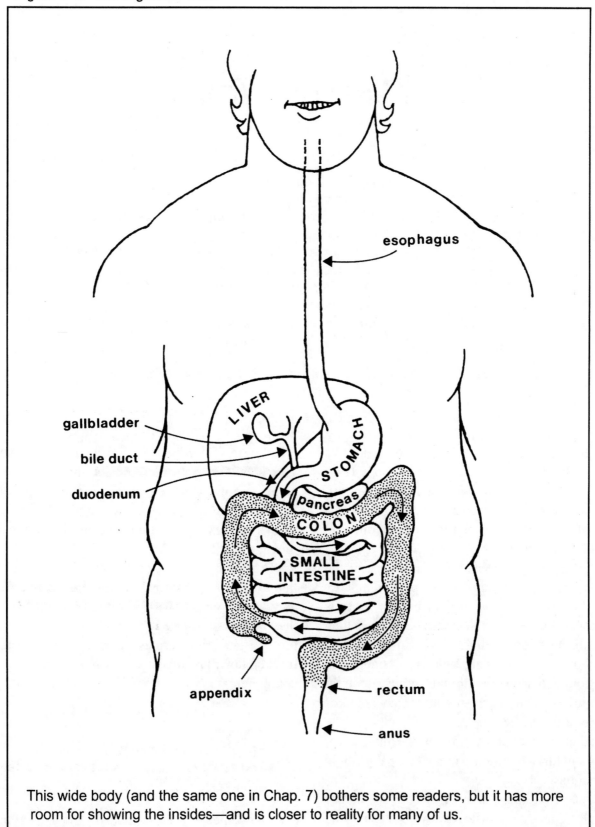

This wide body (and the same one in Chap. 7) bothers some readers, but it has more room for showing the insides—and is closer to reality for many of us.

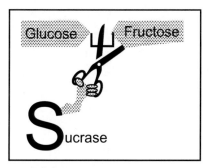

molecule it acts on, ending in *-ase*: lactase acts on lactose, sucrase on sucrose, etc. Digestive actions (chewing, liquefying, mixing) increase the contact between digestive enzymes and the molecules they break apart.

Mouth

The digestive tract begins with the mouth. Food is macerated by chewing, and is made more liquid and slippery by saliva. Just thinking of food can make the mouth water, starting the digestive process even before eating. Saliva has a slightly basic pH, and we secrete about a quart and a half each day. Saliva contains amylase, an enzyme that digests starch (amylose, amylopectin). But very little starch is digested in the mouth because food is usually there so briefly.

Taste

Taste buds are buried in the surface of the tongue. We even have some in the lining of the mouth and at the back of the throat. Though plentiful, they recognize only five sensations—sweet, salty, sour, bitter, and umami ("savory"). All other "tastes" are really smelled. We acknowledge this when we bemoan the tastelessness of food when we have a stuffy nose.

On the tongue, sweet and salty are mostly sensed on the tip, sour at the sides, and bitter at the back. This pattern may have evolved from an ancient need to differentiate between nutritious foods and noxious ones. Tasting sweetness at the tip of the tongue encourages selecting sweet and nutritious foods like fruit. Poisons are often bitter, and when food goes toward the back of the tongue, it's the last chance to spit it out.

Sweetness

Sugar is sweet. Starch is made of sugar (glucose), so why isn't it sweet too? Sweetness depends mostly on how a substance fits into the taste bud. Starch is too big. But if you chew a cracker and hold it in your mouth, it turns sweet. Saliva's amylase enzyme breaks down the starch, releasing some maltose (the double sugar made of two glucoses).

A spoonful of sugar taken straight from the sugar bowl doesn't immediately taste sweet. Sugar crystals are too big to fit into taste buds. As the crystals dissolve in saliva, you taste the sweetness. (Whether sweet, salty, sour, bitter, or umami, "tasty" molecules must be dissolved in a liquid before they can be tasted.)

How the arrangement and composition of atoms in a molecule affect its sweetness isn't fully understood. There are no instruments to measure sweetness, so it's usually measured by dissolving sweeteners in water and having people taste them. Taste tests are carefully controlled, because sweetness is affected by concentration, temperature, etc. Melted ice cream, for example, tastes sweeter than frozen ice cream.

Sweeteners are found mostly by trial and error or by accident. A chemist found aspartame (NutraSweet) when he licked his fingers and noticed they were sweet. Sweeteners aren't necessarily sugars. Aspartame is made up of two amino acids (aspartate, phenylalanine) linked together. The sweetest known substance is thaumatin, a protein from the berry of a West African plant.

When aspartame is sold in food, it's called *NutraSweet;* when sold in powdered form, its brand name is *Equal*. The body treats it as protein: the 2 amino acids are broken apart (digested), absorbed as amino acids, and have 4 cal/g. NutraSweet *does* have calories, but it's so much sweeter than sugar that very little is needed. This is why cans of NutraSweet-sweetened sodas say *Less than 1 calorie per serving.*

NutraSweet is about 160 times sweeter than table sugar (sucrose). A 12-oz soda having 10 teaspoons of sugar is as sweet as one with $\frac{1}{16}$ of a teaspoon of NutraSweet. The next time you see cans of diet and regular sodas chilling in a tub of ice water, note that the diet versions float higher in the water. Carbon dioxide in the carbonated drinks makes the cans buoyant, but the weight of the sugar dissolved in regular sodas makes them sink deeper.

Changing a carbohydrate can change its sweetness, as in the earlier example of maltose being released from starch in saliva. Vegetables like corn and peas lose their sweetness as they age because their sugar converts to starch. To preserve sweetness, producers of frozen vegetables blanch (briefly heat) the vegetables soon after harvest to denature (inactivate) the enzymes that catalyze this conversion. Some fruits, like bananas, get sweeter as they ripen. Starch in the fruit is converted to sugar. (Sugar in fruits is mostly a mix of glucose, fructose, and sucrose.)

Honey is sweeter than table sugar (sucrose), although both have glucose and fructose in a 1:1 ratio. Glucose and fructose are "loose" as single sugars in honey, whereas they're combined as a double sugar in sucrose. The combined sweetness of glucose and fructose is sweeter than an equal amount of sucrose. Honey is also sweeter because its sugar is dissolved in water, so a teaspoon of honey has more sugar (6 g) than dry table sugar (4 g).

High-fructose corn syrup is made from cornstarch and is commonly used to sweeten food products. Liquified cornstarch is broken down to glucose (using enzymes from certain molds), yielding corn syrup. A few atoms in glucose are rearranged (using bacterial enzymes), converting it to fructose (Fig. 5-1). Fructose is more than twice as sweet as glucose, so less syrup (thus, less cost) is then needed to sweeten food products.

Consumers are confused about high-fructose corn syrup. It's been demonized because of its fructose content, although its sugar content (half fructose, half glucose) is the same as honey and table sugar. Fructose in large amounts has adverse health effects, so the problem is simply too much sugar-sweetened drinks, candy, and desserts. Substituting high-fructose corn syrup with honey or regular sugar doesn't lower the fructose content, but the price increase might cause people to cut back.

Tooth Decay

Mouth Bacteria

Tooth decay is a preventable disease caused by mouth bacteria that feast on sugar and excrete an acid waste. When the acid erodes through the enamel, bacteria enter (infect) the tooth, causing decay.

The mouth is a moist and warm habitat for bacteria, and we feed them when we feed

"It's fast, but I miss the chewing and swallowing."

Table 6-1: Sweetness Relative to Sucrose

2000	Thaumatin (a protein)
500	Saccharin (artificial sweetener)
160	Aspartame (NutraSweet; 2 amino acids linked)
100	Cyclamate (artificial sweetener)
30	Tryptophan (an amino acid)
1.7	Fructose (sugar)
1.0	Sucrose (table sugar)
0.7	Glucose (sugar)
0.5	Mannitol, sorbitol, inositol (sugar alcohols)
0.3	Maltose, lactose, galactose (sugars)
0	Starch

ourselves. Bacteria are a key factor in tooth decay. *Bubble-boy David from Houston* (see Chap. 10) didn't get tooth decay because he lived germ-free in a plastic bubble because of his immunodeficiency. The same is true of germ-free animals given sugar-rich diets. In this sense, tooth decay is an infectious disease—caused by bacteria.

It's usually the mother who infects her child during the normal, intimate mother-child relationship. A pregnant woman with decayed teeth or poor dental hygiene should get her teeth filled and begin good dental hygiene. Otherwise, she'll more easily pass decay-causing bacteria to her child through kissing, tasting the child's food, etc.

Colonies of bacteria form in soft plaques that cling to the teeth. The bacteria feed on sugar that comes their way. Sucrose (table sugar) promotes tooth decay the most. Starch can also be a source of sugar for the mouth bacteria because saliva has amylase, the enzyme that can partially break down starch to sugar.

The bacteria break down the sugars and make lactic acid as a waste product. The acid dissolves minerals in the enamel underneath, and begins the process of decay. The initial area of mineral loss shows as a white spot on the tooth. More mineral loss causes erosion that can penetrate the enamel, allowing bacteria to infect the dentin and then the pulp (Fig. 14-2). You'd feel this as a toothache. Of course, it's best to have your dentist remove the decay and fill the cavity long before the infection progresses this far.

Unchecked, the infection can kill the pulp and cause an abscess at the tip of the root. A dead pulp means a dead tooth. Rather than pull the tooth, the dentist usually does a "root canal" by cleaning out the debris all the way to the root tips, and allowing the abscess to drain. The inside of the tooth is then sterilized and filled.

Saliva

Saliva helps prevent tooth decay. It's slightly basic, has antibacterial agents, dilutes the acid made by bacteria, has proteins that neutralize the acid, and continually rinses the mouth of debris. Saliva's neutralizing and diluting action doesn't reach the acid made at the interface of dental plaque and tooth, however. Conditions or medication that lessen saliva production raise the risk of dental decay.

Saliva is rich in calcium and phosphorus and can remineralize enamel—repair some of the mineral loss. Under everyday conditions, this goes on constantly. When we eat, the bacteria eat too, and make acids that demineralize enamel. Between meals, the bacteria don't have much to eat, allowing the plaque and saliva to become slightly basic, setting the stage for remineralization.

Remineralization is possible only at the earliest stage of mineral loss. In other words, mineral loss at a very early stage is reversible, and a cavity can be avoided. Once you get a cavity, it won't repair itself. This is why constant snacking promotes decay, and why cleaning the teeth soon after eating helps prevent it. The time available for mineral loss versus the time available for restoring the minerals can make the difference between healthy and decayed teeth. Sucking on hard candy throughout the day gives bacteria a steady source of sugar with which to make acid—too much time for mineral loss and not enough time for restoration.

A striking example is "bottle mouth"—the rampant tooth decay (sometimes all the way to the gum line) seen in children who go to bed with a bottle of milk (milk has the sugar lactose). The child falls asleep sucking on the bottle, leaving a pool of milk in the mouth, then sucks the bottle intermittently throughout the night. A bottle of fruit juice or sugared water is, of course, just as bad. Children shouldn't get in the habit of going to sleep with a bottle. A pacifier can be used instead.

There are other sources of acid besides mouth bacteria. Continually chewing vitamin C (ascorbic acid) tablets or sucking lemons acidifies the saliva for long periods of time. Frequent vomiting also promotes tooth decay (stomach fluid is very acid). In bulimia,* the dentist is often the first to suspect the disorder because repeated vomiting can cause irritation of the oral tissues and severe erosion and decay of the teeth.

A popular classroom demonstration is to dissolve a tooth in a glass of Coca-Cola, to show how sugar "rots the teeth." Children are impressed but, actually, it's the long-term acidity—not the sugar nor any bacteria—that dissolves the tooth in this demonstration. Vinegar (or diet Coke) would do the same thing.

Sites of Decay

The most common site of decay is the deep and narrow fissures and pits on the biting surfaces of the back teeth. Food and bacteria get caught easily there, and the area is hard to clean. The dentist finds early decay in these areas by probing with a sharp instrument.

Children should visit their dentist before they have any decay, so these natural fissures and pits can be painlessly coated with an acid-resistant sealant that keeps out food and bacteria. It's better for children to have their first dental visit for this, rather than for drilling and filling a tooth. Their teeth are especially susceptible to decay; the enamel of newly emerged teeth isn't yet completely mineralized (hardened).

The second most common site for decay is between teeth, especially just below where they contact each other. This area is hard to clean, and plaque and debris can accumulate easily. Dentists advise using dental floss once or twice a day to clean between the teeth. Dental X-rays detect early decay in these areas.

Sides of the teeth that face the cheeks or tongue are the least likely to decay because they're smooth and kept clean by saliva and the continual movements of the cheeks and tongue. Also, it's easy to clean these areas by brushing.

Later in life, the gums can recede because of periodontal disease (infection of the tissues that surround the teeth). This is why people are said to be *getting long in the tooth* as they age. Receding gums uncover some of the root below the enamel, making it vulnerable to decay. Tooth decay

---

*Bulimia is an eating disorder most common among young white women: continual episodes of bingeing (gorging on huge amounts of food) followed by "purging" (for fear of becoming fat) by self-induced vomiting and/or use of laxatives or diuretics. Regular loss of stomach fluids can cause alkalosis (a dangerous rise in the pH of blood and tissue fluids; see Chap. 3) and, along with losses caused by laxatives and diuretics, such a severe loss of electrolytes (e.g., chloride and potassium ions) that the heart doesn't beat normally. The *gag me with a spoon* line in the song Valley Girls refers to self-induced vomiting. Jane Fonda and Elton John had bulimia. Singer Karen Carpenter died of it.

in middle age and older usually occurs in these newly exposed root surfaces and in new fissures around the edges of old dental fillings. Periodontal disease will be discussed in Chapter 14.

Fluoride

Besides keeping the teeth clean, another way to prevent decay is to make teeth more acid-resistant by incorporating fluoride into their structure. This is done by replacing some of the enamel's hydroxy(OH)-containing crystals $[Ca_{10}(PO_4)_6(OH)_2]$ with harder fluoride(F)-containing crystals $[Ca_{10}(PO_4)_6(F)_2]$.

Optimally, fluoride is incorporated when enamel and dentin form—from birth until permanent teeth erupt fully at about ages 11-13. Although some teeth mineralize before birth, there's no proof that maternal fluoride ingestion during pregnancy helps.

Fluoride is present in all natural water supplies. The recommended level is 0.7 ppm (0.7 part fluoride per million parts of water), to give maximum protection against decay without causing the mottling of enamel that can occur in developing teeth when fluoride is excessive.* Fluoridation can reduce decay by more than half (and might also lower risk of osteoporosis by strengthening bone the same way that it strengthens teeth).

Infants who are exclusively breast fed and children who don't get fluoridated water should get a prescription for daily fluoride drops or tablets from their physician or dentist.

Only about 60% of the U.S. population has access to an adequately fluoridated municipal water supply. Antifluoridation groups have been quite successful in alarming the public when proposals for fluoridation have come up for vote. Many people are scared when told, for example, that fluoride is a rat poison. In big doses, it is a rat poison—and even a human poison. It's all in

the size of the dose. The anticoagulant warfarin, for example, is used in big doses to kill rats, and is used in small doses as a drug to treat people who've had a heart attack (Chap. 7).

When natural water supplies are excessively high in fluoride and removing fluoride to bring the level to recommended amounts has been proposed, communities have, on occasion, voted this down as well, wanting to leave their water "natural."

Water fluoridation has been studied for more than a half-century, has been demonstrated to be safe and effective in about 60 countries, and is promoted by the World Health Organization. Fluoride's main benefit in preventing decay comes from its incorporation into the enamel of developing teeth, but fluoride in drinking water, toothpaste, mouth rinse, etc., also helps protect teeth in adults, mainly by promoting the remineralization of enamel. As noted earlier, tooth decay in older adults often occurs in roots newly exposed because of receding gums. Topical fluoride helps protect this area of the tooth from decay as well.

Feeding the Bacteria

Generally speaking, the amount of sugar in the diet is directly related to the amount of tooth decay. The amount of time that sugar is available to the bacteria is also crucial. Gulping a big glass of a sugared drink is less likely to cause decay than eating a small amount of a sticky food like raisins—unless we thoroughly clean our teeth right after eating (a hard habit to instill, especially among children and adolescents).

A sugary food's potential to cause decay is measured by changes in the acidity (pH) of plaque after eating. Foods like cookies, cake, pie, and candy cause a dramatic rise in acidity in dental plaque, and it takes over 2 hours for the pH to return to normal.

---

*Mottling is the blotching of enamel—"extra-white" spots can occur at 2 ppm fluoride; brown stains at 4 ppm. Mottling looks bad, but isn't harmful. In fact, the discovery that mottled teeth (of people living where water was naturally high in fluoride) were very resistant to tooth decay led to the discovery of fluoride's protective effect. (Other things can cause brown stains on the enamel, e.g., exposure to the antibiotic tetracycline during tooth development from before birth to about 8 years old.)

There are some ways, besides brushing, to lessen this prolonged acidity, but there are drawbacks, especially from a parent's point of view. One way is to eat the sugary food at the start of the meal instead of at the end (yes, dessert first). Cheese, for example, eaten after sweets hastens the neutralization of acid in the plaque. Another way is to chew sugarless gum for about 15 minutes, right after a sugary snack. Chewing motions of the cheeks and tongue, the increased saliva, and the chewing gum itself are what help (no, snapping the gum or chewing with your mouth open doesn't help). Also, sugarless gum often has sorbitol, a sugar-alcohol that doesn't promote (and may possibly even help prevent) decay.

Tooth decay is preventable. Brush and floss daily, and cut down on the frequency and amount of sweets you eat. Good nutrition, optimal levels of fluoride during tooth development, and sealing the natural pits and fissures make teeth more resistant to decay.

Esophagus

Swallowing closes off routes to the nasal cavity and windpipe and sends food down the esophagus. This is why you can't keep drinking without pausing for breath—as a baby can. Babies can breathe and swallow at the same time, as when they nurse or suck a bottle. Their windpipe doesn't have to be shut off when they swallow because their short lower face puts the top of the windpipe at the level of the nasal cavity. (This also means that it's harder for babies to breathe through their mouth.)

The esophagus is straight and short—about 9 inches long and 1 inch wide. Sword-swallowers tilt back their heads to get the sword to go straight down the esophagus; their talent is their ability to suppress the normal gag reflex.* Other than serving as a passageway from mouth to stomach, the esophagus isn't essential to digestion or life.

Each year in the U.S., thousands of children under age 6 damage their esophagus by swallowing caustic chemicals, mostly household products like drain openers. Sometimes the damage is irreparable, and an artificial esophagus must be surgically constructed.

In earlier times, there wasn't much a surgeon could do. In 1895, there was the case of a nine-year-old who took a huge gulp of scalding-hot soup, permanently damaged his esophagus, and had to have a permanent opening made to his stomach. He went on to live an outwardly normal life, but ate by chewing his food and spitting each mouthful into a funnel that led to the special opening in his belly.

Before food goes on to the stomach, it passes through a sphincter (a ring-like band of muscle fibers that act to constrict a passageway) located at the junction between the esophagus and stomach. After food goes into the stomach, the sphincter contracts to keep the food from backing up into the esophagus or the mouth.

Sometimes, especially when the stomach is full, stomach acid may splash up past the sphincter into the esophagus and cause pain. It feels like a burning sensation in the chest and is commonly called **heartburn.** It's really esophagus-burn, and is especially common after dinner among people who eat a small breakfast, a small lunch, and a large, high-fat dinner. Heartburn often can be avoided by eating smaller, lower-fat meals, and not lying down afterwards. If eating large, high-fat meals, it helps to wear clothes that are loose at the waist. Also, drugs that hamper acid production (e.g., Tagamet) can be taken before eating, or antacids (e.g., Tums) after eating. Chronic heartburn should be checked by a physician because it can sometimes lead to cancer of the esophagus.

Stomach

Cells in the stomach lining secrete about 3 quarts of liquid each day. This "gastric juice" includes hydrochloric acid, intrinsic factor, and digestive enzymes that begin the digestion of fat and protein. The fluid is very acid (about pH 2).

---

*Alcohol can suppress the gag reflex, making it easier to choke on food when drinking alcohol before or during eating (food gets further down before gagging, and you can't pull it out like a sword).

Hydrochloric acid is what makes gastric juice so acid. The acid kills much of the bacteria ingested along with food, and denatures proteins (including enzymes in food).* The acidity also aids mineral absorption, because minerals dissolve more easily in acid fluids. As with other nutrients, minerals must be in solution *(dissolved)* to be absorbed.†

Intrinsic factor is a protein secreted in the stomach that's needed to absorb vitamin B_{12}. It attaches to B_{12}, and the combination is absorbed in the lower part of the small intestine. As will be discussed in Chapter 7, some older people develop pernicious anemia, due to B_{12} deficiency. Their deficiency isn't due to lack of B_{12} in their diet, but to insufficient intrinsic factor from the stomach. These people can get B_{12} as an injection or from a nasal gel, or take pills that contain a combination of B_{12} and intrinsic factor.

Very little nutrient absorption occurs in the stomach. But alcohol can be absorbed here, so it can enter the bloodstream that much sooner. It's a small molecule that's already "in solution;" it's readily absorbed "as is."

Alcohol only needs to contact the wall of the stomach or small intestine to be absorbed. So you feel its effects the fastest when you drink on an empty stomach—no food to hinder its contact. Also, liquids leave the stomach faster than solids. This speeds alcohol absorption, because the small intestine provides more surface area for absorption.

Eating fatty foods when drinking helps slow alcohol absorption, because fat stays longer in the stomach. Appetizers served with alcoholic drinks are typically high in fat, e.g., cheese, nuts. They slow alcohol absorption by mixing with it (hindering its contact with the wall of the stomach and small intestine) and by slowing its passage from stomach to small intestine.

The stomach lining also has an enzyme that breaks down alcohol. The enzyme lessens the toxic effects of alcohol by breaking some of it down before it's absorbed into the blood. People vary in how much of this enzyme they have. Women have less than men. As a result, women are more susceptible to alcohol's toxic effects, e.g., cirrhosis of the liver.

Stomach Cancer

Stomach cancer is common throughout the world, but relatively uncommon in the U.S. Stomach cancer has fallen dramatically and steadily in the U.S. for decades (Table 12-1). We now have one of the lowest rates in the world (Fig. 12-4).

Long-term infection with the microbe *Helicobacter pylori* is thought to play a major role in stomach cancer. Throughout the world, the rate of stomach cancer has fallen in parallel with the infection rate, which is lower in developed countries and closely related to socioeconomic status. *H. pylori* can also cause stomach ulcers** and gastritis (inflammation of stomach lining), both of which raise the risk of stomach cancer. (*H. pylori*-caused ulcers and gastritis can usually be cured with a precise regimen of antibiotics and other medication.) Although much of the world's population is infected, only a small fraction get ulcers, gastritis, or stomach cancer, presumably because of people's genetic and environmental differences and different microbial strains.

What's in our food would be expected to be a strong environmental factor. In fact, stomach cancer rates do seem to reflect the amount of carcinogens (cancer-causing substances) in food. A major source has been foods preserved by salt, smoke, and/or nitrite. Salt isn't a carcinogen, as such, but excessive amounts can contribute to inflammation of the stomach lining (gastritis), increasing susceptibility.

---

*A common misconception is that "natural enzymes in food" aid our bodily functions. But the body treats the enzymes as it does other proteins in food—it digests them and absorbs the resulting amino acids.

†Some brands of mineral tablets (e.g., calcium) don't dissolve as they should in the stomach. Put a tablet in a half-glass of vinegar at room temperature, and stir vigorously every 5 minutes. If it doesn't completely dissolve in 30 minutes or less, try another brand.

**Non-steroidal anti-inflammatory drugs (NSAIDs) such as aspirin, ibuprofen, acetaminophen can also cause ulcers.

It's probably not coincidental that stomach cancer rates fell when sanitation improved (lessening *H. pylori* infections) and the use of home refrigerators and refrigerated trucks became widespread. Fresh fruits and vegetables became available year-round in most parts of the U.S., and we no longer had to preserve food with salt, smoke, or nitrite. We now eat fewer preserved foods and more fresh fruits and vegetables (thought to protect against cancer). Also, refrigeration retards spoilage (e.g., formation of molds), and some products of spoilage can be carcinogenic.

Whether stomach cancer occurs probably depends on combinations of factors. Carcinogens in food might not cause stomach cancer if the diet wasn't also high in salt, or the stomach wasn't infected with *H. pylori*. As combinations go, note that bacon is very salty, is cured with nitrite, has nitrosamines, and is sometimes smoked. When bacon is then fried, more nitrosamines are formed—and perhaps people who eat a lot of cured meats eat fewer fruits and vegetables. Nitrosamines and other food and nutrition factors will be discussed in Chapter 12.

Japan has one of the highest stomach cancer rates and one of the highest salt intakes in the world. Stomach cancer is Japan's leading cause of death from cancer. Refrigerating food isn't as common in households as it is here. Foods preserved with salt (e.g., pickled vegetables, pickled fish) and smoked and fermented foods are a traditional part of their diet, whereas fresh fruits and vegetables are not. When Japanese immigrate to the U.S., they get less stomach cancer. Stomach cancer is also decreasing in Japan. Their diet has become more Americanized, and infection with *H. pylori* has fallen.

Small Intestine

Partially digested food leaves the stomach through a sphincter located at the juncture between the stomach and small intestine. The sphincter controls the passage of food into the small intestine, and contracts to help prevent backtracking.

The adult small intestine is about 1½ inches wide and about 20 feet long when it relaxes, and about 10 feet when it contracts—it's not very small! It's the main site of digestion and absorption. The first 12 inches or so is called the duodenum (because so much happens here, this uppermost section has its own name-—derived from *duodeni,* Latin for *twelve each).* Except for the duodenum, the small intestine is unattached, which allows such a long tube to be stuffed into such a small space (Fig. 6-1).

The small intestine's lining is truly remarkable. Like a wadded terry cloth towel (that quickly absorbs water), its surface is expanded by folds and loops to quickly absorb food (Fig. 6-2). The folds are densely covered with villi (finger-like projections), each of which is covered with microvilli (the "ruffled" membrane of intestinal cells).

Many proteins are embedded in these microvilli (see cross section of cell membrane in Fig. 6-2), and are involved in digestion as well as absorption. Examples include sucrase, maltase, and lactase—digestive enzymes anchored in the membrane and protruding into the intestinal passageway. Although these enzymes are named for the double sugars (sucrose, maltose, lactose) that they digest, sucrase and maltase also can digest starch. This gives the digestive tract a large and versatile capacity to digest starch: sucrase and maltase, and the starch-digesting enzymes of the saliva (salivary amylase) and pancreas (pancreatic amylase). Starch is the predominant source of calories for the world's population.

Marketing "starch blockers" pills (amylase blockers) was a popular, short-term money-maker: popular, because the sales pitch was irresistible *(eat all the pasta and potatoes you want without gaining weight);* short-term, because the pills didn't block starch digestion. The pills block only a small amount of amylase. Amylase is made in excess, and maltase together with sucrase also can digest starch.

The surface area of our small-intestinal lining is about 1800 square feet, about the floor space of a three-bedroom house. No wonder our food's

Figure 6-2: Lining of the Small Intestine

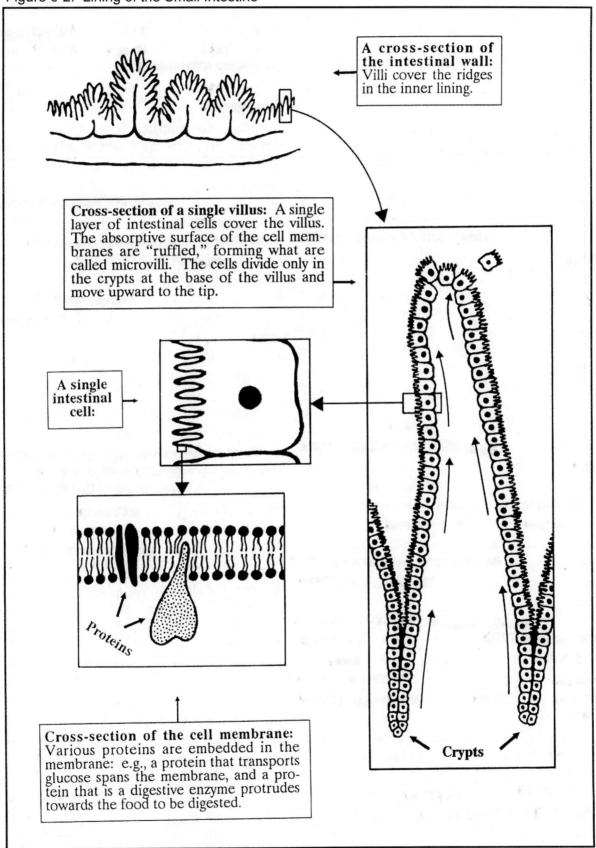

A cross-section of the intestinal wall: Villi cover the ridges in the inner lining.

Cross-section of a single villus: A single layer of intestinal cells cover the villus. The absorptive surface of the cell membranes are "ruffled," forming what are called microvilli. The cells divide only in the crypts at the base of the villus and move upward to the tip.

A single intestinal cell:

Proteins

Crypts

Cross-section of the cell membrane: Various proteins are embedded in the membrane: e.g., a protein that transports glucose spans the membrane, and a protein that is a digestive enzyme protrudes towards the food to be digested.

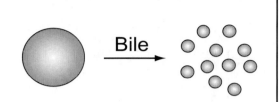

Bile breaks up globs of fat. This creates more surface for the fat-digesting enzymes to do their job, make fat more digestible.

absorbed so efficiently! The lining is renewed continually; it's completely replaced about every 3 days.

The cells that make up this lining are made at the base of the villi (in the crypts, as shown in Fig. 6-2) and then migrate to the tips of the villi where, at an "old age" of 3 days, they come off and become a part of the food that's digested and absorbed there.

About 20-50 million cells per minute are shed into the adult intestine. In fact, dietary protein represents only about half of the protein that we digest and absorb. About 25% comes from shed intestinal cells and another 25% from protein in digestive secretions (remember, enzymes are proteins).

Digestion and absorption take place mainly in the first half of the small intestine (protein, fat, carbohydrate, vitamins, and minerals are mostly absorbed here). Pancreatic and liver secretions enter the small intestine through the bile duct (Fig. 6-1).

The **pancreas** secretes an alkaline solution of sodium bicarbonate *(baking soda)* that neutralizes the acidity of the material coming from the stomach. The pancreas also secretes digestive enzymes that break apart starch, protein, and fat. (As food, pancreas and thymus are called sweetbread; tripe is part of the stomach of a ruminant. Intestine can be used as casing for sausage.)

The **liver**'s job in digestion is to make and secrete **bile**. Bile emulsifies fat, making it easier to digest. As discussed earlier, emulsification finely divides the fat and suspends it in a water-based liquid. It's like homogenizing whole milk, finely dividing the fat (cream) so that it stays suspended rather than rising to the top. In homogenization, globs of fat are made smaller by forcing the milk through a small nozzle, whereas an emulsifier such as bile has chemical properties that finely divide the fat.

Finely dividing the fat increases its exposed surface. This is crucial. The fat-digesting enzymes are in a watery liquid and can't penetrate the fat. The enzymes can reach and digest only the exposed surface. Bile is stored and concentrated in the **gallbladder**, which contracts and releases bile when food enters the small intestine.

A gallbladder isn't essential. Many people have it removed without serious consequences. Without a gallbladder, bile enters the duodenum (the top of the small intestine) directly from the liver in steady and less concentrated amounts. Most fatty foods are comfortably digested, unless a lot is eaten in a short time.

By the time the intestinal contents reach the lower half of the small intestine, most of the nutrients have been digested and absorbed. But the lower part of the small intestine is the site of vitamin B_{12} absorption. Intrinsic factor (secreted in the stomach) bound to B_{12} is absorbed here.

About 90% of the bile acids secreted earlier into the duodenum is also absorbed in the lower small intestine and recycled via the blood to the liver to be made again into bile. Bile acids are recycled about twice during a meal. Without this efficient recycling, the liver wouldn't have enough bile in time to digest the fat in a typical meal.

People who tend to put on weight bemoan the fact that digestion and absorption are so efficient. In the 1970s, some morbidly obese patients underwent a desperate procedure that speaks to the efficiency of the small intestine. All but about two or three feet of the small intestine was surgically bypassed so that they could overeat and steadily lose weight. As you might expect, an undesirable side effect was massive amounts of stool. Some patients also developed serious side effects (e.g., liver failure).

"Hey! Where's my science project?"

Duodenal Ulcers

The acidic liquid from the stomach enters the small intestine at the duodenum, and this was thought to be why the duodenum is a common site of ulcers. A common treatment was to cut out part of the stomach, so less acid would be made. Drugs (e.g., cimetidine/Tagamet) that reduce the stomach's acid production have now replaced surgery as the standard treatment.

To treat ulcers, physicians used to prescribe a diet that avoided certain acid foods. Studies since have shown this was mostly unwarranted. Because the stomach is already very acid, acid food (e.g., citrus fruits) don't appreciably increase the acidity. Today, physicians commonly limit the "forbidden" list to coffee (caffeinated and decaffeinated) and alcohol, both of which stimulate acid production in the stomach.

Ulcers can bleed or cause pain, but pain isn't a dependable sign. About half the people diagnosed with duodenal ulcers don't report pain as a symptom. Sometimes, an ulcer's discomfort is misinterpreted as hunger, which can unwittingly lead to overeating and weight gain. When there isn't pain, a bleeding ulcer is often discovered by blood in the stool, or anemia resulting from blood loss.

It's now known that most duodenal ulcers are caused by *H. pylori* (most of the others are caused by drugs such as aspirin). *H. pylori* infection can be diagnosed by a blood or breath test, and cured with a precise antibiotic regimen (as can the stomach ulcers caused by *H. pylori*). This cure has been very good for those who had to continually take an acid-reducing drug like Pepcid or Tagamet to control their ulcers. This cure hasn't been so good for the profits of companies that make the drugs. The drugs are now intensely marketed for treating heartburn, and are now available without a prescription.

Ulcers also can occur in the esophagus or stomach, but these are much less common. Stomach ulcers raise the risk of stomach cancer, but this doesn't seem to be the case with duodenal ulcers.

Lactose Intolerance

A diminished ability to digest lactose (lactose intolerance)* is common among adults (sucrose intolerance occurs, but is unusual). We're born with generous amounts of lactase enzyme in our small intestine, so we can digest the lactose in milk, our first food. As the intestine matures, lactase—and the capacity to digest lactose—normally falls.

---

*Don't confuse lactose intolerance with the allergic reaction that some babies have to cow's milk. Allergies are hypersensitivity reactions, usually to a specific protein—in this rase, protein from cow's milk. Cow's milk also seems to cause constipation in some young children. They can be given soy milk, goat's milk, human milk, etc., instead.

The term *lactase deficiency* is somewhat misleading in that it suggests it's abnormal. Worldwide, about 75% of adults have low lactase. The high lactase in some populations (e.g., Northern Europeans and the pastoral Fulani tribe of Nigeria) is an anomaly, possibly due to a selective mutation thousands of years ago that conferred an advantage to people who herded milk-producing animals (adults with more lactase could "tolerate" more milk).

About 90% of Asians and about 75% of African and Native Americans—but less than 20% of Caucasians of Northern European origin—have low lactase as adults.

If you consume more lactose than can be digested by your intestinal lactase, you can get unpleasant symptoms such as diarrhea, gas, and abdominal cramps (these malabsorption symptoms will be discussed later). But gastrointestinal symptoms like this are so common that they can be falsely attributed to lactose intolerance.

A well-controlled double-blind study of 30 people (age 18 to 50) who said they were severely lactose intolerant and said they consistently had symptoms after drinking less than a cup of milk showed no difference in symptoms when given a cup of regular or lactose-free milk.

Milk is the only natural source of lactose, so milk and foods made with milk are the only foods with lactose. How much of these foods can a person with low lactase comfortably consume? This is best determined by one's own eating experience (keeping in mind the above study). Some people can't tolerate gulping a glass of milk on an empty stomach, but find no discomfort in drinking a glass of milk leisurely throughout a meal.

Yogurt and "acidophilus milk" are better tolerated because the added bacteria (*Lactobacillus acidophilus*) have "predigested" some of the lactose into its absorbable components (galactose and glucose). Lactose-free milk is also available. Cheese and ice cream are usually well tolerated because they're high in fat and have relatively little lactose. Fat slows the passage of the lactose from the stomach to the intestine. Also, high-fat food is usually eaten in smaller amounts.

Colon

The colon is the main site of bacterial action (lots of bacteria live here). It's about 4 feet long, about 2½ inches wide, and—unlike the small intestine—isn't lined with villi. Water is easily absorbed here, turning the liquid from the small intestine into semisolid stool. (This "easy absorption" makes it possible to administer some drugs as a suppository via the rectum.)

Bacteria make up about 30% of the dry weight of stool. They alter bile pigments to make the stool brown and alter certain residual amino acids to give stool its characteristic odor. The bacteria also make some vitamins, such as K, which are then absorbed. Vitamin K deficiency is uncommon because of its ample production in the colon but a deficiency can occur if you take antibiotics for a long time. A vitamin K injection is given to newborns in this country as a preventative measure, because there are no bacteria in the colon at birth.

Gas

Colon bacteria need nutrients to sustain themselves (they grow by multiplying), and they use whatever they can from what comes their way. They break down substances like undigested lactose and certain indigestible carbohydrates in beans, and can make gas as a byproduct. For this reason, beans cause gas, as does undigested lactose.

Some of the gas is absorbed into the blood from the colon and expelled in the breath (increased breath hydrogen after a dose of lactose is a positive test for lactose intolerance). The rest is expelled through the anus. The expulsion of gas (flatus) through the anus is called flatulence (useful information for those seeking an alternative word). Some jokes are based on the fact that one of the gases is methane, which is combustible.

As a side-note to the earlier mention of starch-blocker pills, people who ingested starch blockers along with their pasta and rice should have been glad that the pills didn't work. Bacteria in the colon would have had a feast on all that starch coming their way. The gaseous result would have been "explosive!"

Diarrhea

Many diseases can cause diarrhea. In developing countries, a common cause is drinking water contaminated by disease-causing bacteria (usually from sewage). Severe diarrhea causes massive water loss, which can cause severe dehydration. It's a major cause of infant death in developing countries. They can't get liquid intravenously (needed to get liquid in fast enough when there's severe diarrhea), as they would here. Lacking the medical care of developed countries, many infants have been rescued from fatal dehydration by their mothers giving them cooled boiled (sterilized) water mixed with a bit of sugar and salt (to speed water absorption).

Some diarrheas aren't related to disease. Emotional upset or lactose intolerance can cause it. The diarrhea of lactose intolerance occurs because the lactose pulls water into the colon. Ingestion of a lot of sugar alcohol such as sorbitol and mannitol can similarly cause diarrhea. Sorbitol and mannitol are commonly used as sweeteners in sugarless gum and dietetic foods, and are only absorbed slowly. Thus, some may remain unabsorbed and proceed to the colon and produce diarrhea (and gas), as in lactose intolerance.

Constipation

Constipation is the difficult or infrequent passage of stool. Many people complain of it because of the mistaken belief that defecation *(bowel movements)* must occur daily to be healthy and normal. In fact, it's quite normal to be irregular. Twice a day or three times a week is well within normal.

The amount of stool depends mainly on the amount of fiber you eat. Fibers like cellulose help prevent constipation by holding water, making the stool bulkier and softer and thus easier to pass. Eating or drinking can cause an urge to defecate (*gets the intestines*

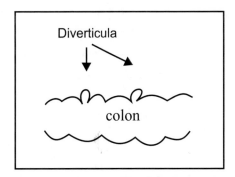

moving); infants usually defecate after a meal. Adults often suppress or ignore this urge. Those worried about constipation might be wise to heed "nature's call," because it's when defecation is easier.

You shouldn't be unduly concerned with bowel movements, but consult your physician if there's a big change in the usual pattern of bowel movements or in the stool's appearance. A change to a very light color might be from fat malabsorption due to insufficient bile production; a change to a black color might be due to blood from a bleeding ulcer.

Diverticulosis

Diverticulosis is an outpouching of the colon wall, much like a hernia. An estimated 30 to 40% of people over age 50 in the U.S. have one or more of these outpouchings (called diverticula),* although many of them don't suffer any ill effects. If an outpouching fills with bacteria and stool or becomes ulcerated, it can be painful. If an ulcer erodes a blood vessel, severe bleeding can occur. If it erodes completely through the colon wall, severe problems can occur from bacteria leaking into the normally germ-free abdominal cavity.

With a low-fiber diet, colon muscles can go into spasm when squeezing against an insufficiently bulky stool. This increases the pressure inside the colon, and can eventually cause outpouchings at weak points (think of the outpouchings between your fingers when you squeeze a partially filled balloon). Fiber such as cellulose helps prevent diverticulosis by providing the bulk that helps the colon move things along with less squeezing.

---

*When diverticula become inflamed, it's called diverticulitis; -itis means inflammation of, as in dermatitis (inflamed skin/derma), appendicitis (inflamed appendix), gastritis (inflamed stomach).

Imagine trying to push mashed potatoes through a resilient rubber tube by squeezing the tube. If the tube is filled with mashed potatoes, you don't have to squeeze very hard to move the potatoes through. If the tube is only half-filled, you have to use more pressure to push against the lesser bulk. Over time, this excess pressure inside the tube may cause outpouchings of any weak spots.

Colon Cancer

Colon cancer is the second leading cause of death from cancer in the United States (lung cancer is first), so there's a lot of interest in the possibility that diet may affect risk. As seen by the array of high-fiber cereals in the supermarket, fiber's possible role is well advertised. Fiber might lower risk, but this hasn't been proven.

In looking at colon cancer throughout the world, high rates have been linked with diets low in fiber and high in fat, refined sugar, and animal protein. (These dietary factors tend to be linked, e.g., diets high in animal protein tend to be high in fat and sugar and low in fiber.) Other studies, e.g., comparing vegetarians with non-vegetarians, also show a link between more fiber and less colon cancer. But these studies show only links rather than causal relationships.

Studies in lab animals have been inconsistent. Some show protective effects, some show no effect, and some even show more colon cancer with more fiber. The probable reason for these variable results is that the diets differ in the kind and amount of fiber. Oat bran, for example, isn't the same as wheat bran. Even differences in how finely the fiber is ground could change the outcome.

As with most diseases, genetic susceptibility varies. For most colon cancers, the cause isn't known, though there are several suspects. A roundabout way of examining some possible causes is to begin by comparing the colon with the small intestine, where cancer is rare. This gives insight into both the logic and the difficulties of determining the relationship of diet to colon cancer.

A key event in cancer is a change that enables a cell to multiply out of control. In the small intestine, cells multiply only in the crypts at the base of the villi. As can be seen from Figure 6-2, the presence of the many villi helps protect these crypt cells from outside contact with carcinogens (cancer-causing agents). If cancer were to occur in any cell on the villus (i.e., a cell that has migrated up out of the crypt) this usually wouldn't matter because that cell would be shed and gone in a matter of hours or days.

In contrast, the colon has crypts but no villi, putting the crypt cells (i.e., the dividing cells) in more direct contact with the contents of the colon. The colon partially protects itself by secreting mucus. Some fibers stimulate this secretion, and this could be one way in which fiber could help prevent colon cancer.

As a general rule, the length of exposure to a carcinogen has a bearing on whether cancer is induced in a cell (e.g., more smoking = more lung cancer). Transit through the colon is much slower than in the small intestine. Fiber helps move substances faster through the colon, which shortens the exposure to any carcinogens there. But if the length of exposure was crucial, we'd expect that people with a history of constipation would be more likely to get colon cancer. This doesn't seem to be the case.

It's also generally true that the higher the concentration of carcinogens, the greater the risk of cancer (e.g., smoking unfiltered rather than filtered cigarettes). Low-fiber diets are typically high in fat, animal protein, and refined sugar, so it's logical to consider whether a high concentration of fat, animal protein, and refined sugars is a direct cause of colon cancer. It's highly unlikely that these are a direct cause. These dietary substances aren't carcinogens themselves, and none of the refined sugar and only small amounts of the fat and protein even reach the colon.

Substances that are ingested but not absorbed might be expected to play a role because they're more concentrated in the colon. But if the ingested substances are carcinogens, they should cause some stomach cancer as well, even though they would be at lower concentrations in the stomach. In other words, we might expect that populations with a lot of colon cancer also have a lot of stomach cancer if ingested carcinogens were responsible. This isn't the case, e.g., Japan has low rates of colon cancer but high rates of stomach cancer, whereas it's the opposite in the U.S.

Where might carcinogens in the colon come from if they aren't ingested? The most likely suspects are breakdown products of some kind, such as components of bile, bacterial breakdown products, etc. Trying to identify a culprit is like looking for the proverbial needle in a haystack.

Each person's colon has a unique blend of hundreds, if not thousands, of substances, including a unique blend of bacteria that subsist on whatever's available. Just as restaurants serving different foods have different clientele, so it is with the colon and its bacteria. Different bacteria can make different substances. Some bacteria, for example, can change bile acids into carcinogens.

If bile or its breakdown products are a major culprit, eating a lot of fat and protein could play an indirect role because both stimulate bile secretion. A prospective study of more than 88,000 nurses found that colon cancer was 2½ times higher among those who ate beef, pork, or lamb as a main dish every day, compared to those who ate meat less than once a month. Most cuts of beef, pork, and lamb are high in fat and protein, so this finding is consistent with the hypothesis that eating lots of fat and protein increases the risk. But keep in mind that the comparison groups probably have other lifestyle differences—dietary and otherwise—that may not have been taken into account.

Clearly, the possible effect of diet on colon cancer isn't simple or straightforward. But based on current evidence, we're advised to eat less animal fat, more fiber, and only moderate amounts of protein as a possible way to lower risk of colon cancer (i.e., eat more vegetables, fruits, and grains, and less animal fat). Also, don't forget that a nutritious diet is needed for healthy tissue, and healthy tissue is less susceptible to disease. The

dietary recommendations discussed in Chapter 4 are the basis of what's currently considered to be the best diet.

Summary

The digestive tract includes the mouth, esophagus, stomach, small intestine, colon, and rectum. In digestion, food is broken down into a form that can be absorbed from the intestine into the body. Starch and double sugars must be broken down (digested) to single sugars; proteins to amino acids; and triglycerides must have at least two of their fatty acids removed. Digestive enzymes do this. Some substances (e.g., alcohol and cholesterol) don't have to be digested; they're absorbed "as is."

Tooth decay is caused by mouth bacteria that colonize in soft plaques that cling to teeth. They break down sugars in our food and make lactic acid that dissolves minerals in the enamel, starting the process of decay. Saliva helps control tooth decay; it has antibacterial agents, and neutralizes some of the acid.

Saliva also has the calcium and phosphorus used to remineralize the demineralized areas of enamel. Fluoride reduces decay by making teeth more resistant to acid. Drinking water that has 0.7 ppm fluoride is recommended for maximum protection.

Pancreas and liver play crucial roles in digestion. The pancreas provides digestive enzymes and sodium bicarbonate, which is alkaline and neutralizes the acid coming from the stomach. Liver provides bile, which emulsifies fat, making it more digestible. Bile is stored and concentrated in the gallbladder.

These pancreatic and liver secretions enter at the top of the small intestine through a tube called the bile duct. Digestion and absorption of food occurs mostly in the small intestine, which has an intricate lining for this purpose.

Lactase, an enzyme found in the lining of the small intestine, normally falls to low levels after early childhood, in which case lactose (the double sugar found in milk) can't be digested as fast. When a person consumes more lactose than the enzyme can handle, some of the lactose doesn't get digested and proceeds to the colon where bacteria break it down and make gas as a byproduct. This can cause discomfort—lactose intolerance. Those with low lactase needn't necessarily avoid milk; they may just need to ingest it more slowly with other foods or switch to lactose-reduced milk.

The colon is rich in bacteria and is where residue from food and digestive secretions is stored until it's excreted through the rectum. The colon extracts water from the residue, so if the residue goes through the colon too fast, it's watery (diarrhea). If it stays in the colon a long time, it can become quite dry. This can be constipating and can contribute to the development of outpouchings of the colon wall (diverticulosis).

Insoluble dietary fiber (fibers that don't dissolve in water) can help prevent constipation and diverticulosis by holding water, thus providing bulk and softness to the stool. Fiber might also help lower the risk of colon cancer, but this isn't proven. Because the mixture of substances that pass through the colon is so complex, it's extremely hard to identify and sort out the factors that contribute to or help prevent colon cancer.

Stomach cancer, duodenal ulcers, and tooth decay were also discussed. The microbe *H. pylori* is thought to play a role in stomach cancer; is a major cause of duodenal ulcers; and can be eradicated with specific medication and antibiotics.

Chapter 7

Circulatory System

All the blood in the body is under the control of the heart ....
The blood current flows continuously in a circle and never stops.

As translated from *Neiching,* a Chinese treatise on internal diseases
written on strips of bamboo in about 2600 B.C.

The circulatory system includes the heart, blood vessels, and blood. The heart pumps blood through an elaborate system of blood vessels (Fig. 7-1), continuously delivering oxygen and nutrients to the tissues, carbon dioxide to the lungs, and waste products to the kidneys. The circulatory system also transports other key substances such as hormones and antibodies and plays a central role in regulating body heat by "transporting" heat from one part of the body to another.

Because blood carries substances to and from cells, it's often sampled and analyzed. Think of trucks (*blood*) that constantly transport material to and from buildings (*body tissues*). If you can't see in the building, you can get a good idea of what's happening there by pulling aside a truck (*taking a blood sample*) to see what it's carrying. To extend the analogy, trucks (*blood*) must have an efficient and well-maintained transportation system (*heart and blood vessels*) to do a good job.

Heart

The heart is an amazing muscle; it beats steadily throughout our lifetime—about 4 billion times. The pulse reflects how fast and hard the heart beats.

How much blood the heart pumps per minute depends on how fast the heart beats and how much is pumped with each beat. When you rest, your heart pumps about 5 quarts per minute. You have about 5 quarts, so this means that your entire blood supply is pumped through your heart each minute—about 0.3 cups per beat and 70 beats per minute in sedentary people. Endurance training increases the amount pumped with each beat, so an athlete's resting pulse is slower. An athlete's heart can pump 5 quart per minute with about 0.4 cups per beat and 50 beats per minute.

How fast can blood circulate? An endurance athlete's performance depends a lot on how fast substances (especially oxygen) are delivered to muscles and how fast waste is removed. A world-class endurance athlete's heart can pump about 40 quarts per minute (the fastest in sedentary college-age men is about 20 quarts/minute)—the entire blood supply is circulated in less than 10 seconds. This is mostly from more blood pumped per beat, because the maximum heart rate in both athletes and sedentary people is about 200 beats per minute.

Figure 7-1: Circulatory System

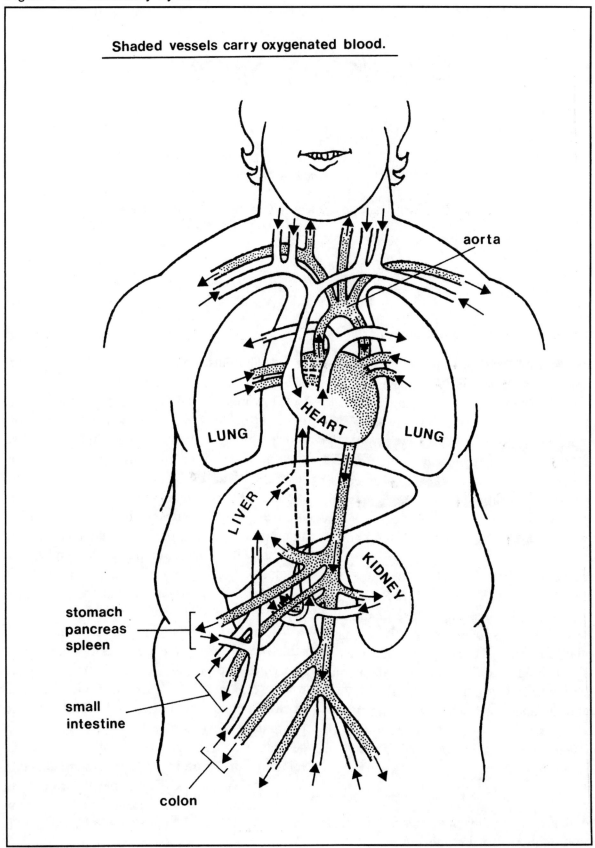

Differences between sedentary people and world-class endurance athletes may not, of course, all be due to training. Some of the differences may be genetic. But endurance training does markedly increase the amount of blood the heart can pump with each beat.

Your heart is a muscle about the size of your fist. As shown in Figure 7-1, the right side of the heart (the unshaded side) pumps blood to the lungs, where carbon dioxide is removed and oxygen is taken up. The blood then returns to the left side of the heart, which pumps oxygenated blood to the aorta that then branches into vessels that supply the entire body. The heart itself is nourished by coronary arteries—the first branches off the aorta (Fig. 7-2). Blockage of a coronary artery causes a heart attack.

Blood Vessels and Blood Pressure

Arteries, veins, and capillaries circulate blood throughout the body. The distribution of blood is changed by constricting (*tightening*) or dilating (*widening*) certain blood vessels. In a resting muscle, more than 95% of the capillaries are unfilled. When the muscle is exercised, blood flows through all its capillaries to provide needed oxygen and nutrients and to remove waste products. In a more familiar example, we look flushed when warm because more blood is diverted to the skin by filling its capillaries (as evaporating perspiration cools the skin, the underlying blood is cooled as well).

The heart begins circulation by pumping oxygenated blood into arteries (Fig. 7-1). This creates high pressure in the arteries, which have thick, muscular walls and can be thought of as high-pressure tubing. Rupturing an artery is often lethal; abnormally high blood pressure raises the risk of damage or rupture.

Figure 7-2: Coronary Arteries Nourish the Heart

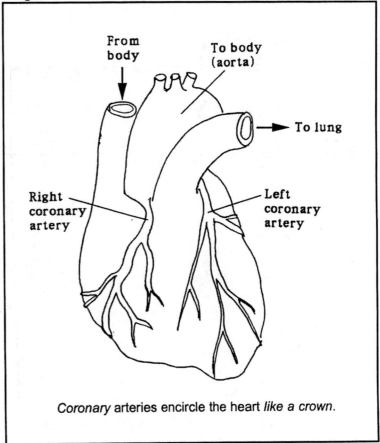

From body

To body (aorta)

To lung

Right coronary artery

Left coronary artery

Coronary arteries encircle the heart *like a crown*.

Blood pressure is routinely measured at the arm, and the numbers (e.g., 120/80) tell how high (in millimeters) the pressure raises a calibrated column of mercury. The top number is the [*systolic*] pressure in the arteries when the heart contracts (*beats*); the bottom number is the [*diastolic*] pressure when the heart rests between contractions. Both pressures are important in terms of stress on the blood vessels.

To illustrate, imagine using a pump to pulse air into a high-pressure rubber air hose. How long the hose lasts depends not only on how much pressure is exerted with each pulse, but also on how much steady pressure there is between pulses. A certain amount of pressure is needed to get the job done, whether with the air hose or with the circulatory system, but excess pressure can cause damage. Obviously, a defective artery doesn't last as long as one that's in good shape.

Blood pressure goes up with age, in part because the arteries become more rigid and, don't

Figure 7-3: Circulatory Route of Blood Vessels Through the Body

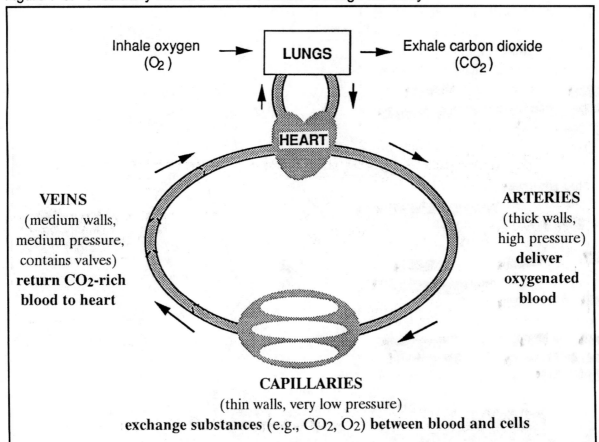

Inhale oxygen
(O_2)   → LUNGS →   Exhale carbon dioxide
                                                               (CO_2)

HEART

VEINS
(medium walls,
medium pressure,
contains valves)
**return CO_2-rich
blood to heart**

ARTERIES
(thick walls,
high pressure)
**deliver
oxygenated
blood**

CAPILLARIES
(thin walls, very low pressure)
exchange substances (e.g., CO_2, O_2) between blood and cells

easily expand slightly as they should with each heartbeat.* A rubber air hose also becomes less flexible as it ages. When air is pulsed in, the hose doesn't expand as much in response, resulting in higher pressure. If the passageway in the hose has also narrowed due to damage and accumulated debris, the steady pressure between pulses will also be higher. This happens with narrowed arteries as well.

Arteries branch into smaller and smaller vessels. The smallest are **capillaries** that go to every living cell in the body (note that you bleed wherever you prick yourself). Capillary walls are very thin, and some capillaries are so narrow that red blood cells can go through only in a single file.

As arteries branch, blood pressure falls from high pressure in the large arteries to the very low pressure in the capillaries. The low pressure allows the exchange of substances between tissue cells and capillary blood.

To complete the circle (Fig. 7-3), blood goes back to the heart via **veins**. Compared to the high-pressure/thick-walled arteries and the low-pressure/thin-walled capillaries, veins are intermediate in pressure, diameter, thickness, and muscularity. Unlike arteries and capillaries, veins have valves that direct blood back to the heart and help prevent pooling of blood in the veins.

The return of blood back to the heart is helped by muscle action—particularly in the legs, where gravity impedes the return. Walking squeezes the leg veins and helps return blood to the heart. Blood can pool in leg veins when a person stands or sits still, thereby reducing circulation. Someone who stands in a crowd for hours while waiting for a

---

*In relatively isolated rural populations in some developing countries, blood pressure doesn't go up, or goes up only minimally with age. These people typically have a low-salt diet, aren't overweight, and are physically active at all ages.

parade may faint from insufficient blood going to the brain.* In contrast, the strong and fast muscle actions of running increase circulation.

Blood

Blood is made up of red blood cells, white blood cells, and platelets suspended in a fluid called plasma. The cells and plasma each make up about half of the blood. Blood continually mixes as it moves through the heart and blood vessels. If a blood sample is put in a tube with an anticoagulant (a substance that prevents clotting), the red blood cells settle to form the bottom half of the blood sample. On top of the red blood cell layer is a thin layer of white blood cells.

The upper half of the blood sample is the plasma, a clear, yellowish fluid. If the plasma has a lot of fat (e.g., after a high-fat meal), it's cloudy and the fat might even rise to form a layer of fat.

Red Blood Cells

Red blood cells are made in bone marrow, and make up most of the blood cells. Their job is to carry oxygen and carbon dioxide. Men normally have a higher concentration of red blood cells than women (about 5.4 vs. 4.8 million per microliter of blood).

Hemoglobin in red blood cells is what actually carries oxygen (O_2) and carbon dioxide (CO_2). It has an iron-containing part (*heme*) and a protein part (*globin*). Heme is red, giving red blood cells (and blood) their color. When carrying oxygen, blood is bright red; it's dark and purplish when carrying carbon dioxide. Routine blood samples taken from arm veins are dark—blood is on its way back to the heart and is carrying mostly carbon dioxide.

Without hemoglobin, the 5 quarts of blood of an average adult would carry only about 1 tablespoon of oxygen. Hemoglobin increases the oxygen-carrying capacity by about 70-fold, to about 1 quart of oxygen.

Hemoglobin can also carry carbon monoxide (CO). In fact, hemoglobin binds tighter to carbon monoxide than to oxygen (or carbon dioxide). Thus, carbon monoxide can displace oxygen in blood. You can die from lack of oxygen when breathing carbon monoxide coming from the deliberate or accidental venting of exhaust fumes into a car, even though there is still a lot of oxygen in the car.†

Tobacco smoke also has carbon monoxide. Smokers can't carry as much oxygen in their blood because some of their hemoglobin is tied up with carbon monoxide. As a result, smokers run out of breath sooner when exercising. Maybe this is why many people quit smoking soon after starting an exercise program or taking up a sport. Smokers are also more prone to heart attacks (Chap. 8). Carbon monoxide adds to this risk, especially when oxygen delivery to the heart muscle is barely adequate due to narrowed coronary arteries.

A red blood cell lasts about four months. Its protein is then broken down to amino acids for reuse; the iron in heme is reused to make more hemoglobin; and the rest of the heme is made into bile pigments and excreted as part of bile. If these bile pigments build up in the blood and tissues, the skin looks yellow (*jaundice*). This abnormal buildup can be from less excretion of bile pigments due to a diseased liver or gallbladder, or a defective bile duct. Accelerated destruction of abnormal red blood cells can also cause bile pigments to build up.

Athletic Competition: A limiting factor in endurance events is how fast blood can deliver oxygen to muscles. Some athletes try to increase blood's oxygen-carrying capacity by increasing the number of red blood cells. One way is "blood doping:" about 2 units (almost a quart) of the athlete's blood is drawn about 2 months before competition and then stored. Meanwhile, the body replenishes the blood cells. A few days

---

*A somewhat different example is a weight lifter who feels dizzy when straining to lift weights. A deep breath is held during the lift, causing a big rise in pressure in the chest cavity. This compresses the vein that passes through this area, obstructing the return of blood back to the heart and to the brain

†Dr. Jack Kevorkian (the "suicide doctor") often used a canister of carbon monoxide attached to a gas mask to help people commit suicide.

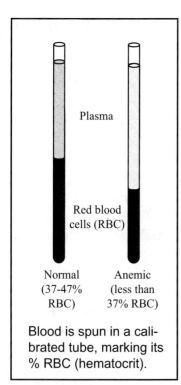

Plasma

Red blood
cells (RBC)

Normal   Anemic
(37-47%   (less than
RBC)   37% RBC)

Blood is spun in a cali-
brated tube, marking its
% RBC (hematocrit).

before competition, the athlete gets a transfusion of the stored blood (*extra red blood cells*).

Another way is injection of erythropoietin, a human protein (made for medical use by biotechnology) that increases the body's production of red blood cells. The use of either of these methods is against the rules of the International Olympic Committee.

A legitimate way is to train at high altitudes just before competition at sea level. At high altitudes, the body responds by making more red blood cells (and hemoglobin) to compensate for the lower oxygen pressure of the atmosphere.

Anemia

The word *anemia is* from the Greek, meaning *without blood.* **Anemic people have fewer red blood cells or less hemoglobin in their red blood cells** from blood loss, impaired production of red blood cells or hemoglobin, or increased destruction of red blood cells. Despite the many possible causes of anemia, the end result is that blood can't carry as much oxygen.

An anemic person tires easily and often has such symptoms as weakness, dizziness, headache, drowsiness, and irritability. In short, there's less physical and mental capacity for work and productivity. Also, anemia can lessen the body's ability to warm itself in response to cold (*cold*

intolerance). Severe anemia can cause cessation of menstrual periods, loss of sexual desire, heart failure, and shock.

Anemia can be diagnosed from a blood sample by measuring the volume of red blood cells (hematocrit), measuring hemoglobin concentration, or examining and counting the number of red blood cells. The values below are for people living at sea level. There are several nutritional deficiencies that can cause anemia. The most common ones are deficiencies of iron, folate, and vitamin B_{12}.

Iron-Deficiency Anemia

Iron deficiency is the most common cause of anemia. Iron is an essential part of hemoglobin, so not enough iron means not enough hemoglobin. Red blood cells become small and pale because they have less hemoglobin.

Iron deficiency can be from needing more iron (as when growing or pregnant), not getting enough in the diet, less of it being absorbed, or a combination of these. The anemia occurs mainly in children and women of childbearing age. Children need more iron for their increasing blood volume and growing bodies.

Women lose iron in menstrual blood. Blood losses vary, so women vary in the amount of iron needed for replacement. It follows that any condition that changes the amount of menstrual blood will also change iron needs, e.g., oral contraceptives lessen menstrual blood losses. Menstruation can stop entirely with extreme thinness, as can happen with anorexia nervosa or among ballet dancers. Although menstruation stops during pregnancy, more iron is needed for the growing fetus and the woman's larger blood volume.

Iron deficiency is unusual among men and postmenopausal women because they have

	Men		Women	
	Normal	Anemic	Normal	Anemic
% Red Blood Cells (RBC) by volume	47	<42	42	<37
Hemoglobin concentration (gm/100ml)	16	<14	14	<12
Number of RBC (million/microliter)	5.4	<4.5	4.8	<4.0

minimal iron losses. Blood donors are, of course, an exception. Blood banks check for anemia, and don't allow donations of more than a pint about every 2 months. Men and postmenopausal women with iron-deficiency anemia are checked for chronic bleeding, especially in the digestive tract, e.g., an undiagnosed bleeding ulcer.

Iron deficiency is usually corrected by ingesting more iron by diet or supplements. Compared to other nutrients, iron is poorly absorbed from the intestine. This is an important safeguard, because excessive iron in the body can be toxic. Aside from blood losses, very little iron is lost from the body once it's absorbed. The intestine serves as a gatekeeper by adjusting the amount absorbed; absorption is normally low, but more iron is absorbed when the body needs more.

Iron in foods: The two main forms of dietary iron are *heme iron*—iron that's ingested as a part of heme (e.g., the iron-containing part of hemoglobin)—and *non-heme iron* (inorganic iron). Heme iron is better absorbed than non-heme iron.

Heme iron is found in animal tissue, mainly in hemoglobin and myoglobin (an oxygen-carrying molecule similar to hemoglobin, but found in muscle). Most of the iron in animal tissue is heme iron, but some—such as iron in egg yolk—is non-heme. About 25% of heme iron is, absorbed, whether or not a person is iron-deficient.

Because of the telltale "bloody" color of heme, we can figure that red meat (e.g., beef) has more heme iron than light meat (e.g., chicken, fish), and that the darker meat of a chicken leg has more than the lighter meat of the breast. Red blood cells are made in the bone marrow and broken down in the liver, making bone marrow and liver rich dietary sources of heme iron. (Eating bone marrow is more common in Europe than in the U.S.)

Amounts of iron in about 3 oz of lean, cooked portions of animal tissues are: beef liver (7.5 mg); hamburger (3.9); lamb (2.6); skinless dark chicken meat (1.4); skinless light chicken meat

(1.1) salmon, swordfish, or trout (1.0). (The RDA is 15 mg iron for menstruating women, and 10 mg for men and postmenopausal women.)

We eat a lot of heme iron in meat, but we eat more non-heme iron (e.g., from fortified breakfast cereals and enriched bread). Plants have non-heme iron, which is more poorly absorbed than heme iron. But the absorption of non-heme iron varies from about 2% to 45%, depending on whether you're deficient in iron, the amount of iron in the meal, and what else is in the meal. Thus, unlike sources of heme iron, it's hard to evaluate dietary sources of non-heme iron.

One can't say that we absorb more iron from ½ cup cooked spinach (2 mg iron) than from an egg (1 mg iron), because other substances in the meals can affect the amount absorbed. For example, meat, fish, or foods having vitamin C, eaten in the same meal increase absorption of non-heme iron. Conversely, substances such as tannins (as in tea), phytic acid (as in wheat bran), and oxalic acid (as in spinach) in the meal can combine with non-heme iron, preventing its absorption.

We get more iron from an egg if the breakfast also includes sausage and orange juice, and less iron from a luncheon spinach salad served with a whole wheat roll and tea. The meat in sausage and the vitamin C in orange juice increases iron absorption, whereas oxalic acid in spinach, phytic acid in the whole wheat roll, and tannins in tea all bind to iron and prevent its absorption.*

As mentioned in Chapter 4, Recommended Dietary Allowances (RDAs) take into account differences in absorption. Only a small amount of the iron ingested is actually absorbed, so the amount recommended (RDAs for iron) is about ten times more than what the body actually needs.

Food rich in non-heme iron (in portions with 1 to 2 mg iron) include: ¼ cup peanut butter, raisins, bran breakfast cereal, or cooked cream of wheat; ½ cup cooked spinach, chard, lima beans, or peas; 2 slices enriched or whole wheat bread; 1

---

*Iron absorption from this salad lunch may not be as good as from the egg-and-sausage breakfast, but it's more in line with the advice to eat less fat and cholesterol and more fiber. A breakfast of orange juice and either peanut butter on toast, or cream of wheat cereal mixed with non-fat milk would be good, in terms of both iron absorption and dietary recommendations.

egg yolk; 3 dried apricot halves; and 5 prunes. Other foods included in the same meal increase the absorption of non-heme iron: a small amount of meat or fish, and especially foods rich in vitamin C (e.g., oranges, grapefruit, strawberries, melon, broccoli, green peppers).

Milk has very little iron (only about 0.1 mg per cup; the RDA for children, ages one to ten, is 10 mg), and milk is typically a big part of a child's diet. When it's top-heavy in milk and milk products, there's risk of iron deficiency. (Newborns normally have about a 6-month supply of iron stored in their liver, to "hold them over" until they get other foods besides milk.)

Iron supplements: Iron fortification of many breakfast cereals and enrichment of white flour with iron have lessened iron deficiency in this country. Also, many people take iron supplements. Absorption of iron in these supplements varies. It's highest for supplements like ferrous (iron) sulfate, ascorbate, fumarate, and citrate.

Iron supplements are easily available and cheap, but it's still a good idea for those at risk of deficiency to work on eating more iron-rich foods. Improving the diet in one nutrient—iron in this case—tends to improve the diet in other nutrients as well. Also, iron supplements can cause side effects, such as constipation, nausea, and stomach cramps.

You can also supplement your diet without iron pills—by cooking acid foods (foods containing vinegar, lemon juice, wine, tomato sauce, etc.) in cast iron pots and pans. Acid dissolves some of the iron in the cookware, putting it in the food. You can increase the iron content of tomato-based (acidic) spaghetti sauce, for instance, by simmering it in a cast iron pot. An old folk remedy for anemia is to put

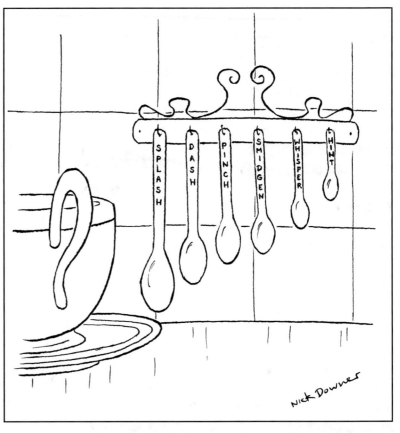

a long iron nail in an apple overnight and then eat the apple (after removing the nail, of course).

Iron toxicity: Our intestines normally protect us from absorbing excess iron, but massive amounts can overwhelm this safeguard and cause acute iron poisoning—an emergency. The typical victim is a child who accidentally ingests the mother's iron pills. Acute iron poisoning also occurs with food or drink heavily contaminated with iron, e.g., acidic drinks brewed or stored in iron vats.

Because iron-deficiency anemia is common among children and young women, it's been suggested that more foods be fortified with iron. But it's argued that this might cause more cases of **hemochromatosis.** In this disease, excessive amounts of iron are absorbed from normal diets because of a genetic error that impairs the intestine's ability to keep it out. The danger is an accumulation of iron to toxic levels in the body.

Hemochromatosis is mostly a man's disease.* Just as many women have the genetic defect,

---

*Jim Clark, founder of Silicon Graphics and Netscape, has been treated for hemochromatosis; his experiences with the health care system led him to create his third billion-dollar company, Healtheon.

but women "get rid of iron" in menstruation and pregnancy. Men don't have a regular outlet unless they're regular blood donors.

Hemochromatosis rarely is found before middle age; it's apparent only after many years of accumulating excess iron in various tissues. It isn't localized to any one part of the body and can be fatal. Iron deposits can, for example, cause liver damage (e.g., cirrhosis) and heart damage (e.g., irregular rhythms). It's estimated that 1 of 10 Americans has inherited the abnormal gene from one parent, and 1 of 250 from both parents.

This is why it's worrisome for men to take self-prescribed iron supplements. Men and postmenopausal women generally don't need them except, perhaps, if they're regular blood donors. Even without genetically increased iron absorption, men taking big doses of iron might, over the years, put themselves at risk for toxicity.

Heavily fortified breakfast cereals often have lots of iron—good for children and young women who need more iron, but not so good for many adult men (especially those who eat several bowls a day) and postmenopausal women.

The story of Jim Becker, named at age 79 to the Green Bay Packers Fan Hall of Fame in 2010, tells of a fortunate combination of genes and environment. At age 21, money was tight, so this devoted fan started selling his blood to pay for game tickets. By age 44, he had given 145 pints of blood. At age 44, he was diagnosed with hemochromatosis when a doctor noted that Jim's father had died of hemochromatosis at age 43 and had Jim tested. All those blood donations literally saved his life.

Sweden used to heavily fortify food with iron but stopped in 1995. It had helped the problem of iron-deficiency anemia, but it also appears to have caused more hemochromatosis. This reminds us that there can be problems with too much of an essential nutrient.

Folate-Deficiency Anemia

Folate (or folic acid) is a B-vitamin needed to make DNA, the genetic material in our cells. Folate has a key role in cell division because DNA must be made before a cell divides. Folate deficiency hampers cell division, most of all in cells that divide fast.*

Cells that become red blood cells divide fast, so folate deficiency causes an anemia in which red blood cells are bigger *(getting ready to divide)* and fewer *(less able to divide)*. The usual remedy is more folate by diet or supplement.

Rich sources of folate include liver (where folate is stored in the body) and leafy, dark-green vegetables. Folate/folic acid was, in fact, first isolated from spinach, and its name comes from the Latin word meaning *foliage.* Other good sources of folate are asparagus, artichokes, brussels sprouts, beans (lentils, lima beans, green beans, peas, etc.), broccoli, avocado, and oranges.

Folate is fragile and can be damaged, especially by heat and acid conditions. Some folate is lost with cooking and processing—good reason for including dark green salads of romaine lettuce or spinach in the diet. The RDA for folate allows for expected losses in food preparation. Also, the liver can store about a three-month supply, which acts as a buffer against short-term deficiencies in the diet.

Folate deficiency is most common when there's both a greater need and low body stores from a long-term dietary deficiency. Pregnant teenagers from low socioeconomic groups are of particular concern. The RDA for folate goes up during pregnancy—cells divide fast in the growing fetus, and teenagers often have a poor diet (and thus marginal stores of vitamins), and many don't get prenatal care or prenatal vitamins.

Folate deficiency can increase the risk of spontaneous abortion and neural tube defects (the neural tube is a structure in the embryo that becomes the brain and spinal cord). Some of these defects occur during the first month of

---

*Cells divide rapidly in the lining of the small intestine—they're continually being replenished (Chap. 6). Folate deficiency impairs this cell division. This, in turn, impairs the small intestine's lining and the absorption of nutrients, making a dietary deficiency of folate worse. Also, as discussed in Chap. 12, cell division is rapid and out of control in cancer; drugs that interfere with folate can be effective in treating cancer.

pregnancy, before most women get prenatal care or take prenatal vitamins, so women who can get pregnant are advised to take folate/ folic acid in a vitamin pill or in a fortified food (e.g., fortified breakfast cereal).

Folate deficiency is common among alcoholics, who often have poor diets. Their folate deficiency is made worse because alcohol itself hampers folate's activity in the body. Also, excessive alcohol intake increases the need for folate, hampers its absorption, and increases its excretion. Alcoholics also often have damaged livers that hampers their storing folate.

Some people are deficient but don't have folate-deficiency anemia, because it generally occurs only in the late stages of deficiency. One way of detecting milder deficiency is to measure blood-homocysteine, which goes up when folate is low.* (High blood-homocysteine also raises the risk of atherosclerosis; see Chap. 8.) As of 1998, folate has been included with some other B-vitamins that are added, by law, to enrich staple grains like white flour, so folate deficiency and related birth defects are now less common in the U.S.

Pernicious Anemia

Pernicious anemia is caused by a vitamin B_{12} deficiency, almost always due to a lack of intrinsic factor, rather than a deficiency of B_{12} in the diet. As discussed in Chapter 6, intrinsic factor is made in the stomach and is needed to absorb B_{12} in the small intestine.

Pernicious anemia seems to be an auto-immune disease in which the body mistakenly makes antibodies against its own intrinsic-factor-producing stomach cells, and destroys them as if they were foreign invaders. So, people with this disease can't absorb B_{12} in their food and must get B_{12} another way, usually by injection.

The liver can store enough B_{12} for about four years. Thus, an actual deficiency may not occur for several years after the loss of the stomach cells that make intrinsic factor, and the symptoms often appear gradually. Pernicious anemia mostly occurs after age 50.

B_{12} deficiency also hampers cell division and causes anemia. The anemia is indistinguishable from that caused by folate deficiency—red blood cells are larger and fewer. The crucial difference is that B_{12} deficiency can also cause permanent nerve damage. B_{12} is needed to make myelin, a crucial component of nerve cells (Chap. 15), so it's very important to detect and treat the deficiency early to prevent permanent nerve damage. Often, the first sign of B_{12} deficiency is the anemia.

The anemia of B_{12} deficiency can be cured by large amounts of folate. This can be a problem, because folate won't do anything about the damage to the nerve tissue from B_{12} deficiency, and can, in fact, make the damage worse. In other words, large amounts of folate can delay the diagnosis of a B_{12} deficiency by curing its telltale anemia. This delay increases the risk of permanent nerve damage.

Pernicious means deadly. In late stages of this disease, the nerves and spinal cord degenerate. Pernicious anemia was a fatal disease until 1926, when two physicians found effective treatment in a dietary regimen that included about a half pound of liver a day. They didn't know what caused pernicious anemia nor what was in the dietary regimen that was effective.† However, for discovering an effective treatment (and discovering that the disease had something to do with nutrition), George Minot and William Murphy won the Nobel prize in 1934.

Liver is a rich source of B_{12}** because it's stored there. By eating all that liver, a small amount of B_{12} is absorbed, despite the absence of intrinsic factor. In 1948, B_{12} was isolated from

---

*Vitamins B_6 or B_{12} deficiency can also cause high blood-homocysteine, but folate deficiency is the most common cause.
†The role of an intrinsic factor was discovered a few years later. (It's made in the stomach, so it's intrinsic to the body; required nutrients are extrinsic.) The enlightening—and unappetizing—experiment: the discoverer (Dr. William Castle) ate some beef (which has B_{12}), and then used a stomach tube to bring up the meat/stomach-juice mixture, which was then fed to patients with pernicious anemia.
**Liver is also a rich source of folate, and the prescribed diet also included a lot of fruits and vegetables (including spinach), many of which are rich in folate. All this folate certainly must have helped remedy the anemia of B_{12} deficiency..

liver (it was the last vitamin discovered). In 1955, Dorothy Hodgkins determined the complex structure of B_{12}, and won the Nobel prize in 1964.

B_{12} is an unusual vitamin because it's made only by microbes. It is, in fact, the only vitamin that plants can't make. B_{12} found in animal tissues and animal products comes from that made by microbes, e.g., microbes in a cow's rumen make B_{12}, which the cow absorbs—and we get in beef and milk.

We need very little B_{12}; the adult RDA is 2.4 micrograms (less than 1/10,000,000 of an ounce). People who eat meat, fish, milk, or eggs get enough B_{12}.

Because B_{12} isn't found in plants, vegans (who don't eat any animal food) are at risk of deficiency. They can get B_{12} from several sources: sometimes, they inadvertently ingest B_{12} when their food or water is contaminated with microbes that make this vitamin. Microbes in soil might be enriched further by the use of bacteria-containing manure as fertilizer.

These bacteria can be a source of B_{12} if food grown in this soil isn't thoroughly washed (B_{12} isn't easily destroyed by cooking). B_{12}-synthesizing microbes in the root nodules of some legumes (beans) can also be a source. Other sources include plant foods fortified with B_{12} (e.g., some breakfast cereals or soy milk) and special yeast grown in a B_{12}-enriched broth.

Vegans develop a B_{12} deficiency only after a severe and long-term shortage (the body can store enough to last several years, and very little is needed). But, one concern is a delayed diagnosis—a strictly vegetarian diet often has a lot of folate, which can cure the telltale anemia of B_{12} deficiency without protecting against nerve damage.

Infants born of mothers who have been vegans for a long time are especially vulnerable. They're born with low body stores of B_{12}, and are commonly fed only breast milk during early infancy. As might be expected, the breast milk of a longtime vegan mother has very little B_{12}. Sometimes, the infant's nervous system is damaged.

White Blood Cells

White blood cells play a key role in immunity by destroying bacteria and other foreign substances. They defend the body against infections and tumors.

Leukemia and AIDS involve white blood cells. We see, again, the familiar theme of *too much* or *too little* as a problem. In leukemia, there's an uncontrolled production of white blood cells. The result is an overwhelming abundance of white blood cells, causing a potentially fatal disruption of normal body processes.

AIDS (Chap. 10) stands for Acquired Immuno-deficiency Syndrome: *Acquired* from an infection rather than a genetic defect; *Immunodeficiency* because white blood cells are infected and destroyed; and a *Syndrome* (set of symptoms occurring together in a disease). Besides destroying white blood cells, AIDS can damage the nervous system and cause unusual diseases, like a pneumonia caused by *Pneumocystis carnii* (a microbe that's ordinarily harmless) and Kaposi's sarcoma, a rare cancer.

Platelets

Platelets are small disk-shaped structures *(small plates)* that can be thought of as sentries on the lookout and at the ready for any injury to a blood vessel. They immediately gather at an injury, temporarily plugging a leak until a clot can form by normal clotting mechanisms.

Injuring a blood vessel's inner lining exposes an underlying layer. Platelets have proteins on their surface that attach to this normally unexposed layer. Because of this feature, platelets normally cluster only at the site of damage. At the injury, the platelets release a variety of substances, including those needed to clot blood. They also release substances that constrict injured blood vessels and promote healing.

Aspirin lessens the platelets' ability to cluster. This alteration lasts for the life of the platelet (less than a week), so blood donors are asked if they've taken aspirin within the past week. If so, the blood won't be used to replace surgical losses. Surgery patients need blood that clots well (to stem the bleeding). Conversely, aspirin is commonly prescribed to people who have had inappropriate clotting (as in a previous heart attack).

Plasma Proteins

Antibodies

Many kinds of proteins are dissolved in the plasma of blood. Among them are antibodies made in response to infection (or vaccination). We make the antibodies when we're exposed to a foreign agent, and usually continue to make them to `protect against any subsequent infections by the same agent. Thus, the presence or absence of specific antibodies in a blood sample can reveal whether we've ever been infected with (or vaccinated against) a particular microbe.

The development of vaccines was a major breakthrough in preventive medicine. Some vaccines have microbes (dead or alive) that are similar to the disease-causing ones—similar in that they cause us to make protective antibodies, but dissimilar in that they don't cause the disease. Other vaccines have only harmless part(s) of the microbe. If, for example, we make protective antibodies in response to a particular protein on the surface of a microbe, that protein alone might be used in a vaccine. Two milestones in preventive medicine involved the smallpox vaccine: the development of the first vaccine and the eradication of a horrible disease that had plagued mankind for centuries.

The first smallpox vaccine was the cowpox virus. English physician Edward Jenner had heard that dairy maids who'd been infected with cowpox virus (from cowpox blisters on nipples of cows they milked) didn't get smallpox. In 1796, he tested the hypothesis that infection with cowpox virus confers immunity to smallpox. Using the fluid from a cowpox blister (on a dairy maid's hand), he infected a healthy boy (Jim

Phipps) by way of two slight incisions on Jim's arm. Seven weeks later, and again several months later, he tried (unsuccessfully, thank goodness) infecting Jim with smallpox by applying fluid from a smallpox blister and then making several slight punctures and incisions on Jim's arms.

Smallpox as a disease was eradicated in 1977, so the vaccine is no longer needed.* This first and only eradication of an infectious disease was made possible by an effective vaccine, a major effort by the World Health Organization, and by the fact that humans are the only natural host of the smallpox virus. This accomplishment is really impressive. As recently as 1967, smallpox killed about two million people that year.

Using mass surveillance and immunization campaigns, the World Health Organization together with other governments and organizations such as Rotary International have been working toward eradicating polio`. On a single day in 1997, volunteers vaccinated 134 million children in India. In Turkey, the Rotary talked soap manufacturers into adding vaccination announcements to their commercials. Where there's war, doctors have negotiated cease-fires to immunize children.

Scientists are working on an AIDS vaccine. One obstacle is that the proteins on the surface of HIV (the virus that causes AIDS) differ and change (mutate). In other words, there are many strains of HIV (unlike many other viruses that have only a few strains), and a vaccine against one strain may not be effective against others.

Albumin

Albumin is the most abundant protein in blood plasma and has many functions, e.g., it helps transport substances like bile components in the blood and helps regulate the pH of blood by acting as a buffer (Chap. 3). Albumin also holds liquid in the plasma (imagine transparent sponges holding water). When there isn't enough albumin,

---

*Ironically, smallpox virus (and anthrax) now poses the greatest threat as a biological weapon by terrorists or in warfare. High-security depots in Russia and the U.S. are the only known and legitimate sources of the smallpox virus today. These were to be destroyed but weren't, mostly because of the fear that there may be unknown (illegitimate) sources. If used as biological weapons, the legitimate depots of the virus could then be used to make and test vaccines.

some of the fluid moves out of blood vessels into the surrounding tissue, causing edema (swelling from excess tissue fluid). A number of diseases can cause low plasma-albumin, as can the severe dietary protein deficiency common among children in some developing countries. These children can't make enough albumin, and they look "puffy" with their bellies and faces swollen from edema.

Clotting Factors

Proteins needed for blood clotting are in blood plasma. Clotting involves more than a dozen clotting factors. Lacking even one can cause life-threatening bleeding from minor injuries. Hemophiliacs genetically lack one and get it from a plasma-extract.* Some clotting factors are now made by biotechnology (Chap. 10). Hemophiliacs avoid taking aspirin—they are especially dependent on the clustering of platelets to prevent bleeding.

Forming a blood clot involves a complex series of reactions in which enzymes are activated; these, in turn, activate other enzymes. Calcium and vitamin K are required (as shown below in a small segment of the clotting process) to form thrombin, the enzyme that catalyzes the final reaction that forms the blood clot (fibrin).† ("Pre-prothrombin," prothrombin, thrombin, and fibrinogen are proteins dissolved in blood plasma.)

Good sources of vitamin K include green leafy vegetables (plants use K for photosynthesis) and liver (where K is stored). Vitamin K deficiency is uncommon because intestinal bacteria make ample amounts under normal circumstances.

As mentioned in earlier chapters, a vitamin K injection is given routinely to newborns in this country because there are no bacteria in the intestine at birth. A deficiency is occasionally seen in people who ingest antibiotics for a long time, or have diseases where there's chronic malabsorption of dietary fat (K is a fat-soluble vitamin).

Drugs that hamper K activity are prescribed as anticoagulants for those who want to reduce their ability to form blood clots (e.g., people who've had a previous heart attack). Dicumarol and warfarin (Coumadin®) are two such drugs. Dicumarol is found naturally in spoiled sweet clover, and when animals feed on this clover, the dicumarol can cause a hemorrhagic disease in the animals called sweet clover disease.

Warfarin is also a very effective rat poison. When rats' food is laced with warfarin, they die from internal hemorrhage. Warfarin (or dicumarol) can thus be a lifesaving drug or the cause of a fatal hemorrhage. It's all in the dose.

There's always enough calcium in the plasma for the clotting process because very little is needed and bone holds a huge reserve. Calcium's importance in blood clotting can be demonstrated in a test tube. If calcium is removed from a blood sample, it doesn't clot (if it clots, the liquid portion is called serum instead of plasma). One way to keep it from clotting is to collect it into a tube that has oxalic acid. Oxalic acid combines with the calcium in the blood, making it unavailable in the clotting process.**

There's a fine balance between clotting and the prevention of clotting. We need a clot to stop bleeding, but if a clot forms when it isn't needed,

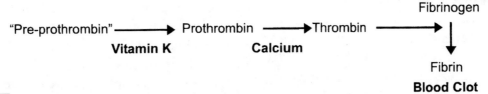

---

*The plasma comes from blood pooled from about 2,000-200,000 donors. Thus, many hemophiliacs were inadvertently infected with HIV before it was known that it could be transmitted in blood, making AIDS their leading cause of death.

†Danish scientist Henrik Dam discovered Vitamin K (from the Danish word koa*gulation*). He and Edward Doisy (who determined the structure of vitamin K) shared a Nobel prize in 1943.

**Oxalic acid was mentioned earlier in this chapter as a substance found in some foods (e.g., spinach) that can combine with iron (as with calcium) and prevent the absorption of that iron from the intestine.

it could impair the normal flow of blood and even cause a life-threatening heart attack, stroke, or blood clot in the lung (*pulmonary embolism*).

Sometimes, a clot forms because of impaired circulation. For example, as mentioned earlier, blood can pool in leg veins when a person stands or sits still for a long time. The "sluggishness" (reduced circulation) of blood in these veins may cause a local accumulation of clotting factors that can cause a clot to form. The clot might then be carried in the bloodstream to block a blood vessel elsewhere.

Note that blood returning to the heart from the legs goes through the lungs to be oxygenated before it goes to the coronary arteries and brain (Fig. 7-1). This is why a clot formed in the leg is more likely to block a blood vessel in the lung than in the heart or brain.

As a preventive measure, people with narrowed arteries are often advised to get up and walk around occasionally during a long, cramped, airplane flight. Likewise, patients recovering from surgery are encouraged to take walks (despite the discomfort) in the hospital corridor soon after surgery. Many years ago, the common practice was for patients to lie in their hospital beds for a week or more after surgery.

As expected, plasma also has substances that help prevent clotting and help dissolve any clots that do form. This "anti-clot" system is also complex (though not as complex as clotting). One substance that triggers the breakdown of clots is tissue plasminogen activator (TPA). Activase is TPA made by biotechnology (Chap. 10) and sold as a drug.

Activase can be injected into the bloodstream to rapidly dissolve the clot in a patient with a heart attack or stroke caused by a clot blocking an artery. The sooner the clot is dissolved to clear the blockage, the less the heart or brain damage and the better the chance of recovery. An injection of Activase also, of course, increases the risk of bleeding in the brain or elsewhere. Activase isn't selective. It acts on any clot it encounters.

Lipoproteins

Fat (lipid) alone would clump together in plasma (plasma is water-based; fat doesn't dissolve in water), so it's combined with protein (which does dissolve). These lipid-protein packages are called lipoproteins. They're ball-shaped—a core of fat surrounded by a protein-containing outer layer.

Lipoproteins are grouped by how dense they are (*how heavy they are for their size*). Fat is less dense (*lighter*) than protein, so the fattier a lipoprotein, the lower its density (Table 7-1). Chylomicrons are the fattiest, biggest, and least dense. High-Density Lipoproteins (HDL) are the leanest, smallest, and most dense. Think of lipoproteins as fat-carrying vehicles that "ride" the blood to transport fat throughout the body.

Chylomicrons* originate in the intestine and transport fat from food (food fat is mainly triglycerides, as discussed in Chap. 5). As expected, chylomicrons increase in the plasma after eating a meal. If the meal is fatty, the abundant chylomicrons give plasma a cloudy appearance and, in a blood sample, they rise to form a layer of fat above the plasma.

As the chylomicrons travel through the capillaries, an enzyme in the capillary lining breaks apart the chylomicron's triglycerides into fatty acids and glycerol, which then move out of the capillaries for use by nearby tissues. After unloading much of their triglycerides in this way, chylomicrons are taken up by the liver, where they're repackaged into lipoproteins called VLDL.

VLDL (Very Low Density Lipoprotein) is rich in triglycerides, and delivers them to tissues in much the same way as chylomicrons. As VLDL makes its deliveries, it becomes smaller and more dense (removing fat increases the proportion of protein, which is denser). The proportion of cholesterol also goes up as triglycerides are selectively removed.

At this stage, VLDL is taken up by the liver, which alters the protein portion, turning

---

*They're called chylomicrons because dietary fat comes into the blood mainly as a fluid called chyle, and the size of lipoproteins is measured in microns. Chylomicrons are about 0.1 microns wide (HDL are about 0.01 microns wide).

Table 7-1: Composition of Plasma Lipoproteins

	Approximate Composition (%)			
	Protein	Triglyceride	Cholesterol*	Phospholipid
Chylomicrons	2	90	5	3
Very Low Density Lipoprotein (VLDL)	8	55	20	17
Low Density Lipoprotein (LDL)	20	6	55	21
High Density Lipoprotein (HDL)	50	5	20	25

* Includes cholesterol with a fatty acid attached

Chylomicron → triglycerides → VLDL → triglycerides → LDL → cholesterol → HDL

Mostly triglycerides

Mostly triglycerides

Mostly cholesterol

Mostly protein

it into a lipoprotein called LDL (Low-Density Lipoprotein). LDL is mostly cholesterol and delivers cholesterol for use in making cell membranes, sex hormones, etc.

HDL (High-Density Lipoprotein) is mostly protein, but also is rich in cholesterol. But in contrast to LDL, it generally delivers cholesterol to the liver, where it can be made into bile acids and secreted into the intestine for use in digestion. The relationship of these lipoproteins to heart disease will be discussed in the next chapter.

Summary

The main parts of the **circulatory system** are the heart, blood vessels, and blood. There are 3 main types of blood vessels. Thick-walled high-pressure **arteries** carry blood from the heart and branch extensively into thin-walled, very-low-pressure **capillaries** that make intimate contact with each of the body's cells. Capillaries then converge into medium-walled, medium-pressure veins that return the blood back to the heart (veins have valves that help).

Blood is made up of red blood cells, white blood cells, and platelets suspended in a liquid called plasma. **Red blood cells** have hemoglobin, which carries oxygen to cells throughout the body and carries carbon dioxide back to the lungs. **White blood cells** are an essential part of the immune system, and **platelets** play a key role in blood clotting.

Anemia is a reduced capacity of the blood to carry oxygen due to insufficient red blood cells or hemoglobin. Less oxygen is delivered to the tissues, so an anemic person tires easily and can feel weak, dizzy, drowsy, irritable, and have a headache. Several nutritional deficiencies can cause anemia. The most common ones are deficiencies of iron, folate, and vitamin B$_{12}$.

Iron deficiency is the most common cause of anemia, and is common among children and premenopausal women. Iron deficiency is unusual among men and postmenopausal women, because they aren't growing like children and don't have regular blood losses like menstruating women. Without enough iron, normal amounts of hemoglobin can't be made, since iron is an essential part of hemoglobin. So red blood cells are smaller because of less hemoglobin.

Folate and **vitamin B$_{12}$** are needed to make red blood cells. Fewer (but bigger) red blood cells are made when there's a deficiency of either of these B-vitamins. Though the anemia caused by folate deficiency looks the same as that caused by B$_{12}$ deficiency, the one from a B$_{12}$ deficiency is called pernicious *(deadly)* anemia. This is because, in addition to anemia, untreated B$_{12}$ deficiency can cause permanent nerve damage and ultimately death.

Vitamin B$_{12}$ is unique in that it's the only vitamin that plants can't make. Those who include animal foods like milk or eggs in their diet get enough B$_{12}$. (Of all the vitamins, it's required in the smallest amount.) B$_{12}$ deficiency generally occurs only when the stomach doesn't make enough of the intrinsic factor needed for B$_{12}$ absorption. The stomach normally makes plenty. Longtime vegans (those who eat only plant foods) should see to it that they get enough B$_{12}$ (e.g., as a supplement or in plant foods fortified with B$_{12}$). Exclusively breast-fed infants born of long-term vegans are particularly at risk of developing a B$_{12}$ deficiency.

Plasma is the fluid portion of blood. **Plasma proteins** (proteins dissolved in the plasma) include:

- **Antibodies**, which protect against infections.
- **Albumin**, which carries various substances, holds fluid, and regulates the pH of blood.
- **Blood-clotting factors**, which are needed to form blood clots.
- **Lipoproteins**, which transport fat in the blood. Fat (lipid) doesn't dissolve in water/plasma, but does when combined with protein (lipoprotein).

Chapter 8

Atherosclerosis

An ounce of prevention is worth a pound of cure.

Benjamin Franklin (1706-1790)

Atherosclerosis is a disease characterized by damaged and narrowed arteries (Fig. 8-1). It's first seen as fatty streaks in the lining of the arteries. It can begin early in life. Autopsies of young American men killed in war or accidents often show early stages of atherosclerosis.

Over time, increased fatty deposits form plaques and damage the lining, causing scar tissue and progressive narrowing. The thickened and damaged lining becomes rigid and lessens an artery's elasticity.

Athero means *gruel* in Greek—cutting open a plaque yields a thick, yellow, cholesterol-rich substance with the consistency of gruel. *Sclerosis* means hard. *Arteriosclerosis* means *hardened arteries.* A plaque can break open on its own, causing a clot that can block the artery there, or travel in the blood and cause a blockage elsewhere.

Arteries deliver oxygenated blood to vital tissues and organs, so the effects of atherosclerosis depend on which arteries are affected. If it's those feeding the heart, it's coronary artery disease and a possible heart attack. If it's those feeding the brain, it's cerebrovascular disease and a possible stroke.

Figure 8-1: Narrowing of Arteries in Atherosclerosis

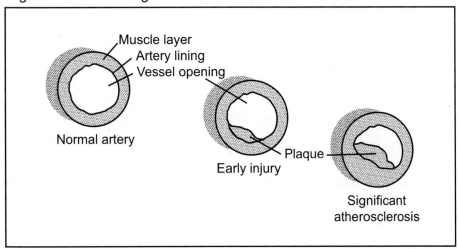

"It was touch and go for a while. I'm lucky to be dead."

If arteries don't deliver enough oxygen to the heart muscle, it's felt as chest pain (or chest discomfort, nausea, numbness, or even a pain in the jaw) and is called *angina pectoris* (anger of the breast) or simply *angina.* Angina is commonly triggered by physical activity and relieved by rest. Physical activity increases the heartbeat to provide more oxygen to the muscles. A faster heartbeat increases the heart muscle's own need for oxygen, which can't be met if the arteries are severely narrowed.

With narrowed arteries, there's risk of a sudden, complete blockage. A sudden lack of oxygenated blood to the tissue served by that artery leads to tissue death in a short time. When a coronary artery, which supplies the heart muscle (Fig. 7-2), is blocked, it's called a *heart attack.* If a significant portion of the heart is damaged, it can't contract, resulting in sudden death. When an artery feeding the brain is blocked, it's called a *stroke.*

A rupture of an artery in the brain also causes a stroke—a *hemorrhagic stroke.* It often starts as an outpouching *(aneurysm),* usually from a weak spot in the arterial wall and/or high blood pressure. (Outpouchings can occur in any blood vessel, but the ones in the brain aren't as accessible for surgical repair.)*

Whether an artery in the brain is blocked or ruptured, the effect is similar. In both cases, the flow of oxygenated blood is interrupted (warning signs: sudden weakness or numbness of the face, arm, or leg; sudden dimness or loss of vision; sudden difficulty speaking or understanding speech; sudden severe headache; sudden unexplained dizziness, unsteadiness, or sudden falls). Getting help is urgent. The longer the delay, the more the damage.

Heart disease is the leading cause of death in the U.S., but the age-adjusted death rate has fallen dramatically since the 1950s (Fig. 1-4).† Less smoking by men, changes in diet, and improved treatment of high blood pressure and heart disease have certainly helped.

In 1964, the Surgeon General issued a report on the health hazards of smoking, and the American Heart Association advised eating less saturated fat and cholesterol. Since then, intake of animal fats has fallen, and the percent of U.S. men who smoke fell from 51% in 1965 to 23% in 2009. For women, comparable figures are 34% in 1965 and 18% in 2009.

Atherosclerosis is a disease that develops over a lifetime. As with many other chronic diseases, symptoms don't usually appear until late in the disease. The passageway in arteries is often narrowed to a quarter of its normal size before symptoms develop. In all too many cases, the first symptom is sudden death.

Premature Death

If sudden death happened only at an old age, many of us wouldn't mind dying this way. But heart attacks and strokes kill many people prematurely or leave them severely disabled. In the U.S., the risk of suffering or dying from heart

---

*Outpouchings of arteries remind one of diverticuli—outpouchings of the colon discussed in Chap. 6.

†When looking at changing rates of death or illness over the years, age-adjusted rates should be used. Otherwise, higher rates could simply be from a larger proportion of elderly (Chap. 2).

Figure 8-2: 2007 Death Rates, Ages 15-64

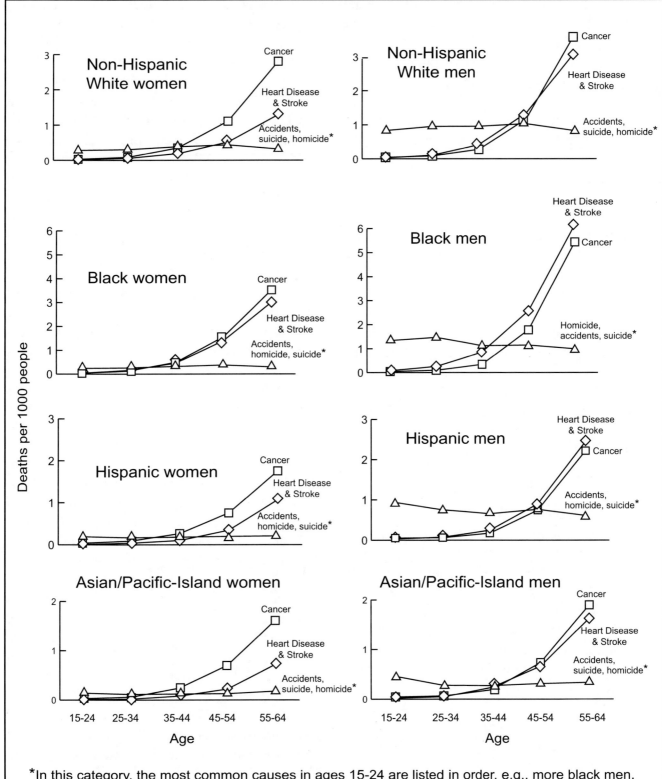

*In this category, the most common causes in ages 15-24 are listed in order, e.g., more black men, ages 15-24, die by homicide than from accidents.

National Center for Health Statistics, 2011

disease goes up dramatically after age 45 for men, and 55 for women. Figure 8-2 shows death rates for some common causes of death among people 15-64 years old.

The aim is to prevent premature death (*dying before age 65* is the standard definition of premature death, although today 65 isn't very old). Don't be discouraged by such statements as, "even if all heart disease were prevented, life expectancy would only go up by 3 years." Preventing a fatal heart attack in a 45-year-old man who lives to be 66 extends his life by 21 years. But when his extended life is averaged with 6 other people whose ages of death weren't affected, the *average* life expectancy is higher by only 3 years ($^{21}/_7 = 3$).

Risk Factors

The main risk factors for atherosclerosis are genetic predisposition, high LDL-cholesterol, smoking, high blood pressure, and male gender. Diabetes also increases risk substantially. Obesity increases risk in several ways, including a higher risk of diabetes and high blood pressure, and lower HDL-cholesterol.

High LDL-Cholesterol

As discussed in Chapter 7, LDL (low-density lipoprotein) carries cholesterol to various cells for use in making sex hormones, cell membranes, etc. LDL gets into the cells by attaching to LDL-receptors that protrude from the surface of the cell. When LDL locks into these receptors, the entire complex (LDL and its receptor) enters the cell, and the cholesterol is released inside. This reduces the amount of LDL in the blood and cuts back the cell's own cholesterol production.

When LDL in the blood is excessive, LDL can deposit in the lining of the artery. Scavenger (*clean-up*) cells in the lining of the artery take in the LDL and release enzymes that cause local inflammation, contributing to the atherosclerotic process. LDL-cholesterol (the cholesterol carried in LDL) is called *bad cholesterol,* because the higher the LDL-cholesterol, the higher the risk of atherosclerosis.

HDL-cholesterol (the cholesterol in high-density lipoprotein) will be discussed later, but is mentioned here to contrast it to LDL-cholesterol. HDL generally takes up excess cholesterol and transports it to the liver, where it can be made into bile acids and secreted into the intestine to aid digestion (Chap. 6). Most of the bile acids in the intestine are absorbed back into the blood, but some of it can get trapped by dietary fiber and excreted in the stool. Losing cholesterol via bile is about the only way the body gets rid of cholesterol. HDL-cholesterol is thus called *good cholesterol.*

It should be emphasized that the cholesterol itself is the same whether it's carried in the blood by LDL (*bad*) or HDL (*good*).* People are often confused into thinking that there are two kinds of cholesterol in the diet—*good* cholesterol and *bad* cholesterol. In food, cholesterol is simply cholesterol.

Genetic Predisposition

A family history of a heart attack or stroke—especially in a parent or sibling before age 55—suggests a genetic susceptibility. But keep in mind that families not only share genes, but often share eating, smoking, drinking, and exercise habits.

A very severe genetic defect is seen in the disease *familial hypercholesterolemia* [*familial* (inherited) *hyper-* (excessive) *-emia* (in the blood)]. Due to a defect in the gene for LDL receptors, cells can't take in LDL, and blood-cholesterol skyrockets. Those with the disease have inherited the defective gene from both parents, and have blood-cholesterols of about 500 to 1200 mg/100 ml (normal is less than 200 mg), and can die of heart disease before age 20.† Luckily, only about 1 per million people have this disease.

---

*To remember which is bad and which is good, think of LDL as Lousy (high blood-levels raise the risk of heart disease) and HDL as Healthy (high levels protect).

†The first person to get a simultaneous heart-liver transplant was Stormie Jones, who had familial hypercholesterolemia. Following a heart attack, she had the double transplant in 1984 at age 6 and died of a heart attack in 1990 at age 13.

Figure 8-3: % Men and Women Smokers in 2009 by Education

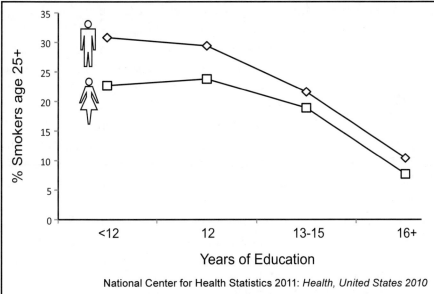

National Center for Health Statistics 2011: *Health, United States 2010*

About 1 of 500 people inherit the defective gene from only one parent, and have about half the number of normal LDL receptors and a blood-cholesterol of about 300 mg/100 ml. They have severe atherosclerosis—especially men. In the past, one of six men with this genetic defect died of heart disease by age 40, and about two thirds of them died by age 60. The outlook now is better with earlier diagnosis and new drugs and treatments.

A cell's LDL receptors and their role of pulling in cholesterol from blood were found by comparing cells from normal people with cells from people with familial hypercholesterolemia. For these discoveries, Michael Brown and Joseph Goldstein shared a Nobel prize in 1985.

Smoking

Most people know that smoking causes lung cancer, but many don't know that it markedly increases the risk of a heart attack or stroke. Carbon monoxide (from the smoke) displaces oxygen in the blood, so less oxygen gets to the tissues (Chap. 7). Nicotine constricts blood vessels, which means even less oxygen delivery and easier blockage by a clot.

Smoking also injures blood vessels, increases blood pressure, hastens the heart beat, and increases the risk of blood clots. Among those who

have heart attacks, sudden death is much more common in smokers. (Chewing tobacco has nicotine and carcinogens. Marijuana doesn't have nicotine, but its smoke has carbon monoxide and carcinogens.)

As expected, the risk goes up the more a person smokes. The risk for cigar and pipe smokers lies between that for cigarette smokers and nonsmokers. About one in five adults in the U.S. smokes. Men who didn't finish high school smoke the most (Fig. 8-3).

About 90% of smokers begin smoking during childhood and adolescence. An effective way to cut smoking, especially in this age group, is to raise cigarette taxes. Canada's smoking rate fell by a third when their cigarette tax was raised from 38¢ to $3.25/pack. But despite protests from antismoking groups, Canada then lowered the tax because of problems associated with smuggling in the lower priced/taxed cigarettes from the U.S. Cigarette tax in the U.S. is low compared to other developed countries.

High Blood Pressure

High blood pressure especially increases the risk of a stroke. High pressure can damage the lining of arteries and can be a determining factor in the formation and rupture of outpouchings in arteries. In the U.S., high blood pressure is much more common in blacks than in whites. Blacks of ages 25-54 have about a 3-fold greater death rate from stroke than whites of the same age and sex.

Male Gender

Men have a higher death rate from diseases resulting from atherosclerosis than do women of the same age and ethnicity (Fig. 8-2). Men do smoke more, but the difference has more to do with sex hormones. Male sex hormones lower

HDL.* Premenopausal women have higher HDL than men of the same age. At menopause, women's risk of heart disease goes up a lot, but it takes years to catch up to men. Men have a head start.

High Blood-Homocysteine

The link between atherosclerosis and high levels of homocysteine in the blood was first seen in the genetic disease homocysteinuria.† Patients with this disease have extremely high levels of homocysteine and have severe atherosclerosis in childhood. In the general population, the most common cause of high homocysteine is a folate deficiency. Since 1998, folate (a B-vitamin) has been added to refined staple grains like white flour. As a result, folate deficiency—and high homocysteine—is much less common.

Treatment

Treating atherosclerosis is like trying to keep the plumbing clear. The goal is to see that enough oxygenated blood is delivered through the narrowed arteries, and that clots don't form inappropriately and block an artery.

Blood flow can be improved by widening the narrowed portion of an artery by physically removing or flattening the plaques,** or using drugs that dilate arteries. Sometimes, a section of a healthy blood vessel elsewhere in the body is used to bypass a narrowed section of a coronary artery (*a coro-*

nary bypass). In a quintuple bypass (as had TV hosts Larry King at age 53 and David Letterman at age 52), five sections are bypassed. Also, drugs can be used to lower the heart's need for oxygen, e.g., drugs called beta-blockers can be used to slow the heartbeat, reducing the heart's need for oxygen.††

Widening or bypass procedures often have to be repeated. When a narrowed coronary artery is widened by flattening the plaques, it narrows again in about 3 to 6 months in about 30 to 50% of the cases.*** Also keep in mind that not all arteries are as accessible as coronary arteries. There is a risk of permanent brain damage in trying to surgically reach a narrowed artery (or an outpouching of an artery) in the brain.

"We're going to name the drug after you, Haskins. We'd like you to change your name to miracle."

---

*Anabolic steroids used illegally by some athletes are similar to the male hormone testosterone and lower HDL, raising the risk of atherosclerosis.

†Homocysteinuria is like phenylketonuria (Chap.3) in that both are due to a genetic deficiency of an enzyme needed to metabolize an essential amino acid (methionine or phenylalanine). A back up occurs, and homocysteine or phenylketone accumulates to toxic levels in the blood and spills over into the urine.

**A balloon-like device is threaded into the narrowed portion of the artery, and then inflated to flatten the plaque. This procedure is called angioplasty.

††Beta-blockers may have been used by some athletes in the 1988 Olympic archery competition to slow the heartbeat for another reason—to minimize disturbing the aim of the arrow by the heartbeat.

***A tube-like device (a stent) can be inserted to help keep it open.

Drugs that hamper the forming of blood clots (e.g., dicumarol, warfarin, heparin, aspirin) are often prescribed to patients with atherosclerosis. When a clot blocks a blood vessel, a clot-dissolving drug (e.g., streptokinase or Activase) is often injected into the bloodstream to dissolve the clot as fast as possible.

It appears that intensive treatment to lower LDL in the blood can halt or even reverse the progression of atherosclerosis in some people. But the first symptom is all too often a heart attack or stroke, and the person must, of course, survive long enough to be treated; many die before getting help or shortly thereafter. For 1 of every 4 fatal heart attacks, the heart attack was the first symptom.

Treatments of diseases resulting from atherosclerosis make up a major part of our health care costs and come with their own risks and side effects. This—and quality-of-life issues—is why prevention is so important.

Prevention

Prevention relies on understanding the causes and development of diseases like atherosclerosis. This requires extensive studies of the subtle interplay between genetics and environment and how a normal cell works. Discovering how a cell makes cholesterol and how it takes in cholesterol from the blood via LDL receptors markedly advanced the understanding of the disease process. Think of how hard it would be to keep a car in good working order—or diagnose or fix a problem—if we didn't know how cars work!

We can't change our gender or genetics, but we can alter other risk factors. Atherosclerosis develops over many years, so even a modest reduction in its progression delays the onset of symptoms. Modest changes starting at age 20 might be enough to delay to age 70 or older a heart attack or stroke that might have otherwise happened at age 60. This same logic applies to early detection and treatment of high blood pressure to delay an outpouching and rupture of a blood vessel. The three most significant risk factors that can be altered are smoking, high blood pressure, and high LDL-cholesterol.

Smoking

It goes without saying that smokers should quit smoking or smoke less (nonsmokers should avoid breathing other people's smoke). It's very hard to quit because nicotine is highly addictive (more so in some people than others). Nicotine chewing gum, inhalants, or skin patches, together with behavior modification techniques can help.

Studies indicate that the risk of a heart attack falls significantly within a year after quitting. Some risks fall immediately, e.g., those associated with the constricted blood vessels caused by nicotine and the reduced blood-oxygen due to the carbon monoxide inhaled in smoke.

Blood Pressure

Treating high blood pressure before the onset of symptoms plays a big part in preventing heart disease and stroke.* Adults should have their blood pressure checked regularly. High blood pressure has both genetic and environmental components. There are effective treatments, including medications.

If you have high blood pressure and are overweight, **weight loss** may, in itself, normalize blood pressure. (Obesity also raises the risk of diabetes, which more than triples the risk of dying from heart disease.) If you can't get down to a normal weight, maintaining a loss of even a few pounds can help. If you can't do this, try to keep from gaining more.

Psychological stress can cause high blood pressure, but at least some of the added risk can be from ways in which people cope with stress, e.g., smoking, drinking, over-eating. Someone who is stressed and has high blood pressure certainly is advised to take measures to **lower stress**. There are, of course, many good reasons for keeping stress (and body weight) to normal levels, whether or not a person is prone to high blood pressure.

*High blood pressure can also directly damage the kidney and heart. Think of the strain on the pump (heart) and filter (kidney) in a high-pressure water filtration system.

Table 8-1: Lowering Risk for Heart Disease

	Start	1 year	2 years
Weight (lbs)	191	164	153
% of Ideal Weight	135%	116%	102%
Body Fat (lbs)	59	35	20
Lean (lbs)	132	129	133
% Body Fat	31%	21%	13%
Resting Heart Rate	78	56	60
Maximum O$_2$ Uptake	27	42	60
Max. minutes on Treadmill	12	19	23
Blood Pressure	114/82	110/71	110/70
Diet: % Calories from Fat	40%	34%	30%
LDL-cholesterol	182	102	116
HDL-cholesterol	33	40	47

The subject is a half-Chinese, half-Caucasian 5'6" man, age 34, who was at risk for heart disease. His wife saw a news ad about a 2-year study (by Peter Wood, PhD and other Stanford Univ. scientists) to lower risk by exercise and diet, and signed him up. His job involved a lot of travel; he hadn't exercised since high school. He started running, working up to 10 miles/week (2 milesX5 days/wk), traveling or not, & eating better (more fruits/veggies, less fat).

Some people with high blood pressure can lower their blood pressure by **limiting sodium**, which we get mostly from salt.* The salt comes mainly from fast foods, chips, processed meats, olives, crackers, etc. The average daily sodium intake in the U.S. for those age 2 and older is about 3,400 mg. The highest intake (more than 4,000 mg/day) is in males ages 12-49. On average, the higher the sodium intake, the higher the blood pressure.

The Dietary Guidelines for Americans (see Chap. 4) recommend lowering daily salt intake to 2,300 mg sodium, further lowering it to 1,500 mg if you are African-American or have high blood pressure or diabetes or chronic kidney disease or are over age 50. About half of the U.S. population is in this 1,500 mg group.

Salt restriction to treat high blood pressure works for some people. But does following a low-salt diet prevent high blood pressure from developing in the first place? High blood pressure is more common and tends to rise with age in populations with a high-salt diet, so it's thought that a high-salt diet brings to light the genetically susceptible. There's also a strain of rats that develops high blood pressure only when fed a high-salt diet, suggesting that there are such "strains" of people.

Some people simply don't develop high blood pressure despite eating a lot of salt, presumably because they don't have the genetic tendency. But most people don't know whether they have the genetic tendency, and there's no known advantage to consuming excess salt, so it's considered prudent to limit salty foods.

Diets rich in vegetables, fruit, and low-fat dairy products can be helpful in preventing and treating high blood pressure. Such diets are rich in magnesium, calcium, and potassium. Low intakes of these minerals may increase the risk of high blood pressure, perhaps by increasing salt-sensitivity.

Alcohol intake shouldn't be excessive. There's substantial evidence that more than two drinks a day raises blood pressure and also raises the risk of a hemorrhagic stroke independently of high blood pressure. One drink has about ½ oz alcohol, e.g., a 12-oz bottle of beer or wine cooler, 5 oz table wine, 1 jigger (1½ oz) vodka, rum, whisky, or gin.

Blood Cholesterol

Adults age 20 and older are advised to check their blood-cholesterol regularly. A consensus of the National Cholesterol Education Program is: **total blood-cholesterol of less than 200 mg/100 ml is desirable**; borderline high is 200-239; high is 240. People who are high (or borderline with other risk factors) should have their LDL and HDL checked (these tests cost more).

It can be hard to lower LDL(*bad*)-cholesterol because the body makes cholesterol. As mentioned in earlier chapters, cholesterol is an essential

---

*5 grams (5000 mg) of salt (NaCl) is about 1 teaspoonful. Sodium chloride (NaCl) is 40% sodium. So a teaspoon of salt has about 2000 mg sodium. See Chap. 3 for how to calculate this.

molecule needed as a part of cell membranes and as starting material for essential substances like bile acids and hormones. The body is limited in ways to get rid of cholesterol. Unlike triglycerides, for example, the body can't dispose of cholesterol by breaking it down to carbon dioxide and water.

How much cholesterol a cell makes depends on the amount already in the cell. If there's plenty, cells make less. If there isn't enough, cells make more. This is why people with familial hypercholesterolemia have such high LDL. Their cells, lacking the proper LDL-receptors to take in LDL from the blood, make cholesterol unabated because cholesterol can't get in to hamper production.

LDL can often be modified by diet within a few weeks. But people vary widely in how they respond to diet. Amounts of saturated and trans fats, and fiber in the diet have the biggest potential effect. Even if blood-cholesterol is at the recommended level, lowering LDL seems to further lower the risk of atherosclerosis. Also, cholesterol tends to rise as one gets older, so a "prudent diet" may help keep it from rising.

Saturated and Trans Fat

Saturated and trans fat (see Chap. 5) in the diet increases LDL in the blood, possibly by lessening the uptake of cholesterol into cells via LDL receptors. This effect is quite consistent, although some people are much more responsive than others.

We're advised to keep trans fat intake as low as possible and limit the saturated fat in our diet to less than 10% of our calories (Chap. 4). Saturated fatty acids don't affect LDL equally, however. The saturated fatty acids lauric (12:0), myristic (14:0), and palmitic (16:0) acids increase LDL more than other saturated fatty acids. Food, however, has a mixture of fatty acids (Table 5-3).

As we learn more about differing effects of particular fatty acids, food companies may manufacture and use fats with only one kind of fatty acid or another to get the desired sensory effect in their food products without getting the undesired effect of raising blood-cholesterol. If food companies in fact do this, we can expect this information to be touted in advertisements for the food product.

We can replace fatty cuts of meat with poultry, fish, or lean cuts of meat; drink nonfat or low-fat milk instead of whole milk; and eat sherbet, ice milk, or frozen low-fat yogurt instead of ice cream. Butterfat (as in whole milk, ice cream, cheese, and croissants) is a big source of saturated fat in the American diet. Trans fat comes mostly from foods that contain partially hydrogenated oils (Chap. 5).

Monounsaturated and polyunsaturated fat generally lowers LDL. Again, some people are more responsive than others.

Fiber

Eating more fiber-rich foods can help lower LDL. Plant foods have a variety of fibers, some of which lower blood cholesterol. Animal foods don't contain dietary fiber.

As to their action in the body, fibers can be roughly categorized by whether they dissolve in water. Soluble fibers (those that dissolve in water) can help lower blood cholesterol. In contrast, insoluble fiber can help prevent diverticulosis, and constipation (Chap. 6). Cellulose (an insoluble fiber), for example, adds bulk to the stools and can thus help prevent constipation, but doesn't appear to help lower blood-cholesterol.

Plant foods have a mix of soluble and insoluble fiber. Some foods that are particularly rich in soluble fibers are oats, beans, and fruits. You get a lot of soluble and insoluble fiber by following the advice to eat lots of fruits, vegetables, and whole grains (Chap. 4).

There are at least three ways in which some kinds of fiber might lower blood cholesterol:

- **Lessening the amount of bile absorbed from the small intestine.** Bile acids are made in the liver from cholesterol and are secreted into the upper part of the small intestine to aid fat-digestion (Chap. 6). Bile acids are then absorbed from the lower part of the small intestine and recycled (via the blood) back to the liver to be used again in bile. Soluble fiber (e.g., pectin) hampers this absorption of bile acids, so less is returned to the liver, and the liver uses more blood-cholesterol to make bile acids to replace what's lost in the stool. A drastic treatment to lower blood-cholesterol is to lessen the absorption of bile acids by surgically bypassing part of the lower small intestine.

- **Interfering with the absorption of dietary cholesterol in the small intestine**.

- **Interfering with the body's production of cholesterol.** Colon bacteria break down some kinds of fiber into products that are then absorbed into blood and may hamper cholesterol production.

Dietary Cholesterol

Cholesterol in the diet generally has much less of an effect on LDL than trans or saturated fat. Again, individual responses vary. Some people can lower their LDL by eating less cholesterol; others can't. If the body makes more cholesterol in response to less in the diet, blood-cholesterol may not go down.

Because cholesterol isn't required in the diet, and some people can benefit from eating less of it, the general advice is to keep the average daily intake to less than 300 mg. Cholesterol is found in all animal fats and animal tissue, but the main source in the American diet is egg yolks.

One egg yolk has about 215 mg of cholesterol (Table 5-4). Eggs with moderately less cholesterol are sold at a premium price—you can do about as well with regular eggs by discarding a bit of the yolk. Egg white is cholesterol-free and virtually fat-free. Remember that the amount of cholesterol isn't related to the amount of total fat in a food (Table 5-4), and that cholesterol isn't found in plants or plant products (fruits, vegetables, grains, vegetable oils, and margarine).

There's an understandable argument as to whether the advice to limit cholesterol intake should be made to the general, healthy population without regard to blood-cholesterol levels. The basis of the advice is that many people in a healthy population don't know their blood-cholesterol, eat a lot of cholesterol and can potentially benefit from eating less. There are no known adverse effects of a low-cholesterol diet. As mentioned earlier, cholesterol isn't required in the diet (strict vegetarians eat cholesterol-free diets).

The main argument against this advice is that it mainly limits eggs. Other rich sources of cholesterol (organ meats—liver, brain, etc.) aren't widely eaten. There are people whose LDL isn't raised by dietary cholesterol and for whom restricting eggs may present an undue hardship.

Eggs have many practical advantages because they're inexpensive, keep a long time in the home refrigerator, and are easy and quick to cook. Also, the softness of eggs is desirable for many people, e.g., those with missing teeth or ill-fitting dentures. These are important considerations, especially for the poor and elderly. For many of these people, eggs are an important source of nutrients. There isn't much research on the benefit—or lack of benefit—of lowering dietary cholesterol in the elderly. Studies showing benefit are mostly of middle-aged men and women.

Foods have a variety of nutrients, and individual foods have their pluses and minuses. The concern isn't only atherosclerosis, but overall health. For a healthy person whose LDL is increased by dietary cholesterol, reducing or eliminating eggs can, on balance, be beneficial. But among people whose LDL is not affected by cholesterol in the diet, there are those who eat a lot of eggs for such reasons as they simply can't get to the grocery store very often. For these people, reducing or eliminating eggs could have a negative effect on their diet and health. As discussed in Chapter 4, it's one's overall diet—not an individual food itself—that tends to be "good" or "bad."

HDL-Cholesterol

Low HDL(*good*)-cholesterol raises the risk of atherosclerosis. Some people are genetically endowed with extraordinarily high HDL, but this is unusual. This genetic aberration seems to protect against atherosclerosis and is linked to longevity. Most of us have either normal or low HDL. Smoking, lack of exercise, and obesity are all linked to low HDL. Of course, quitting smoking, exercising, etc., have additional health benefits besides raising one's HDL.

Moderate alcohol intake is linked to higher HDL and less heart disease in middle-aged men and postmenopausal women. The guideline *If you drink alcoholic beverages, do so in moderation* (Chap. 4) applies here. It's not generally advised that people who don't drink start drinking simply to raise their HDL. As noted earlier, excessive alcohol is linked to high blood pressure and a higher risk of hemorrhagic stroke.

Although moderate alcohol intake lowers the risk of heart attacks, this doesn't necessarily mean it improves overall health or the overall death rate. The French, for example, drink more alcohol and have less heart disease, but have more alcohol-associated cancers and more cirrhosis of the liver.

There's only a subtle difference, but it may be more accurate to say that low HDL is linked to higher risk of heart disease, than to say that a high HDL is linked to lower risk. We repeatedly hear that exercise increases *good cholesterol* and that people with high levels have a lower risk of a heart attack. This can mislead us into thinking that more and more exercise will lead to such high HDL that we can overcome other risk factors.

Instead, if we're told that a sedentary lifestyle lowers HDL, we can see more easily that moderate exercise is beneficial because it helps maintain normal HDL levels. Added exercise (beyond moderate) doesn't proportionately raise HDL. Furthermore, low HDL isn't as much of a risk factor as is high LDL, smoking, or high blood pressure. While regular exercise is important in lowering the risk of heart disease, its importance shouldn't be either under or overemphasized.

In 1984, Jim Fixx, the avid long-distance runner and popular author of books and articles on running, died suddenly at age 52 of a heart attack while on his way back from a run. People were shocked and dismayed, especially runners. At age 32, he gave up a 2-pack-a-day smoking habit. At age 35 (the age his father had a first heart attack), he started running, and got to a normal weight by losing more than 50 pounds. At age 43 (the age his father died of a heart attack), he took a leave of absence from his high-stress job as a magazine editor in New York City to write *The Complete Book of Running*. The book was an immediate success, earned him over a million dollars, and allowed him to quit his job.

Jim Fixx apparently didn't have a regular physician. An autopsy showed severe heart disease, including signs of earlier, mild heart attacks. His father's early death from a heart attack was certainly a strong risk factor. The question is what his fate might have been if he had had regular medical care and treatment, or hadn't been running 10 to 15 miles a day.

"Be my valentine?"

Omega-3 Fatty Acids

Eating fish is linked to a lower risk of heart disease. Omega-3 fatty acids (Chap. 5) in fish are thought to be what lowers risk. Only small amounts are found in vegetables and meats (see *18:3* and *>18:3* fatty acids in Table 5-3); the main source is fish.

The native Eskimo diet includes a lot of fish, seal, and whale, and is very rich in omega-3 fatty acids. Eskimos have a low incidence of heart disease, even though their diet is high in cholesterol and total fat (mainly polyunsaturated).

Omega-3 and omega-6 fatty acids are essential nutrients (Chap. 5) that are needed as starting material to make substances like prostaglandins, which have a wide array of effects on such things as acid secretion in the stomach, allergic response, and constriction and dilation of blood vessels.*

Many of these substances made from omega-3 or omega-6 fatty acids are counterbalancing, e.g., either lessen or enhance the blood's ability to clot. Thus, the relative amounts of omega-3 and omega-6 fatty acids in the diet can tip the balance. If omega-6 predominates (as in the American diet), the body makes more of its products. If omega-3 predominates (as in the Eskimo diet), products made from omega-3 predominate.

Eating foods rich in omega-3 fatty acids seems to tip the balance toward a lower risk of heart disease as shown by widened arteries, a reduced ability of platelets to cluster, lower blood pressure, and higher levels of TPA (called *Activase* when made by biotechnology)—the substance in blood that triggers the breakdown of clots.

Besides lessening the formation of clots that might block narrowed arteries, omega-3 fatty acids may retard the development of atherosclerosis itself. Studies of hundreds of men followed for many years have found that men who eat fish regularly have a lower rate of death from heart disease. (Keep in mind that linking "eating fish regularly" to fewer deaths from heart disease doesn't prove that it's omega-3 fatty acids in fish that protect. It might be other substances in fish,

or it might be that "eating fish regularly" is simply a marker for other healthful aspects of a person's life.)

It seems that the American diet would be healthier with fewer foods rich in omega-6 and more foods rich in omega-3. On the other hand, the Eskimo diet might be healthier with less omega-3 and more omega-6; In fact, the Eskimos' reduced ability to form blood clots was noted long before the discovery of the relationship to omega-3 fatty acids.

Gontran de Poncins, a French aristocrat who lived among the Eskimos, wrote in his 1941 book *Kabloona*:

Manilak and his wife both began to suffer from nosebleeds, a thing common among the Eskimos and likely to be serious. I have known it to go on for several days, and men have died among them as the result of the loss of blood. These two bled for hours and left a stain on the snow behind the gliding sled.

Nosebleeds are a side effect of a high intake of omega-3 fatty acids, and Eskimos eating a native diet are prone to hemorrhage and hemorrhagic stroke. One suspects that omega-3 in the native Eskimo diet is excessive.

The American Heart Association advises eating at least 2 servings/week of fish (particularly oily fish like salmon, tuna, mackerel, herring, trout). Fish-oil supplements and omega-3 fatty acid capsules are classified as dietary supplements rather than drugs, so keep in mind that they aren't subjected to the strict regulations of content, safety, purity, dosage, etc., established for drugs (and food additives).

Medication

Drugs are used as a preventive measure in people who don't have symptoms of heart disease. For example, drugs to lower blood pressure are prescribed for those who have high blood pressure but no symptoms (high-blood

---

*For discoveries relating to prostaglandins, Drs. Bergstrom, Samuelsson, and Vane shared a Nobel prize in 1982.

pressure not only raises risk of heart attack and stroke, but can damage the heart and kidneys). Similarly, high blood-cholesterol is treated with cholesterol-lowering drugs.

A number of drugs lessen the formation of blood clots. Aspirin, warfarin, and dicumarol are examples that were discussed earlier. Nicotinic acid (niacin)* is used in huge doses (1000 to 9000 mg/day) as a drug to lower LDL-cholesterol. Niacin is a B-vitamin (adult RDA =14-16 mg/day), but functions as a drug when taken in such large doses.

Aspirin and nicotinic acid (and capsules of omega-3 fatty acids) can be bought without prescription, leading many people to use them casually.† Drugs, including nutrients used as drugs, have side effects that must be taken in consideration in weighing benefit vs. risk.

For example, a study of male physicians, showing that a single aspirin taken every other day lowered risk of heart disease, was widely publicized. As discussed in Chapter 2, what wasn't publicized was that the physicians were carefully selected so as to exclude those whose health might be endangered by aspirin (e.g., people with ulcers or people at risk of hemorrhagic stroke).

As another example, large doses of nicotinic acid can cause irregular heartbeats and damage the liver; physicians prescribe liver-function tests during treatment. Milder side effects include itching and hot flushes in the skin, and digestive upsets.

Some drugs, such as cholestyramine (Questran) and colestipol, are used because they combine with bile acids in the intestine and promote the excretion of bile products. This method of lowering blood-cholesterol was discussed earlier in relation to the dietary fibers that promote the excretion of bile products.

"Statin" drugs (e.g., lovastatin) lower the body's production of cholesterol and are among the most effective in lowering blood-cholesterol.

Drugs are sometimes used in combination, e.g., a drug to promote excretion of bile products plus a drug that lowers cholesterol production.

Summary

Atherosclerosis is a disease in which the passageway in arteries becomes progressively damaged and narrow. The process can begin early in life. If the flow of blood is abruptly blocked by a clot, the clot can cause a heart attack if the affected artery feeds the heart.

If the artery feeds the brain, it can cause a stroke. A stroke can also occur from a rupture of an artery that feeds the brain (a hemorrhagic stroke). Such a rupture is generally caused by a defect in the arterial wall and/or high blood pressure.

Atherosclerosis is the main cause of heart disease—the leading cause of death in the U.S. The age-adjusted rate of death from heart disease has fallen dramatically since the 1950s, but heart disease is still our leading cause of death because of the increased proportion of elderly people in our population.

Although heart disease is most common among the elderly, it's also a common cause of death among those under age 65. In this younger group, heart disease is more common among men than women, and more common among Blacks than Whites.

The major risk factors in the development of atherosclerosis are genetic predisposition, smoking, high LDL-cholesterol, high blood pressure, and male gender. Smoking markedly increases the risk of a heart attack, even more so for sudden death from a heart attack. Carbon monoxide in the smoke displaces some of the oxygen carried by red blood cells, and nicotine constricts blood vessels. Both effects result in less oxygen delivery to tissues.

Adults age 20 and over are advised to have their blood pressure and blood-cholesterol checked periodically. If either of these measurements is

---

*The B-vitamin nicotinic acid is called niacin to avoid confusion with nicotine, the addictive drug in tobacco. Another form of niacin called nicotinamide or niacinamide doesn't have the same effect as nicotinic acid in lowering LDL.

†Several dietary supplements, e.g., ginkgo, have anti-clotting effects. This is why it's important to let your physician know which supplements you take. They can potentiate or interfere with other drugs, affect blood clotting during surgery, etc.

high, they should seek the advice of a physician. The initial blood-cholesterol test is usually one that measures total blood-cholesterol. If this is high, LDL and HDL components of blood-cholesterol are measured.

The higher the LDL(*bad*)-cholesterol, the higher the risk of a heart attack. Genetics can be a major factor. Dietary factors also have an effect. Of these, a high trans and saturated fat intake seems to have the greatest effect in increasing LDL-cholesterol. Diets rich in soluble fibers tend to lower LDL-cholesterol, and diets rich in saturated fat and cholesterol tend to raise LDL-cholesterol.

Low HDL(*good*)-cholesterol is linked to a higher risk of a heart attack. Men have lower HDL than premenopausal women, as do people who are sedentary or overweight.

To lower risk of heart attacks and strokes, we're advised to not smoke, exercise regularly, include fish in the diet, and follow the dietary guidelines outlined in Chapter 4. These guidelines include advice to: maintain a healthy weight; minimize trans and saturated fat; eat fruits, vegetables, and whole grains; limit salt intake; and, if you drink alcohol, drink only moderate amounts.

Chapter 9

Cells and Metabolism

Aloft, floating free beneath the moist, gleaming membrane of bright blue sky, is the rising earth, the only exuberant thing in this part of the cosmos .... It has the organized, self-contained look of a live creature, full of information, marvelously skilled in handling the sun.

It takes a membrane to make sense out of disorder in biology. You have to be able to catch energy and hold it, storing precisely the needed amount and releasing it in measured shares. A cell does this ....

From *Lives of a Cell* by Lewis Thomas

How does food become you? After it's digested and absorbed, the nutrients are delivered to cells throughout the body. The nutrients then take part in a series of chemical reactions that are collectively called metabolism—from *metaballein* (to change) in Greek. The nutrients become you.

Metabolism includes: (1) breaking down energy-providing nutrients (fat, carbohydrate, and protein) into smaller molecules and (2) building big molecules from small ones.* These chemical reactions are interdependent. Breaking down the energy-providing nutrients provides the ATP (chemical energy) needed to build big molecules from small ones.

Only the bare essentials of metabolism are discussed here. In reality, nutrients take part in a multitude of chemical reactions, guided by what the body needs at the time. For example, amino acids from your lunch burrito can be used to make protein—muscle protein, antibodies, enzymes, membrane proteins, insulin, etc. Or used for energy, and broken down completely to carbon dioxide and water. Or made into glucose to fuel the brain. Or made into triglycerides stored as body fat. These are but a few of the "or" s.

The body can make almost everything it needs from a variety of nutrients, e.g., the sex hormones testosterone and estrogen can be made from either fat, carbohydrate, or protein. These chemical conversions—metabolism—take place in our cells.

---

*These "build-up" (synthesis) reactions are called anabolic. The anabolic steroids used by some athletes (Chap. 13) promote the synthesis of muscle protein, and their 4-ring structure—like that of cholesterol (Fig. 5-2)—identifies them as sterols/steroids. Anabolic steroids are similar to testosterone, the male sex hormone that's made from cholesterol.

Figure 9-1: Some Parts of Cells

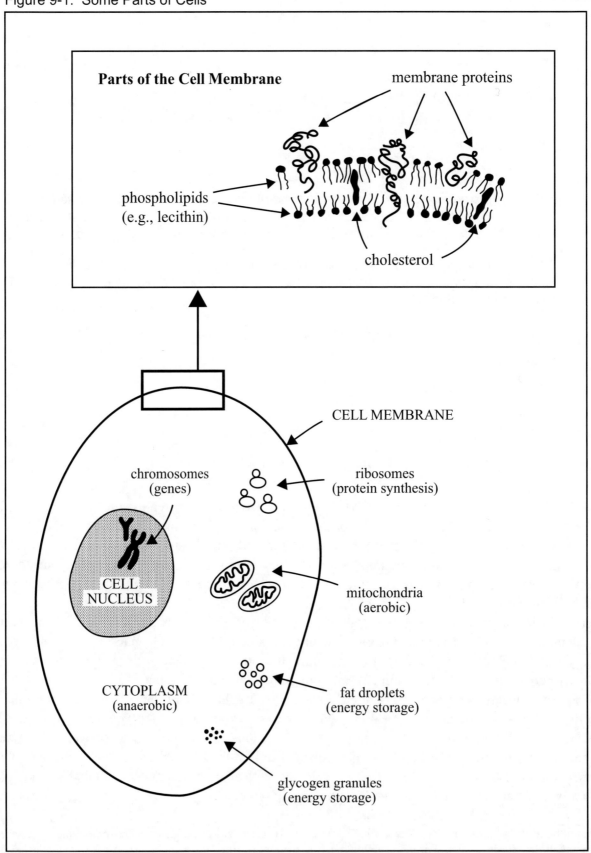

Cell Structure

A cell (from *cella,* Latin for small room or cubicle) is the basic unit of life. With few exceptions, our many kinds of cells have some common features, shown in Figure 9-1: A **cell membrane** surrounds the cell, which is filled with a fluid called **cytoplasm** (*cell plasma*). Within the cell are the cell **nucleus, ribosomes** for protein production, **mitochondria** (where oxygen-requiring reactions take place), and a store of energy-providing nutrients—glycogen granules (carbohydrate) and fat droplets (triglyceride). The cell membrane is discussed below. Other parts of the cell are discussed where relevant in this chapter and the next.

Cell Membrane

A cell membrane is made of a double layer of lecithin (Fig. 5-5) interspersed with cholesterol (Fig. 9-1) and studded with proteins (called *membrane proteins* or *surface proteins*). Membrane proteins differ according to the cell's function. Two were discussed earlier: lactase (enzyme that digests lactose) and LDL-receptors that allow cells to take in cholesterol from the blood. Even with just these two examples, we see how important these membrane proteins are. Lactose intolerance occurs when there isn't enough lactase in the membrane of cells lining the small intestine (Chap. 6), and heart disease can occur at a young age when there aren't enough LDL-receptors (Chap. 8).

Insulin receptors are another example. These are found in the membrane of almost all our cells. Insulin (a hormone made in the pancreas) works by attaching to insulin receptors, which then triggers a number of events within the cell, including the production of more glucose transporters—membrane proteins that allow glucose to enter a cell (Fig. 6-2). (This is how insulin "tells" a cell what to do.)

Membrane proteins also play a role in AIDS. HIV (like all viruses) can do damage only by entering cells. HIV enters (infects) by attaching to a membrane protein called CD4—much like the way LDL-cholesterol enters by attaching to LDL-receptors. Cells use membrane proteins to interact with the "outside world." Think of cells as houses. Someone wanders around with a key. Only if the key fits, does the person get in.

CD4 is mostly in the membrane of certain white blood cells, making them the prime target for HIV infection. In the search for ways to control the infection, CD4 was made by biotechnology for use as a possible drug. The hope was that HIV would attach to this "loose CD4" drug in the blood, instead of the actual CD4 in the membrane of the white blood cells. In other words, the drug was intended as a decoy to prevent HIV from infecting these cells (it worked in the test tube, but it was too hard to continuously keep enough of the CD4 drug in a person's blood).

Metabolism

As said earlier, metabolism includes the energy-releasing reactions that break apart molecules, and the energy-requiring reactions that put molecules together. When the energy-providing nutrients (fat, carbohydrate, protein) are broken apart, two forms of energy are released—heat and ATP (Chap. 3). ATP is used for things like muscle action and the synthesis of enzymes, hormones, and tissues.

Metabolism is controlled by many substances, including enzymes, coenzymes, minerals, and hormones. **Enzymes** catalyze the reactions, enabling them to occur. They play a key role in directing metabolism, since each reaction requires its own special enzyme. **Coenzymes** work with enzymes (*cooperate with enzymes*) usually by carrying a key substance that's made or used in a reaction. Coenzymes aren't as choosy as enzymes. Each typically works with many enzymes, whereas specific enzymes are needed for specific reactions.

Minerals also are essential coworkers with enzymes, e.g., calcium is needed in a blood-clotting reaction (Chap. 7). **Hormones** help direct and coordinate metabolism by carrying "messages" to various parts of the body, e.g., the sex hormones appearing at puberty start the reactions that lead to a boy's deepening voice and a girl's developing breasts.

B-vitamins

There are eight B-vitamins: thiamin, riboflavin, niacin, folate, biotin, pantothenic acid, vitamin B_6, and vitamin B_{12}. All are water-soluble. Some of their functions, food sources, and symptoms of deficiency and toxicity are given in Appendix A-5.

Each of the B-vitamins is an essential part of a different coenzyme. Coenzymes act as carriers between reactions, much like delivery trucks that continually ferry lumber between lumber mills and construction sites. The B-vitamins riboflavin and niacin, for example, are parts of coenzymes that ferry hydrogen atoms.

Because coenzymes play a crucial role in the metabolism of all living things, all the B-vitamins, except B_{12}, are found in both plants and animals. B_{12} isn't found in plants; its coenzyme isn't needed for a plant's metabolism.

Plants and many microbes don't need an outside source of B-vitamins, because they make them. It could be said that we eat their coenzymes and use the B-vitamin portions to make our own coenzymes. The cow, for example, gets its riboflavin from that made by bacteria that live in the cow's rumen. We, in turn, ingest that riboflavin when we eat beef or drink milk.

Niacin-Tryptophan-Pellagra Connection

The body can make the B-vitamin niacin from tryptophan, an essential amino acid. We don't need niacin in our diet if we get enough tryptophan. In other words, to become niacin deficient, the diet has to be low in both niacin and tryptophan. This helps explain the distribution of the disease pellagra in the early 1900s.

Niacin deficiency causes pellagra, which was especially prevalent in the South, where the diet commonly was based on corn products, with very little added meat, eggs, or milk (Chap. 1). Niacin in corn happens to be tightly bound to other substances in corn, hampering its absorption from the digestive tract. In addition, corn is particularly low in the amino acid tryptophan (Fig. 11-1). Meat, eggs, and milk are low in niacin but are good sources of tryptophan. Thus, meat, eggs, or milk can prevent pellagra because we can make

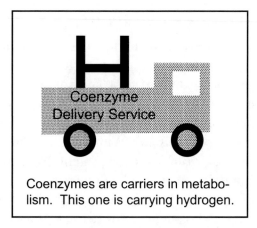

Coenzymes are carriers in metabolism. This one is carrying hydrogen.

niacin from the tryptophan in these foods.

The diet in Mexico was also based on corn products with little added meat, eggs, or milk, but pellagra wasn't as prevalent as in the southern United States. One explanation is that in making tortillas, corn is first soaked in a solution of lime (calcium oxide). This makes niacin in corn easier to absorb, thus providing more niacin (and more calcium) than untreated corn. Also, coffee was more widely consumed, and coffee contains niacin.

Energy-Releasing Reactions

When energy-providing nutrients are broken down, energy is released. There are two kinds of energy-releasing reactions—those that don't require oxygen (anaerobic) and those that do (aerobic). Figure 9-2 outlines these energy-releasing reactions, indicating where glucose, fatty acids, amino acids, and alcohol come in.

Let's begin with glucose, our most handy fuel. Starch—the main source of energy for the world's population—is absorbed from the intestine as glucose. We always carry glucose in our blood, and store glucose as glycogen in liver and muscle for quick release of glucose.

Anaerobic Energy Production (Glycolysis)

Glucose (a 6-carbon molecule) is broken down to pyruvate (3-carbons) in a set of reactions called *glycolysis* [from the Greek *glycos* (sugar) and *lysis* (to break apart)]. The reactions take place in the cell cytoplasm and are anaerobic [*an*(without) *aerobic*(air)], meaning that oxygen isn't used.

Figure 9-2: Energy-Releasing Reactions

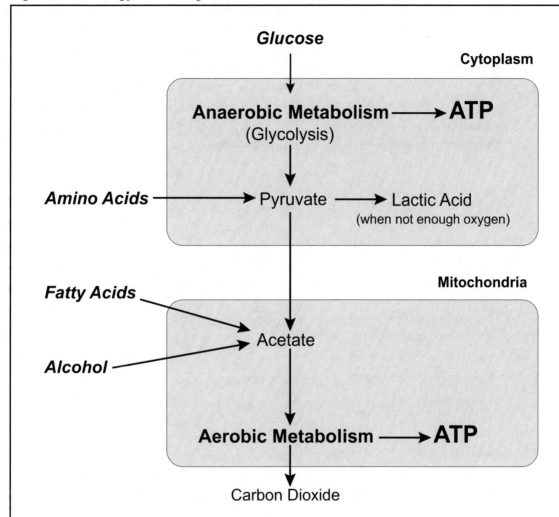

- Energy is released as ATP and heat. Glucose, fatty acids, and alcohol are made of carbon, hydrogen, and oxygen, and their final breakdown products are:

$$\text{Carbon Dioxide } (CO_2) + \text{Water } (H_2O) + \text{ATP} + \text{Heat}$$

Amino acids also have nitrogen (from the "amino").
So, they have an additional breakdown product: Urea (NH_2-CO-NH_2).
Amino acids vary a lot in size, structure, and ATP production.

- Net ATP production:

Without oxygen: **1 glucose = 2 ATP**

With oxygen (fatty acids release energy only aerobically):

1 glucose: $C_6H_{12}O_6 + 6\ O_2 = 6\ CO_2 + 6\ H_2O +$ **38 ATP** + heat

1 fatty acid (16:0): $C_{16}H_{32}O_2 + 23\ O_2 = 16\ CO_2 + 16\ H_2O + 129\ ATP + heat$

Only a small amount of the potential energy in glucose is released here, but it's important because this ATP is made without oxygen. In weightlifting, for example, the muscle contractions squeeze the capillaries in the muscle, temporarily limiting its oxygen supply. ATP generated from anaerobic metabolism of glucose fuels the muscle action needed for the lift and hold. The glucose is conveniently stored as glycogen in muscle cells.

Pyruvate (the end-product of glycolysis) normally proceeds to a set of aerobic (oxygen-requiring) reactions in the mitochondria (Fig. 9-2). But the reactions can't proceed if oxygen is scarce, as in endurance events. In these cases, pyruvate is converted to lactic acid, which helps sustain anaerobic ATP production a little longer.*

The price paid for this is a slightly higher acidity in the cell, from accumulating lactic acid. This local acidity is thought to contribute to muscle fatigue during sustained exercise. For example, the acidity might change the 3-dimensional structure of local enzymes (Chap. 5), making them less able to catalyze the reactions needed for sustained exercise.

There are some interesting side notes concerning glycolysis. When cows are killed, glycolysis continues briefly, using glucose from muscle glycogen. But oxygen is unavailable (breathing and blood circulation have stopped), so lactic acid accumulates. This added acidity of the carcass improves meat's appearance and texture, and there's less spoilage because the acidity hampers microbial growth. If muscle glycogen is depleted before slaughter (e.g., stress-induced muscle tension), all this doesn't happen. There are thus commercial as well as humane reasons for treating animals well before slaughter.

Glycolysis is synonymous with fermentation. Both use the same reactions to break down glucose into pyruvate. But some organisms such as yeast convert the pyruvate to alcohol. The yeast takes the sugar in grape juice and, by glycolysis, makes ATP for itself and wine for us. In converting pyruvate to alcohol, carbon dioxide (CO_2) is released. Trapping this CO_2 gives the fizz of champagne and beer.

Aerobic Energy Production

The next set of reactions† is aerobic (uses oxygen) and takes place in mitochondria, the site of all oxygen-requiring reactions.** Pyruvate (3-carbon molecule) goes from the cytoplasm (anaerobic) to the mitochondria (aerobic), and is broken down to acetate (2-carbons).†† Acetate breaks down to carbon dioxide (1-carbon), completing the breakdown of energy-providing nutrients.

Considerable energy is made in mitochondria. The use of oxygen enables a net production of 38 ATP molecules from 1 glucose molecule. In the absence of oxygen, there's a net production of only 2 ATP. Clearly, mitochondria enable cells to make a lot more energy.

It's thought that mitochondria are former microbes that hundreds of millions of years ago permanently infected our cells. Mitochondria do, in fact, have their own DNA. Without mitochondria, cells can't use oxygen and are limited to the ATP made by glycolysis. Cells "infected" with mitochondria would have had a huge advantage in evolution. When the supply of nutrients was limited (the usual situation), cells with mitochondria could make much more ATP than other cells. The extra ATP could fuel greater growth, movement, and synthesis of complex molecules.

---

*Converting pyruvate to lactic acid frees a coenzyme (NAD) needed in glycolysis. NAD (nicotinamide adenine dinucleotide) is a niacin-containing coenzyme that ferries hydrogen (H) atoms. Pyruvate takes H from NADH to become lactic acid. This frees NAD. In the trucks-carrying-lumber analogy: H is lumber; glycolysis needs empty trucks (NAD). In everyday activities, oxygen isn't limiting. H is easily unloaded by aerobic metabolism; making lactic acid isn't necessary.

†This set is called the citric acid cycle, TCA (tricarboxylic acid) cycle, or Krebs cycle. Hans Krebs discovered these reactions and shared a Nobel prize in 1953 with Fritz Lipmann.

**The poisonous gas hydrogen cyanide blocks oxygen-requiring reactions in mitochondria. It has been used in the gas chamber for capital punishment, and is made by dropping cyanide pellets into acid.

††Acetate is carried by Coenzyme A, which contains the B-vitamin pantothenic acid. In the trucks-carrying-lumber analogy, the lumber is acetate. Franz Lipmann discovered Coenzyme A and its role in metabolism and shared a 1953 Nobel prize with Hans Kreb.

Aerobic is a familiar word in reference to exercise. It's called aerobic because continuous and sustained exercise (e.g., running) requires fatty acids as fuel, and ATP production from fatty acids is completely dependent on oxygen availability. In other words, the use of fatty acids for energy is entirely aerobic and takes place exclusively in mitochondria. Aerobic exercise enhances the cardiovascular system's ability to circulate more oxygen to exercising muscles, thus promoting cardiovascular fitness.

Fatty acids are broken down to acetate* and then to carbon dioxide (Fig. 9-2). Because energy is stored in the body mainly as fat (triglycerides), fatty acids are the main source of energy whenever cells need to call on substantial energy reserves (perhaps when a person is on a weight-loss diet, or is running a marathon).

Amino acids can also be used as fuel, but aren't the best source (Chap. 10). The nitrogen-containing (amino) part is removed. The remaining structure is converted to pyruvate† and enters the energy-releasing set of reactions (Fig. 9-2). When fat stores are depleted (e.g., by starvation), amino acids from protein in our organs and muscles are used as a source of energy. When this happens, the body "wastes away."

Athletic Performance

Athletes are useful examples in explaining anaerobic and aerobic energy production. Athletes push ATP production to its limits. Athletics can be roughly grouped according to whether glucose (strength-and-power events) or fatty acid (endurance events) is the main fuel.

Strength-and-power events (e.g., weight-lifting, gymnastics, sprints, shot put) mainly use ATP generated anaerobically from glycolysis. Oxygen isn't a limiting factor—the event is short. The reactions of glycolysis are very fast and make ATP much faster for "bursts of energy."

"Aerobics is down the hall—this is robotics."

Don't confuse speed of ATP production with the total amount made from one molecule of glucose. Most of the energy released from glucose comes from the aerobic reactions of metabolism, but these are rather slow. In contrast, glycolysis breaks down many glucose molecules to make a lot of ATP quickly.

Recall that ATP isn't stored, but is made as needed. A sprinter doesn't gather ATP while anticipating the starting gun. The ATP to fuel that sprint is made during the sprint itself. It needs to be made fast!

Types of muscle cells: It follows that athletes with a greater capacity for glycolysis will be more successful in events that call for a short and intense burst of energy. Muscle cells differ in their anaerobic and aerobic capability, and can be roughly divided into two types: white (*fast-twitch*) fibers and red (*slow-twitch*) fibers. (Muscle cells are often called fibers, because they're long and cylindrical.) Muscles are made of both white and red fibers; most of us have both in about equal amounts.

White fibers are geared for glycolysis (e.g., have more glycolysis enzymes), allowing them to contract (*twitch*) rapidly. Red fibers are geared toward the slower, aerobic production of energy;

*For his part in this discovery, Feodor Lynen won a Nobel prize in 1964.
†Some amino acids are converted to acetate, depending on the amino acid's structure.

they have more fat and mitochondria. Red fibers are also rich in myoglobin, which is similar to the hemoglobin in red blood cells.

Both myoglobin and hemoglobin are proteins that contain heme (which contains iron) and carry oxygen. Myoglobin in muscle holds oxygen that can be used when oxygen from blood is restricted (as when muscle contractions squeeze the capillaries). Muscles of seals and whales are exceptionally rich in myoglobin, to provide oxygen to generate ATP when they dive and swim under water.

Studies show that muscle fibers in the relevant muscles of elite strength-and-power athletes are more than 70% white, whereas those of elite endurance athletes are more than 70% red. These proportions seem to be genetic. (Quarter horses and greyhounds are bred for speed; the fibers in their leg muscles are about 95% white.) For athletes intending to break world records, heredity could well be destiny. Training, however, can markedly enhance the aerobic (and possibly the anaerobic) capacity of both types of fibers.

The iron-containing heme in myoglobin (and hemoglobin) is red, giving a reddish color to muscles rich in red fibers. People are already familiar with these muscle fibers in their preference for either dark or white meat in the Thanksgiving turkey.

The dark meat of the turkey leg is mostly red fibers, and is thus well adapted to turkeys running around (endurance). The white breast meat is mostly white fibers, needed for the burst of power that turkeys use to flap their wings in making a fast move. (In contrast, the breast of migratory birds is dark meat, needed for the endurance of long, nonstop flights.) As a food, this makes dark turkey meat higher in fat and iron than white meat.*

The flesh of fish is mostly white fibers. Survival depends a lot on a fish's ability to make quick movements—to catch prey, or avoid being one. Fish don't need much power to cruise the waters; for this, fish have thin bands of red fibers just under their skin and/or near their fins. (The flesh of salmon is actually white, but looks pink, because of pigments from insects and such that salmon feed on.)

Oxygen delivery: Endurance athletes need a steady production of ATP over a long time—more ATP than glycogen (glucose) stores can provide. But even the leanest athlete has more than enough body fat to fuel a marathon. Oxygen is needed to "burn" fat, so the amount of oxygen available to the muscles is what becomes limiting. Endurance athletes work for cardiovascular fitness (to deliver oxygen and remove carbon dioxide and lactic acid as fast as possible), and they train to enhance the aerobic capacity of their muscles. Also, as discussed in Chapter 7, some endurance athletes attempt to boost the amount of red blood cells (i.e., the oxygen-carrying capacity) in their blood.

Glucose supply: Aerobic metabolism is sluggish when glucose is scarce. In other words, a muscle doesn't "burn" fatty acids as well if it runs out of glucose. Endurance athletes often use a technique called *carbohydrate-loading* to temporarily increase glycogen (the storage form of glucose) in the relevant muscles.† The extra supply of glycogen delays muscle fatigue.

Endurance athletes also work to "spare" the use of glucose so it won't run out as fast. Drinking carbohydrate-containing beverages during events of more than 90 minutes helps (Chap. 4). Caffeine can also help, because it promotes the use of fatty acids as fuel, thus sparing

---

*Looking for good sources of iron in the diet, we can make a visual appraisal of the heme-iron content of meat (Chap. 7). Myoglobin in muscle has the red iron-containing heme, so the redder meats generally have more heme iron. Beef liver has more iron than hamburger, which has more iron than chicken or fish. Whale and seal meat is very dark and rich in iron because it's so rich in myoglobin.

†About a week before competition, athletes train hard and then taper training, resting on the day before the event. For 3 days before the event, they eat a high-carbohydrate diet. The intense exercise depletes the muscles of glycogen. Upon repletion with a high-carb diet, there's a rebound effect, and glycogen stores are temporarily raised to higher-than-normal levels in time for the event.

the use of glucose. But caffeine also is a diuretic (i.e., increases water loss through urine) and can thus contribute to dehydration (which impairs performance).

Neutralizing muscle acidity: Local acidity in muscle, caused by lactic acid production, can cause muscle fatigue and can be a limiting factor in events like the 400- and 800-meter races—"all-out" events of 1 to 2 minutes.

In "soda-loading," a small amount of sodium bicarbonate (*baking soda*) is consumed prior to the event. Bicarbonate is alkaline in pH and counters the acidity of the lactic acid build-up.* Taken at the right time and dosage, soda loading has been shown to improve running times by about 1½ seconds in a 400 meter race and about 3 seconds in an 800-meter race—times that can mean the difference between first and last place. But a common side effect is "urgent diarrhea" which, of course, can deter performance if it occurs at the wrong time.

Energy-Requiring Reactions

Energy-requiring reactions use ATP. In many cases, what's broken apart can be put together again with an input of energy. All the chemical reactions in which big molecules are made from small ones require energy. ATP energy is needed to connect the molecules. Making protein from amino acids and making glycogen from glucose are examples.

Fig. 9-2 shows only a very basic outline of the breakdown of the energy-providing nutrients. In fact, these reactions can branch in many directions, and can even change directions in some parts. Examples: The 27-carbon structure of cholesterol is built entirely from acetate (2-carbons). Pyruvate can be made into the amino acid alanine by transferring the amino (-NH$_2$) to pyruvate.† Thus, we don't need this amino acid in our diet.

Protein Synthesis

Protein synthesis is an energy-requiring process in which amino acids are linked together. The topic of protein synthesis is complex and broad (and thus has its own chapter). How does a cell know which amino acids to link together to make a protein? How does protein synthesis relate to our dietary protein requirement? Examples of what can happen when cells make a protein incorrectly (e.g., the hemoglobin in sickle cell anemia) or when cells don't make enough of a protein (e.g., in lactose intolerance, PKU, familial hypercholesterolemia) have been discussed earlier. Protein synthesis also is relevant to viruses and biotechnology—and even cancer. These aspects will be discussed in upcoming chapters.

Storing Excess Calories

What happens when we take in more energy-providing nutrients than we need? In other words, what happens to those excess calories when we over-eat? As we know from personal experience, the excess is stored as body fat. The body does this by using some of the same reactions that break down carbohydrates, protein, and fat.

As shown in Fig. 9-2, all the energy-providing nutrients can be broken down to acetate, and most of the energy from these nutrients comes from the breakdown of acetate. If the energy isn't needed just then, the cell doesn't break down acetate. There's also no need to break down dietary fatty acids to acetate. When you eat more calories than you need, acetate and fatty acids are diverted from energy production to energy storage as fat.

It's clear from Fig. 9-3 that we can become fat from excess calories, whether from over-eating carbohydrate, protein, or fat. But note how much easier it is to make body fat from dietary fat. In contrast, protein and carbohydrate first have to be broken down to acetate before they can be made into fatty acids (an energy-requiring process).

---

*In the digestive tract, sodium bicarbonate from the pancreas neutralizes the acid material coming from the stomach (Chap. 6).

†Alanine and pyruvate can be interconverted:
$$CH_3\text{-}\overset{O}{\overset{\|}{C}}\text{-}COOH + \text{-}NH_2 \longleftrightarrow CH_3\text{-}\overset{NH_2}{\underset{|}{CH}}\text{-}COOH$$
pyruvate   alanine

Figure 9-3: Excess Energy-providing Nutrients are Easily Stored as Fat

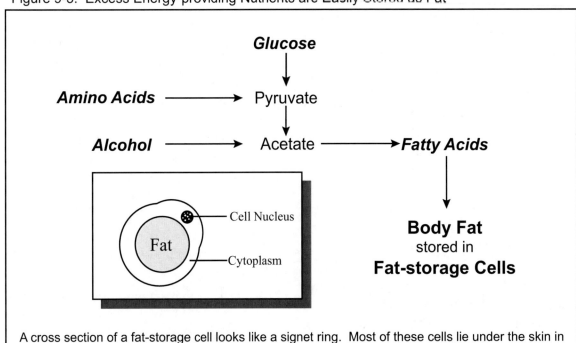

A cross section of a fat-storage cell looks like a signet ring. Most of these cells lie under the skin in a layer held in place by strands of connective tissue. The strands can cause dimpling in the skin. This lumpy-looking layer is called "cellulite" in marketing products that claim to remove it, but it's just ordinary fat. The lumpiness can sometimes be improved with normal weight loss and exercise.

This is thought to be one reason why it's easier to become fat on a high-fat diet.

Maintaining Blood-Glucose

The body constantly uses glucose. The brain continuously needs a lot of ATP energy, but—unlike other organs—can't use fatty acids as fuel. **Glucose is the only fuel that the brain can use under normal circumstances.** The blood transports the needed glucose to the brain.

How do we keep enough glucose in the blood if we don't consume any carbohydrates and our glycogen stores are used up, as during starvation or while on a low-carbohydrate diet? The answer is that **glucose can be made from some amino acids** (Fig. 9-4).* Glucose can be made from pyruvate, but not from acetate (Fig. 9-4). Since fatty acids are broken down only to acetate, **glucose can't be made from fatty acids**.

Carbohydrate-Free Diets

Carbohydrate makes up the bulk of most diets throughout the world, and is the usual source of glucose. When a person isn't consuming carbohydrate for whatever reason, glycogen—our storage form of glucose—is soon gone, giving the body no choice but to use amino acids from protein to make the needed glucose. Throughout history, the usual reason why people aren't consuming carbohydrate is that there's no food—they are starving.

During starvation, the body first breaks down the proteins least essential for survival (e.g., some proteins in liver and skeletal muscle) and, as a last resort, starts breaking down proteins in the heart muscle, etc. Obviously, starvation would be rapidly fatal if the body had to incessantly break down its protein to provide the brain with glucose.

At the start of starvation, anyway, most people have stores of body fat. If the brain could in some

---

*Some amino acids (those made into pyruvate) can be made into glucose, whereas others (those made into acetate) can't. Vitamin B_6 is a part of a coenzyme used in reactions that convert amino acids to pyruvate or acetate. In the trucks-carrying-lumber analogy, the lumber is aminos (NH_2).

Figure 9-4: Glucose and Ketone Production in Starvation and Carbohydrate-free Diets

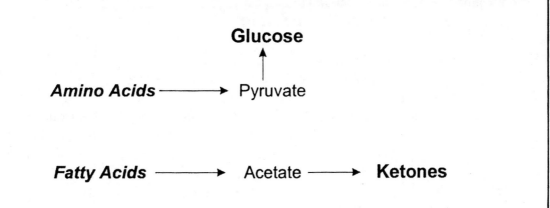

When glucose is scarce, body protein is broken apart into amino acids, which then are used to make glucose for the brain. The scarcity of glucose hampers the normal breakdown of acetate in aerobic metabolism. Acetate then accumulates and combines to form ketones. Ketones provide an alternate fuel for the brain, thus slowing the breakdown of body protein.

way use fatty acids as fuel, it would slow the breakdown of body protein and lengthen survival. The body does, in fact, make an alternate fuel from fatty acids, using the scarcity of glucose as a signal of starvation.

When glucose is scarce, aerobic metabolism is sluggish, and acetate accumulates, like cars jamming up behind a stalled car. This unusual accumulation of acetate causes them to combine to form ketones (Fig. 9-4). The brain uses the ketones as fuel in increasing amounts during starvation, lessening its need for glucose and slowing the breakdown of body protein. Of course, once the body's fat stores are used up, body protein is used unremittingly as fuel, and death is imminent.

Low-carbohydrate diets show up regularly in the steady stream of popular weight-loss diets. This diet is popular because it promotes fast weight loss—a lot of water is lost. Glycogen is depleted, and protein is broken down to provide amino acids for glucose production. Glycogen and protein hold about 3 times their weight in water, whereas fat doesn't hold any (Chap. 5). When the dieter goes back to a normal diet, the body rapidly restores the lost glycogen, protein, water—and weight, much to the dieter's dismay.

Dieters also like low-carbohydrate diets because the ketones cause a loss of appetite,* and some of the ketones are lost in urine and breath. Ketones have caloric value, and this "easy loss of calories" is touted in popular books promoting these diets. But this loss usually amounts to less than 60 calories a day.

Keep in mind that ketone production is basically an emergency response to starvation, in which case the benefit far outweighs risk. A risk of ketone production is that ketones are acidic, and excessive amounts can cause a condition called ketosis or acidosis. This lowers the pH of blood and tissue fluid, which can be life-threatening (Chap. 3). About 50 grams (200 calories worth) of carbohydrate a day prevents ketosis.

Blood Glucose

Glucose in the blood (*blood glucose*) is kept within a normal range by the action of two hormones made in the pancreas: insulin and glucagon. After ingesting carbohydrate, blood glucose rises, and insulin is secreted in response. Insulin lowers blood glucose by promoting the entry of glucose into cells and the production of glycogen. When one hasn't eaten for a few hours,

---

*This is a blessing for the starving—it eases the pain of hunger in a famine. But sometimes the ketones cause nausea.

blood glucose falls, and glucagon is secreted in response. Glucagon triggers the breakdown of liver glycogen to glucose, which is then released into the blood.

Although glycogen is stored in both liver and muscle, liver glycogen is used to maintain blood-glucose levels, whereas muscle glycogen is used locally to provide glucose to fuel muscle activity.

Diabetes

Diabetes is characterized by an abnormally high blood glucose that "spills over" into the urine (glucose isn't normally in urine). Glucose brings water with it, so a lot of water is also lost through the urine. Often, the first sign of diabetes is increased urination and thirst.

More than 20 million people in the U.S. have diabetes. One of the most severe effects of diabetes is damage to blood vessels. Since blood vessels deliver blood throughout the body, the consequences depend on which vessels are affected and how severely they're affected: Diabetics have a much higher risk of stroke, and heart, eye, and kidney diseases. Sometimes, a foot or toe has to be amputated when tissue there dies from lack of circulation.

How fast diabetes progresses varies a lot. Some diabetics develop severe symptoms fast, whereas others have only mild and non-progressing disease. In the U.S., diabetes is the leading cause of blindness, kidney failure, and amputations in the lower leg.

Type 1 and type 2 diabetes are the most common kinds.* In **type 1 diabetes**, there's a shortage or complete lack of insulin due to destruction of the pancreatic cells that make insulin. It seems to be an autoimmune disease, triggered in susceptible people by certain viruses. In autoimmune diseases, the body mistakenly sees a normal part of the body (in this case, the pancreatic cells that make insulin) as foreign, and the immune system destroys it.

Type 1 diabetes isn't related to obesity, and occurs most commonly among children and

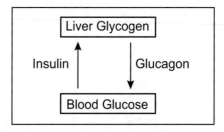

adults under age 30. It's controlled with insulin injections, diet, and exercise. Before insulin was available as a drug, diabetes was quite rapidly fatal. Effective treatment came with the discovery of insulin and its use as a drug.†

Glucose can't enter cells without insulin. Without insulin, the cells lack glucose, in spite of large amounts in the blood. The cells make ketones in response to this lack of glucose. In severe, untreated, insulin-dependent diabetes, this persistent ketone production can lead to fatal acidosis (high acidity of blood and tissue fluids).

About 90-95% of diabetics have **type 2 diabetes**. About 90% of those with type 2 diabetes are obese (overweight by 20-30% or more). But not all obese people develop this disease, since a genetic susceptibility is involved. The diabetes usually occurs after age 40, and is characterized by a resistance to insulin action. This means that the cells can't adequately take in glucose from the blood, despite plenty of insulin.

A cornerstone in preventing and treating this diabetes is a healthy diet and regular exercise to prevent obesity, or if already overweight, to lose weight or not gain any more. Regular exercise, in addition to helping maintain a healthy weight, increases a cell's responsiveness to insulin. There are also various drugs that help. Treatment focuses on maintaining normal blood pressure and normal blood levels of glucose and fat.

As might be expected, type 2 diabetes is common in the U.S., where obesity is common. Obesity brings out a genetic susceptibility to diabetes, just as alcohol consumption can bring out a genetic susceptibility to alcoholism, or a high-salt diet can bring out a genetic tendency to salt-sensitive high blood pressure. Interaction of

*There's also gestational diabetes, which occurs in about 3-5% of pregnancies, and is usually controlled by diet. It usually goes away after delivery, but the woman has a high risk of developing type 2 diabetes later.
†For this discovery, Frederick Banting and John MacLeod won the Nobel prize in 1923.

environment and genetics is a common theme in disease.

This "expression of certain genes" applies to many other situations as well, e.g., people who are genetically endowed with Olympic-caliber endurance (muscles of mostly red fibers, etc.) may not know it because their endurance has never been put to test. Likewise, inherently superior musical ability, computer skills, etc., may go unrealized.

Hypoglycemia (Low Blood Sugar)

By now, the problems of *too much* or *too little* is a familiar theme. Hypoglycemia is a condition of abnormally low blood glucose—hypo(*low*) glyc(*glucose*) emia(*in the blood)*—combined with symptoms that are relieved by sugar. Symptoms range from mild (e.g., dizziness, nervousness, hunger) to severe (e.g., convulsions, coma).

Although severe hypoglycemia can result from excess insulin made by a pancreatic tumor, the most common cause is excess insulin taken by a diabetic. An insulin overdose can lower blood glucose to the point of fainting or coma (the brain is dependent on glucose from the blood).

A diabetic can also lose consciousness from a lack of insulin. If a diabetic feels dizzy or weak and the cause isn't known, sugar (e.g., fruit juice, candy) will help if the problem is low blood-glucose. If the cause is a lack of insulin, the blood sugar will already be high, and a bit more won't make much difference.

For those who don't have diabetes, the most common cause of hypoglycemia is a burst of insulin in response to ingesting a lot of carbohydrate on an empty stomach *(reactive hypoglycemia)*. The symptoms are fairly mild and occur 2 to 4 hours after eating.* The advice is to ingest smaller "doses" of carbohydrate (an apple rather than a candy bar) in more frequent and well-spaced intervals (regularly spaced meals and snacks vs, skipping breakfast and then grabbing a sweet-roll in late morning). All cases of hypoglycemia should be checked by a physician, to rule out more serious causes.

Many people decide on their own that they have hypoglycemia when they actually don't. This is because symptoms are vague, and a diagnosis of "hypoglycemia" is promoted by some misguided health-practitioners and some best-selling diet-and-health books. A common and effective tactic in selling is to create a "non-disease" and then sell its cure in the form of books, nostrums, etc. Many who do this are truly sincere. But sincerity doesn't make up for a lack of supporting scientific evidence.

Summary

In a cell, the **nucleus** houses DNA (our genetic information), which is packed into chromosomes. Surrounding the nucleus is a fluid called **cytoplasm**. Floating in the cytoplasm are **mitochondria** (where oxygen-requiring reactions take place) and **ribosomes** (for protein synthesis). The cell-covering is called the **cell membrane**.

The cell membrane is a lineup of lecithin molecules that form a double layer around the cell. Cholesterol is embedded in this membrane, as are a variety of proteins called **membrane proteins**. Membrane proteins vary, e.g., the digestive enzyme lactase is a protein in the intestinal cell membrane, and have a variety of functions, e.g., serving as receptors for low-density lipoproteins (LDL) or insulin.

Metabolism refers to the chemical reactions that occur in cells, and can be subdivided into energy-releasing ones and energy-requiring ones. They are interdependent. When ATP energy is needed for muscular activity, or to make protein, etc., the energy-providing nutrients are broken down to provide the needed ATP.

A basic design in the breakdown of energy-providing nutrients is that they break into a few key substances so that they can funnel into the same chemical reactions. For example, carbohydrate, fat, and protein can all be broken down to **acetate** (a 2-carbon molecule), which can then take several directions. If ATP is needed, acetate can

*More severe reactive hypoglycemia sometimes occurs in athletes during an athletic event, from a combination of carbohydrate-loading just before an event and the rapid use of glucose during the event.

be broken down further to release energy. If ATP isn't needed just then, acetate can be made into fatty acids and stored as body fat. Acetate can also be used to make other substances like cholesterol.

For glucose and some amino acids, there are two phases of ATP production. The first phase is **anaerobic** (oxygen not used), which takes place in the cytoplasm of a cell. ATP is made in the systematic breakdown of glucose to pyruvate. Although each molecule of glucose provides only small amounts of ATP, these anaerobic reactions are fast, and ATP can be made quickly, using many molecules of glucose.

The second phase is **aerobic** (oxygen used), and takes place in the mitochondria of a cell. ATP is made when acetate is broken down to carbon dioxide (which we exhale). Although a lot of ATP is made here, these aerobic reactions are relatively slow. Fatty acids (and some amino acids) are broken down directly to acetate and don't participate in the anaerobic phase of ATP production. They participate only in the aerobic phase. Without oxygen, fatty acids can't be used to make ATP.

Glucose is an especially important substance because the brain constantly needs ATP, and under normal circumstances, the brain can use only glucose to make ATP. The liver has the responsibility of providing the brain with glucose via the blood. It does this by storing glucose as glycogen when glucose is abundant, and releasing glucose into the blood when glucose is low.

The glucose supply is severely limited during starvation (and other extremely-low-carbohydrate situations). The body must then use certain amino acids to make glucose to feed the brain. (The body can't make glucose from fatty acids.) This is a rather extreme measure. Body proteins must be broken down to provide those amino acids when there's no food coming in.

The scarcity of glucose causes a buildup of acetate, causing the acetates to combine to form **ketones**. The brain then uses some of these ketones as fuel, reducing the brain's need for glucose. This has obvious survival value, since it lessens the need to break down body proteins. When a person is near death from starvation, the body has to break down proteins from the heart and other key tissues.

Blood glucose is normally kept within a narrow range by two hormones made by the pancreas: **Insulin** lowers blood glucose by enabling tissue cells to take in glucose from the blood; **glucagon** raises blood glucose by breaking down liver glycogen to glucose, which is then released into the blood.

Blood glucose is abnormally high in **diabetes**, because cells can't take in glucose adequately from the blood. In **type 1 diabetes**, there's simply a lack of insulin, because the pancreatic cells that make it have been destroyed. This kind of diabetes isn't related to obesity, usually occurs during childhood or young adulthood, and is controlled with insulin injections, diet, and exercise.

Type 2 diabetes is related to obesity, although a genetic susceptibility is involved. It accounts for about 90-95% of the diabetes in the U.S. The cells can't take in enough glucose from the blood because of a resistance to insulin action. It's generally a cell problem rather than an insulin problem. This diabetes usually occurs in adults over age 40, and is controlled with weight loss (if the person is overweight), diet, exercise, and oral medication (and sometimes insulin injections to try to overcome insulin resistance). One of the more serious health risks of diabetes—insulin-dependent or not—is blood-vessel damage, which can result in serious damage to the tissues served by the vessels.

Hypoglycemia is a condition of low blood sugar accompanied by symptoms that are alleviated by sugar. Aside from hypoglycemia that results when a diabetic injects too much insulin, the most common kind is reactive hypoglycemia. This typically involves a big burst of insulin (thus hypoglycemia) as a reaction to a surge of blood glucose from ingesting a lot of carbohydrate on an empty stomach. The advice is to eat a good diet in frequent and regularly spaced intervals.

Chapter 10

Genes, Proteins, and Viruses

The web of our life is of a mingled yarn, good and ill together.

from Shakespeare's *All's Well that Ends Well*

Genes, proteins, and viruses may seem like an odd mix, but they're closely related. Genes are recipes for making proteins, and a virus isn't much more than a strand of genes enclosed in a protein shell.

In the world of molecules, proteins are giants of complexity and diversity. A protein is a long chain of amino acids (typically 200-900). Genes specify which amino acids will be linked together and in what order. The largest protein known is nearly 27,000 amino acids long—a muscle protein called *titin*. Chemists can't make the proteins found in nature. Only cells can.

Genes and DNA

Genes are a part of DNA, the genetic material packed into our chromosomes (Fig. 10-1). Thus, DNA is the master file of recipes for all our proteins, including hemoglobin, insulin, membrane proteins, and enzymes. Enzymes direct the construction of substances other than protein, e.g., cholesterol. Our DNA provides a complete set of directions for producing the entire human body.

Each of us (except identical twins) has unique DNA, making each of us different from everyone else. But the DNA in every cell of a single person is identical—brain and skin cells alike. Cells use the genes in their DNA selectively, depending on a cell's specialty. Think of different factories making ice cream, bread, and sausages, using only one big recipe book. Different cells make what they need, using only the pertinent recipes in identical DNA.

DNA is made of two long strands bridged together by molecules called bases (Fig. 10-1, 10-2). The bases on one strand fit with (match) the bases on the other. There are only four kinds of bases (A,T,G,C) that form two matching pairs: A always pairs with T. G always pairs with C. Discovering DNA's structure was momentous because it revealed how genetic material (DNA) could be duplicated from cell to cell (Fig. 10-2).

The language of DNA uses the bases as letters. It spells out its message by lining up the bases in a certain sequence, just like we line up letters of our alphabet to write books. How can a language with just 4 letters (bases) encode our entire genetic make-up? The sequence of bases is read in sets of 3 (*3-letter words*). With 4 letters, we can make 64 ($4^3 = 4X4X4 = 64$) 3-letter words—more than enough to code for the 20 kinds of amino acids

135

Figure 10-1: DNA is the Genetic Material Packed in Chromosomes

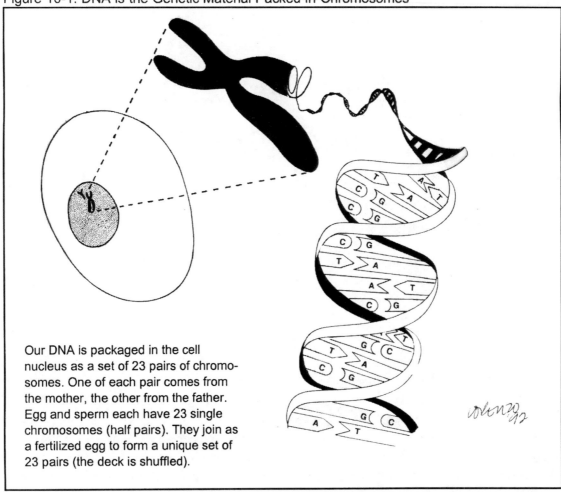

Our DNA is packaged in the cell nucleus as a set of 23 pairs of chromosomes. One of each pair comes from the mother, the other from the father. Egg and sperm each have 23 single chromosomes (half pairs). They join as a fertilized egg to form a unique set of 23 pairs (the deck is shuffled).

needed to make protein (Table 10-1).* Sixty-one of these words code for amino acids; 3 of them mean stop, which signals the end of the directions to make that protein. **This genetic language is the same in all living things**, plant or animal.

Genes (recipes for proteins) **have precise locations in DNA**, e.g., the gene for TPA/Activase (the clot-dissolving enzyme discussed in Chap. 7) has an exact position in the DNA in chromosome #8, and is a section of over a thousand bases. There are about 22,000 genes and about 3 billion pairs of bases in human DNA.†

How A Cell Makes Protein

DNA could be likened to a huge recipe book bolted in a safe because of its 22,000 valuable recipes. When a certain recipe is needed, a copy of the recipe is made and taken to the chef who uses it to make the product. In DNA, the recipes are for proteins.

Copying and Delivering the Recipe

To make the protein insulin, for example, **the first step is to make a copy of the gene** (*the recipe*) for insulin. The gene makes up a very tiny section of DNA. The two strands of DNA pull apart there so the gene can be copied (Fig. 10-3).

---

*These very words appear on the computer screen via a binary code: ASCII (American Standard Code for Information Interchange) has a "2-letter alphabet": off (zero) and on (one). The size of a "word" in ASCII is 7 "letters," so there are 128 possible ways to arrange the 0s and 1s ($2^7 = 2 \times 2 \times 2 \times 2 \times 2 \times 2 \times 2 = 128$), more than enough to code for the upper and lower case of the 26-letter alphabet, punctuation, numbers, carriage return, etc. (e.g., the code for E is 1000101).

†We're not tops here. The tiny water flea *Daphnia* has about 31,000 genes, and the flower *Paris japonica* has about 149,000 billion pairs of bases.

Figure 10-2: Duplication of DNA

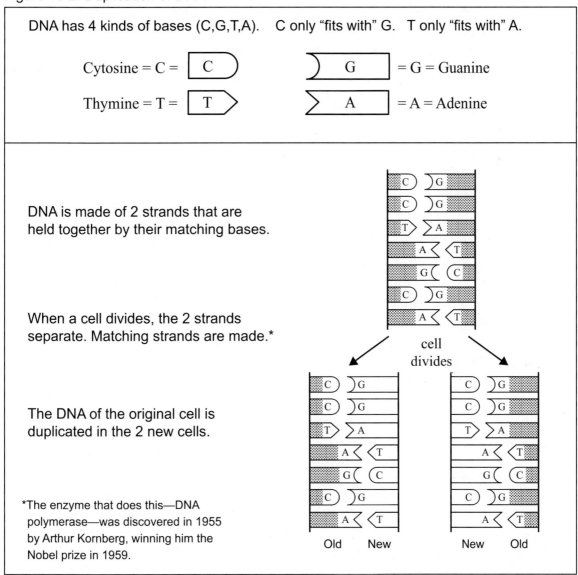

DNA has 4 kinds of bases (C,G,T,A).   C only "fits with" G.   T only "fits with" A.

Cytosine = C = C   G = G = Guanine

Thymine = T = T   A = A = Adenine

DNA is made of 2 strands that are held together by their matching bases.

When a cell divides, the 2 strands separate. Matching strands are made.*

cell divides

The DNA of the original cell is duplicated in the 2 new cells.

Old   New   New   Old

*The enzyme that does this—DNA polymerase—was discovered in 1955 by Arthur Kornberg, winning him the Nobel prize in 1959.

Using the sequence of bases in that section as a template, a matching copy is made. **This copy of the gene is called messenger RNA*** (mRNA). mRNA then goes to a ribosome—a protein-making factory. mRNA is a messenger in that it delivers the recipe from the cell nucleus (*the safe*) to a ribosome (*the chef*) in the cytoplasm (*the kitchen*).

Making the Protein

The messenger RNA threads through the ribosome† (Fig. 10-3). **The ribosome "reads" the sequence of bases in groups of 3** (*3-letter words*). Each of the 20 kinds of amino acids has its own 3-letter word(s) (Table 10-1). As the "words" are read, **each amino acid called for connects to the growing chain of amino acids.** The amino acids are carried by transfer RNAs (Fig. 10-3).

---

*RNA (ribonucleic acid), like DNA (deoxyribonucleic acid), is made up of bases hooked to a chain of sugars. But the sugar chain in RNA is made of ribose; in DNA, the sugar is deoxyribose. Also, 1 of the 4 bases in RNA differs. RNA uses U instead of T to pair with A. The 2 pairs in RNA are A-U and G-C.

†For their work in revealing the atomic structure and inner workings of the ribosome, Ana Yonath, Thomas Steitz, and Venkatraman Ramakrishnan won a Nobel prize in 2009.

Amino acids differ in size, shape, and chemistry, so their sequence in the chain is crucial in determining how **the chain twists and folds into the elaborate structure that is characteristic of that protein and its function.**

Using the analogy of a chef making a cake, the chef is like a ribosome, because the chef reads the recipe and makes the cake. The recipe determines whether the cake is Angel Food or Chocolate Decadence. Like a cake leaving the chef's hands when it's done, the protein leaves the ribosome when it's "done."*

DNA Analysis

The Human Genome Project began in 1989, and the first draft of the genome† was announced in 2001. The aim of the project: to determine the sequence of the 3 billion pairs of bases in human DNA, locate its 22,000 or so genes and identify the functions of proteins they make, and examine the societal/ethical implications. Do we want to know if we've inherited a susceptibility to cancer? Would such information be kept private? Would we be discriminated against in getting health insurance? Congress passed a law in 2008 *"To prohibit discrimination on the basis of genetic information with respect to health insurance and employment."*

The first director of this huge international project was James Watson, who in 1953 (at age 25) with Francis Crick discovered DNA's structure.** Identifying genes helps develop tests, treatments, and cures for genetic defects that cause diseases like phenylketonuria (Chap. 3) and familial hypercholesterolemia (Chap. 8). It advances the treatment and prevention of more complex diseases like cancer, diabetes, and Alzheimer's.

The field of pharmacogenomics looks at a drug's effectiveness based on a person's DNA. We know that some drugs work for some people and not for others. Ideally, we'd know who's

who ahead of time (e.g., tamoxifen is helpful for estrogen-receptor-positive breast cancer; patients can be tested in advance to see if theirs is positive or negative). A drug that cures some patients but seriously harms others isn't approved for use. But perhaps it could be approved if its use could be restricted to those it helps. Determining who these people are by DNA screening is a giant step toward tailor-made treatment to optimize benefit and minimize side-effects.

DNA analysis has led to unforeseen applications. Molecular paleontology is a new area of anthropology. DNA of various species resemble each other (have similar sequences of bases) only if they have a common ancestor. The more the resemblance, the more recently they branched apart in their evolutionary development.

DNA fingerprinting (Fig. 10-4) can identify people and their offspring with almost absolute certainty (many paternity disputes are settled this way). It's had a huge impact on the criminal justice system. Even the DNA from a bit of blood or tissue under a victim's fingernail can provide incriminating evidence. To get enough to analyze, traces of DNA can be increased billions-fold by a process called PCR (Polymerase Chain Reaction, Fig. 10-5).

DNA fingerprinting was first used to solve a murder in 1987. A girl in an English village was raped and strangled near where, 3 years earlier, this happened to another girl. A "likely suspect" confessed—the crime was "solved." But his father sought DNA testing to prove his son's innocence. Semen DNA found on the girl didn't match his son's, but did match the semen DNA found on the earlier victim—the same man raped both girls. Over 4500 possible suspects (all 17-34-year-old men without a valid alibi who lived nearby or were nearby at the time of the murder) gave blood and saliva to find the DNA match. The real culprit (who had no prior criminal record) was found.

---

*Protein synthesis is more complicated with some splicing of messenger RNA, later modifications in the chain of amino acids, etc., but you don't really have to know this.

†A genome is an organism's genetic material, e.g., a cat's DNA is the cat genome.

**Watson, Crick, and Maurice Wilkens won a 1962 Nobel prize for this discovery. Wilkens and Rosalind Franklin made the X-ray diffraction photos of DNA that gave Watson and Crick crucial information on DNA structure. Franklin died in 1958 at age 37. Nobel prizes aren't given posthumously.

Figure 10-3: Making Protein

1. Step 1 takes place in the cell nucleus—the permanent home of our **DNA**. The double-stranded DNA opens up at the location of the **gene**, and a matching copy of the bases in that section is made. The copy is called **messenger RNA (mRNA)**.

Nucleus of Cell

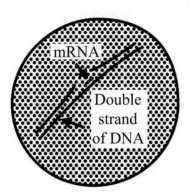

The bases in messenger RNA (mRNA) are a matching sequence to the DNA section. C always pairs with G.

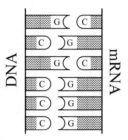

2. The mRNA (the copy of the recipe) moves out of the cell nucleus and into the cytoplasm, where it attaches to a **ribosome** (the protein-making factory).

3. The ribosome "reads" the sequence of bases in mRNA, 3 bases at a time, and **transfer RNAs (tRNA)** carry the amino acids called for. Each tRNA has the matching 3-base code word for the **amino acid** it's carrying. When the entire mRNA is read this way, the newly-made **protein** leaves the ribosome.

Cell

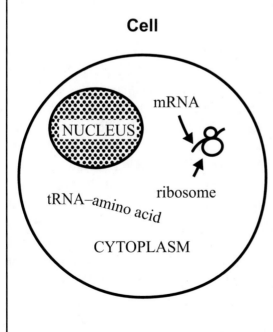

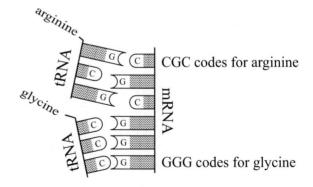

CGC codes for arginine

GGG codes for glycine

When the messenger RNA says CGC (the code for the amino acid arginine), the transfer RNA for arginine "fits." Arginine is then added to the growing chain of amino acids. Glycine is the next amino acid called for in this example.

Table 10-1: The Amino Acid Code in Messenger RNA

Don't be intimidated by this table; just look to see how a sequence of these "letters" can be translated into a sequence of amino acids

The 4-Letter Alphabet of the Code
U = Uracil   **C** = Cytosine   **A** = Adenine   **G** = Guanine

With a 4-letter alphabet,* you can write the 64 different 3-letter words shown below. Sixty-one of them code for the 20 amino acids used to make protein.† The other 3 code for stop—a signal to stop linking the amino acids together.

UUU = Phenylalanine	UCU = Serine	UAU = Tyrosine	UGU = Cysteine
UUC = Phenylalanine	UCC = Serine	UAC = Tyrosine	UGC = Cysteine
UUA = Leucine	UCA = Serine	UAA = Stop	UGA = Stop
UUG = Leucine	UCG = Serine	UAG = Stop	UGG = Tryptophan
CUU = Leucine	CCU = Proline	CAU = Histidine	CGU = Arginine
CUC = Leucine	CCC = Proline	CAC = Histidine	CGC = Arginine
CUA = Leucine	CCA = Proline	CAA = Glutamine	CGA = Arginine
CUG = Leucine	CCG = Proline	CAG = Glutamine	CGG = Arginine
AUU = Isoleucine	ACU = Threonine	AAC = Asparagine	AGU = Serine
AUC = Isoleucine	ACC = Threonine	AAU = Asparagine	AGC = Serine
AUA = Isoleucine	ACA = Threonine	AAA = Lysine	AGA = Arginine
AUG = Methionine	ACG = Threonine	AAG = Lysine	AGG = Arginine
GUU = Valine	GCU = Alanine	GAU = Aspartate	GGU = Glycine
GUC = Valine	GCC = Alanine	GAC = Aspartate	GGC = Glycine
GUA = Valine	GCA = Alanine	GAA = Glutamate	GGA = Glycine
GUG = Valine	GCG = Alanine	GAG = Glutamate	GGG = Glycine

* The 4 letters/bases in messenger RNA are U, C, A, G. In DNA, they are T, C, A, G.
† For their part in deciphering this code, Robert Holley, H. Gobin Khorana, and Marshall Nirenberg won a Nobel prize in 1968. For devising a method to determine the sequence of bases in DNA, Frederick Sanger and Walter Gilbert won a Nobel prize in 1980.

Alec Jeffreys, the molecular biologist who did this DNA match-up, also identified, in 1992, the exhumed bones of Joseph Mengele, the "Angel of Death" of Auschwitz. The bone DNA was compared with DNA from Mengele's son, who gave a blood sample when told that bones of his father's dead relatives might be exhumed for their DNA.

In March, 1998, an 11-year-old girl was raped, stabbed, and killed in Germany. Blood DNA from a knife at the scene matched semen DNA taken from another 11-year-old girl raped in 1996. Police collected and tested saliva from 16,400 local men, ages 18-30 (based on the 1996 rape victim's description). They found the DNA match and arrested a 30-year-old from a neighboring town. He confessed to both crimes.

The first person in the U.S. convicted of murder on the basis of DNA evidence was a man who raped and killed four women in 1987 in a series of break-ins. There were no witnesses, but semen DNA at the crime scenes matched his. He was convicted in 1988 and executed in 1994 at age 32.

Identifying people by DNA fingerprinting has broad uses. In 1976-1983, thousands of people "disappeared" during an Argentine military campaign to silence political opposition. The disappeared included children and pregnant women who were killed after giving birth. Many of the youngest children, including the newborn, were taken by military couples or sold. Their grandparents have spent years searching for them.

Figure 10-4: DNA Fingerprinting

The fingerprint looks like a bar code. The bars *(bands)* are pieces of double-stranded DNA, sorted by size:*

1. **Chop the DNA into pieces**, using enzymes that cut only at a specific sequence of bases, e.g.,

...GATATC... → ...GAT ATC...
...CTATAG...   ...CTA TAG...

We each have a unique sequence of bases in our DNA, so the sizes and numbers of pieces that you get from this chopping vary for each of us.†

2. **Put the chopped-up DNA into a rectangular hole near the edge of a thin slab of gel.**

3. **Apply an electric current to the gel**,‡ with the positive charge at the top. DNA is negatively charged, so the DNA pieces move up toward the positive charge. The shortest ones move the fastest (they slip through the gel faster).

   When the shortest/fastest ones reach the top of the gel, **the pieces are sorted by size**: the shortest in the bar at the top, the longer ones in the bars below.

shortest pieces

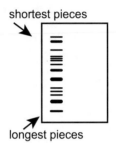

longest pieces

4. **Make the bars visible**. Stain the bars right on the gel. If you want to see only a specific bar that has a certain sequence of bases *(the target sequence)*, it's a bit more complicated:

   a. Separate the DNA pieces into single strands. Then, pour on the custom-made, radioactive, single-stranded pieces of DNA that have the sequence of bases that matches the target sequence. These radioactive pieces will stick to only the bar with the target sequence.

...GGTGGGC...(from bar DNA)
...CCACCCG...(radioactive pieces)

   b. Rinse off the excess radioactive pieces, so that the only radioactive area is the bar with the DNA pieces that have the target sequence of bases.

   c. Lay an X-ray film over the bars. The underlying radio-active bar will darken the X-ray film at that spot.

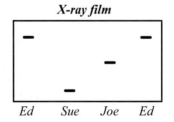

X-ray film

Ed   Sue   Joe   Ed

   Which bar darkens the film varies among people. Ed has the target sequence in shorter DNA pieces than does Joe or Sue. (Several bars with different target sequences can be done at one time.)

*Called RFLP: *Restriction Fragment-Length Polymorphism*. *Restriction* enzymes (from bacteria) chop DNA at restricted places. *Fragment-Length Poly*(many)*morphism*(forms): you get DNA fragments/pieces of many lengths that vary from person to person.

† In your own cells, DNA is the same. So it chops the same way each time the same enzyme is used: Your DNA, whether from blood or skin, chops into identical pieces.

‡ The gel is like wet finger-Jell-O.

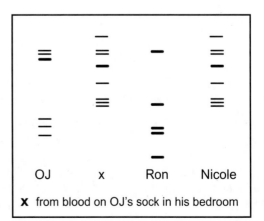

OJ   x   Ron   Nicole

x from blood on OJ's sock in his bedroom

Figure 10-5: PCR (the Polymerase Chain Reaction)

PCR can make unlimited copies of a targeted DNA section, and is used to get enough for analysis,*
e.g., a fragment of DNA from a speck of blood or an ancient insect caught in amber can be made
into the much larger amount needed for DNA fingerprinting (Fig. 10-4) or sequencing.

Mixture in the Test Tube

- **DNA sample**

- **Primers** that bracket the target DNA section. The primers are custom-made,
  short (e.g., 20-30 bases long), single-stranded DNA with a sequence of
  bases that match, and thus attach, to the ends of the target DNA sections.

- **A,T,C,G building blocks** of DNA

- **DNA polymerase** enzyme makes copies of the target DNA section, using
  the A,T,C,G building blocks (Fig. 10-2), using the primer as a starting point.

Method

1. Heat the mixture. This separates the double strand of DNA into 2 single strands.

2. Cool the mixture. Primers attach to the ends of the target on the single stranded DNA.

3. DNA polymerase completes the matching section, doubling the amount of that DNA section.

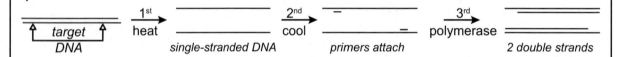

This completes cycle 1. Each cycle (steps 1-3) doubles the target DNA section.**

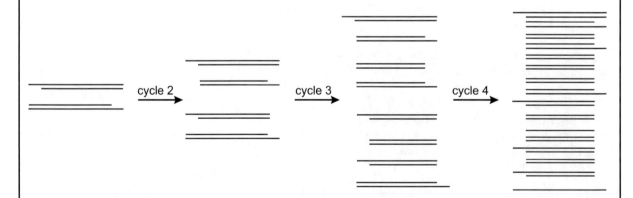

*Kary Mullis conceived of PCR in 1983, winning him a Nobel prize in 1993.

**PCR first used a DNA polymerase that was destroyed by the heat of step 1; new polymerase
had to be added for step 3 of each cycle. The remedy was to use heat-stable polymerase from
microbes living in hot springs—one scientist fell in, trying to scoop some up, and suffered burns!
A commonly used polymerase is made by biotech, using the gene from the microbe *Thermus
aquaticus* from hot springs in Yellowstone National Park. All the PCR machine has to do is alter-
nately heat and cool the test tube; billions of copies of a DNA section can be made in hours.

Even when circumstantial evidence almost certainly identified a child as one of theirs, it wasn't proof enough. Matching DNA from the grandparents was. Over 55 cases have been resolved this way. The hope is that in the years to come, these children will themselves come forward to be identified, using DNA samples left by their grandparents.

Comparing DNA to family members was used in identifying victims of the 9/11 attack and Osama bin Laden. Also, the remains of an American pilot killed in Vietnam in 1972, buried in the Tomb of the Unknown Soldier in 1984, and exhumed in 1998 was identified. Blood and saliva are now routinely collected from U.S. military personnel—DNA is a much better "dog tag." DNA identification also has more mundane uses, e.g., checking for fraudulently labeled fish fillets in stores and restaurants.

Viruses

Viruses are extremely small—much smaller than bacteria. They can, in fact, infect bacteria. Their basic structure is simply a short strand of RNA or DNA (the viruses' genes) enclosed in a protein coat. The protein coat allows the virus to enter a cell (as in the example given in Chap. 9 for HIV), much like a key getting you into a house with a matching lock. So it is that a flu virus infects respiratory cells; HIV infects white blood cells; etc.

The protein coat of a virus is unique, causing us to make a specific antibody in response to a specific virus. After an infection, we keep making that antibody to protect us against subsequent infections with that same virus. Good for us, not so good for the virus.

The influenza (*flu*) virus continually alters its protein coat (altering the sequence of bases in its *RNA—changing the recipe for its protein coat*). If it didn't, it eventually wouldn't have anyone but children to infect; others would have developed an immunity from their first encounter with the flu virus (or the vaccine).

Scientists try to track changes in the virus, to provide effective vaccines in advance of flu season. A different flu shot is offered each year. If there's only a minor change in the virus, antibodies from earlier exposures partially protect us. If there's a major change, a bigger epidemic is expected, since only a few people, if any, have partial antibody-protection. The severity of symptoms depends on how and how much the virus has changed.

The biggest pandemic (worldwide epidemic) in recent history was the flu epidemic of 1918-1919. A major change in the virus caused severe symptoms, resulting in about 50 million deaths, many within hours of the first symptom. Unlike most flu epidemics, about half the deaths were in ages 20-40. Their healthy immune systems worked to their disadvantage, causing a massive immune response with severe consequences, e.g., suffocation from the lungs filling with fluid. Influenza experts are on edge in expectation of another pandemic.

Viruses can't multiply outside of cells. They don't even have the equipment (ribosomes, etc.) to make their own protein coat, and must infect cells to survive. Once inside, they commandeer the cell's enzymes, transfer RNAs, etc., to duplicate their own genes and make the proteins encoded in their genes (remember, the genetic code is universal—GGG "means" the amino acid glycine, whether in a pea, a human, or a virus). Many copies of the virus are made this way, and can go on to infect other cells (the virus can spread).

How can we hamper a virus's ability to multiply without also hampering the function of our own cells? Because of a virus's simple structure and the similarity of its molecules to our own, effective treatments are hard to find. There aren't many chinks in its armor.

In contrast, bacteria are independent single-cell organisms—they multiply all by themselves. They need only nutrients (from dirty dishes, undigested lactose in the colon, candy stuck on teeth, etc.) to survive. They also have cell walls (our cells have cell membranes instead). So, a substance that hampers cell-wall production is devastating for them, but not for us. Penicillin (the first antibiotic discovered) blocks the production of some types of bacterial cell walls and prevents the bacteria from multiplying. The discovery of antibiotics was, of course, a medical milestone.*

AIDS Virus (HIV)

HIV (human immunodeficiency virus)—the AIDS virus—carries its genetic material as RNA and has several unusual enzymes, including *reverse transcriptase, integrase,* and *protease.* Normally, a cell makes messenger RNA as a matching copy of a small section of DNA (*normal transcription;* Fig. 10-3). But when HIV infects a cell, DNA is made as a matching copy of HIV's RNA (*reverse transcription*).† Cells can't normally do this, but HIV's *reverse transcriptase* enzyme makes this possible.

This "foreign" DNA is then inserted into the cell's own DNA. Our cells can't normally do this either, but HIV's *integrase* enzyme makes this possible. Luckily, HIV doesn't infect sperm and ova, so directions to make the virus can't be passed to one's offspring through a parent's DNA. But an infected mother can infect her unborn child. An infected father can only infect his unborn child indirectly, by infecting the mother.

HIV infection can proceed in a matter of months or years to the disease AIDS. In adults without anti-viral therapy, the median time is about 10 years. In general, the more virus in the blood (a sign that the virus is winning the battle against the immune system), the sooner the infection proceeds to AIDS, and the shorter the survival time among those who already have AIDS.

Drugs target HIV's enzymes, which the virus needs to reproduce. AZT was the first such drug. It was first made as an anticancer drug in 1963, but failed in this use. It was one of hundreds of substances screened in an urgent search for a drug effective against HIV. It works by hampering HIV's *reverse transcriptase* enzyme that allows DNA to be made from viral RNA.** Drugs ddI (dideoxyinosine) and ddC (dideoxycytidine) act similarly.

Protease inhibitors were approved in 1995. These drugs target HIV's *protease* enzyme, which cuts newly made HIV protein into the pieces needed to make more virus. Protease inhibitors, combined with drugs that inhibit reverse transcriptase, can dramatically lower blood levels of HIV, and has dramatically improved the course of AIDS in many patients.

HIV multiplies very fast and produces many mutants, some of which are resistant to the drugs. As resistant forms begin to predominate, the drugs lose their effectiveness. There's less chance of HIV becoming resistant to drug combinations that inhibit more than one of its enzymes. If you're given a bin of keys, there may be one that locks your house or car, but it's much harder to find one that locks your house *and* car.

For all the scariness of HIV, it's very fragile outside the body—more fragile and much more difficult to get than herpes or hepatitis. Even a ten-fold dilution of ordinary household bleach (sodium hypo-

---

*Alexander Fleming, Ernst Chain, and Howard Florey won a 1945 Nobel prize for discovering penicillin and finding a way to make useful amounts.

†Most viruses can't do this; those that can are called retroviruses. The first human retrovirus (one that causes a rare leukemia) was discovered in 1978 by Robert Gallo. He and Luc Montagier are credited with discovering HIV in 1984.

**AZT resembles a DNA building-block (thymidine), so AZT—instead of the building-block—attaches to the DNA being made from viral RNA. This halts the process. AZT lacks the "molecular tail" to which the next DNA building-block can attach. If DNA were a chain of 100 monkeys, each holding onto a tail, the chain couldn't be completed if any 1 of the 1st 99 monkeys lacked a tail. AZT is the monkey without a tail.

chlorite) destroys it. HIV isn't transmitted casually. It infects by entering the bloodstream via the transfer of infected blood, semen, or vaginal secretions. Infected blood and semen have the highest concentration of virus. Transmission via semen is more likely if there are breaks in the skin of the recipient (e.g., genital sores, abrasions/tears in the anus/rectum from anal penetration).

In heterosexual intercourse with an infected partner, women have a much higher risk of getting infected. But a man's risk goes up if the HIV-infected woman has a cervical or vaginal infection—this increases vaginal discharges rich in the white blood cells that can harbor the virus.

Now that blood donations are screened for HIV antibodies, HIV infection from blood transfusions and clotting factors extracted from blood is rare in this country. With only a few exceptions, it's transmitted by contaminated needles and syringes (drug users commonly draw blood into a syringe to be sure they're in a vein before injecting), unprotected sexual intercourse with an infected person, and in-the-womb transmission from mother to child. An infected mother also can pass the virus to her infant through breast milk.

Practically speaking, the epidemic in this country can be halted in the short term only by the use of clean needles and syringes (new or cleaned with a 1:10 dilution of household chlorine bleach), the proper use of latex condoms (viruses can pass through condoms made from animal tissue), and the use of antiretroviral treatment to lessen HIV-transmission to the fetus or uninfected partner.

The search is on for a vaccine to prevent infection and for more effective ways to prevent HIV from progressing to AIDS. Once infected, the infection is permanent. Only one person, Timothy Ray Brown, is known to have cleared the infection. He had been infected with HIV for 10 years when, in 2006, he came down with leukemia unrelated to his HIV infection. To treat the leukemia, he needed a bone marrow/stem cell transplant (preceded by wiping out his own immune system—including his HIV-infected CD4 cells). Since it was known that some people have a mutation that makes their CD4 cells highly resistant to HIV infection, a person with such a mutation was found as the donor. The transplant cured his leukemia and HIV infection.

Biotechnology

Making Human Protein

Proteins can be made only in cells. Until the advent of biotechnology, we got them by extracting them from natural sources. Insulin-dependent diabetics need an outside source of insulin (a protein). Pancreases from animal slaughterhouses used to be the only source. The ability to make insulin by biotech came in the nick of time. More people need insulin, and the amount of insulin extracted from pancreases is limited by availability of pancreases.

Large amounts of human proteins can be made by biotechnology, in cell cultures or bacteria (single-cell organisms). The amount isn't limited as it is when insulin is extracted from pancreases. Activase, the drug for dissolving blood clots (Chap. 7), is made by biotech, the only way this human protein can be made in amounts needed for use as a drug.

The basic method: (1) locate the gene (*recipe*) for the protein in human DNA, (2) cut out the gene, using special enzymes, (3) insert (splice) the gene into DNA of bacteria (or cell cultures), (4) grow the bacteria to make the proteins (now including the human protein) encoded in their DNA, and (5) extract the human protein that's been made. Accomplishing all this is easier said than done!*

Bacteria that carry human genes serve as miniature factories for making human proteins. Bacteria multiply fast, so a flask-full can be made quickly. Raw material for this factory is simply the normal nutrients that bacteria need. Some kinds of human and animal cells can also be grown in flasks and genetically altered to make specific proteins.

It's not only human proteins that are made this way. Calf stomach used to be the source of

---

*For work in developing this technology, Paul Berg won a 1980 Nobel prize. It's genetic engineering, but the general term biotechnology is often used instead; genetic engineering sounds ominous to nonscientists.

the enzyme rennin used to make cheese (rennin curdles milk). Rennin made by biotech (the calf gene for rennin was inserted in yeast) is a more reliable and cleaner source. It's been used since 1990 to make most of our cheese.

Besides being able to make specific proteins in large amounts, there are other advantages to making proteins this way. When insulin is made by biotech, human insulin is made, whereas it's cow insulin that's extracted from cow pancreas. Cow insulin works in humans, but it's not exactly the same. When injected with a protein that's not exactly the same as the human protein, some people get an allergic reaction.

Making proteins by biotech avoids such hazards as HIV contamination of blood-clotting factors. When taken from plasma pooled from many donors, an entire batch of blood-clotting factors can be contaminated by just one infected donor. As said earlier, many hemophiliacs were infected with HIV via contaminated blood-clotting factors before the cause of AIDS was known.

Gene Therapy

Gene therapy experiments proceed very cautiously. The first experiment in the U.S. to put a foreign gene (i.e., from an outside source) into a human was approved in 1989. After 7 months of intense scrutiny, the experiment was approved by the Food and Drug Administration, the Recombinant DNA Advisory Committee, the Human Gene Therapy Subcommittee, the Institutional Biosafety Committee, and the Director of the National Institutes of Health.

The purpose of this experiment was to test a new cancer treatment: Take cancer-fighting white blood cells (tumor-infiltrating lymphocytes—TIL cells) from tumors of patients with advanced cancer, tag the cells with a foreign gene to follow their course, use a special protein made by biotech (the only way it can be made in sufficient amounts) to grow large amounts of these cells, and then put the cells back into the patients.

Because the TIL cells are taken from the tumor itself, they come close to "magic bullets" that leave healthy cells alone and seek and destroy cancer cells in the tumor and wherever it has spread. Side effects were severe. The outcome ranged from no improvement, to an apparent cure in a 29-year-old woman with advanced cancer.

The experiment was reported in the popular media, resulting in a flood of requests from terminally ill cancer patients wanting to participate. But only a few could participate—preparation of TIL cells is difficult and expensive (patients aren't charged).

What about using biotech to correct for defective genes in diseases like hemophilia? Even if the correct gene could be put into liver cells of hemophiliacs so that they could make their own missing blood-clotting factor, they would still pass the defect to their offspring. Their sperm or ova DNA wouldn't have been corrected. Making permanent corrections (in sperm or ova) is very difficult, and hasn't been attempted.

"Dr. Farnsworth is attempting to isolate the gene that makes people do this sort of thing for a living."

The first human *gene therapy* experiment began in 1990. A 4-year-old girl, Ashanti DeSilva, was severely ill with an immunodeficiency disease caused by a genetic deficiency of a key enzyme. (Experiments on mice with a similar disease had suggested that this therapy would work in humans.) White blood cells taken from her were infected with a retrovirus that was altered to carry the normal gene she needed (a retrovirus inserts its genes into a cell's DNA). The cells then made the enzyme from its newly inserted gene, and were infused back into her. The therapy wasn't entirely successful in that she still has to take some of the enzyme, but it has enabled her to live an active life as an adult.

In 1993, gene therapy, using umbilical cord blood, was used to treat two affected newborn boys diagnosed prenatally with another severe immunodeficiency disease.* Although gene therapy has been successful in treating others with this disease, the treatment suffered a setback in 2002 when a child developed a leukemia-like disease after treatment.

In 1989, the defective gene that causes cystic fibrosis was found.† Sticky mucus fills the lungs, making it hard to breath and causing lung infections and damage. About half of the patients die of lung damage by age 30. By locating defective genes, scientists can find out what protein is made by a normal version of that gene. Then, by finding out what that protein does, they can begin to figure out the disease.**

In 1990, some lung cells from cystic fibrosis patients were removed and corrected in the test tube, using retroviruses to insert a normal version of the defective gene (this experiment didn't go past the test tube). In 1991, a normal version of the gene was inserted into a common cold virus (altered so it can't cause a cold). The virus was then dripped into rats' lungs, causing the lungs to make the desired protein. But when this procedure was tried in cystic fibrosis patients, it caused unacceptable lung inflammation.

In 1999, gene therapy studies had a major setback with the death of 18-year-old Jesse Gelsinger 4 days after gene therapy for a disease caused by a defective gene for a liver enzyme. He died from a massive immune response to the common cold virus that was to deliver the normal gene for the enzyme to his liver.

In 2006, gene therapy was used successfuly to treat two patients with metastatic melanoma. In 2007, gene therapy was used successfully for an inherited blinding disease. The normal gene was inserted into a common cold virus and delivered to the retina, resulting in improved vision without apparent side effects.

Aside from gene therapy, genes can work as a drug-delivery system. Diabetics who need insulin must inject it their whole lives. One therapy being investigated is to implant the gene for insulin in diabetics so they can make their own insulin.

Cloning

Cloning creates a genetic duplicate of an animal. The DNA-containing nucleus of an animal's cell is removed and inserted in an ovum that has had its own nucleus removed. This means the entire set of genes in the resulting embryo is from the one animal.

The 1997 birth of the lamb Dolly was sensational. It was the first time a mammal had been cloned

---

*This disease has been called bubble-boy disease—David Vetter from Houston lived his life (12 years) in a sterile, plastic bubble because the disease was untreatable then.

†The gene is for a membrane protein that lets chloride ions leave a cell. In cystic fibrosis, chloride ions accumulate inside lung cells, pulling in water from the surrounding mucus, making the mucus thick, hard to cough up, and a favorable site for bacterial infection. White blood cells come in to fight the infection; when the cells die, their DNA (which is thick and viscous) spills into the mucus, thickening it even more. The biotech-made drug pulmozyme was approved in 1993 (the application exceeded 150,000 pages)—the first new treatment in more than 30 years. The inhaled drug is an enzyme that chops up DNA in the lung mucus, thinning it, making breathing easier, reducing lung infections and damage.

**There are huge databases of gene sequences and their proteins, e.g., a certain sequence of bases suggests it's part of a gene for a membrane protein, just as the phrase add ½ cup oatmeal suggests it's part of a recipe book. Databases are used to find a match to unidentified base sequences, just as we might search databases to find out exactly what books contain the sequence, *"his knees felt weak as she kissed him."*

"*Very good, Michaels—you're a DNA molecule. Now get back to work.*"

in the animal's ova). Cloning provides a way of reproducing an animal in which the gene has been successfully inserted and can be passed on to its offspring.

Plant Genetics

In crossbreeding, genes mix "by chance." It takes many crosses and a long time to get what you want (we crossbreed when we mate—when a Lyle Lovett mates with a Julia Roberts, there's no guarantee that the child will have his voice and her looks). Biotech is faster and more precise. You can transfer a single gene to get what is wanted in one shot. The gene also can be from another species, e.g., a gene that protects fish against freezing put into a plant to prevent frost damage.

Agricultural biotech can have a huge impact on health, especially in developing countries where food is scarce and the nutritional quality of the staple diet is inadequate. Often, the scarcity isn't from a deficit in production, but from losses—pest infestation, harsh weather, deterioration of the harvest during transport or storage, etc. Also, dietary protein in developing countries is often inadequate. Biotech is used to get crops with higher quality protein and more resistance to viral infection, pests, deterioration, etc. Making a tastier tomato pales by comparison.*

Using altered retroviruses to insert genes into animal DNA has a counterpart in the plant world. *Agrobacterium tumefaciens* normally causes disease by inserting its genes into plant DNA. Plant geneticists can remove the disease-causing genes from this bacterium (*disarm it*), and then use the bacteria as a vehicle to transfer a desired gene into plants.

from an adult cell. In becoming liver cells, heart cells, etc., certain genes are turned on or off in an embryonic cell's DNA, e.g., brain cells don't make the digestive enzyme lactase because the gene to make it is turned off—permanently it was thought. It didn't seem possible that DNA from an adult cell could revert back to where it could develop into a multicellular animal like Dolly. Dolly was cloned from a mammary (breast) cell (and named after Dolly Parton), making her the genetic twin of the ewe from which the mammary cell was taken.

Cloning has practical uses in animal husbandry (e.g., cloning a steer that grows fast and lean on small amounts of feed), medical research, the pharmaceutical industry, etc. One way to get a steady and large source of a particular human protein is to insert the human gene into a lactating animal, such that the protein is excreted in the milk. One then milks the animal and extracts the human protein from the milk. (It isn't sold to drink!) The stumbling block has been that not only is it very difficult to get the gene inserted in this manner, but the gene isn't passed on to offspring (it isn't

*The Flavr Savr tomato was patented in 1989. The gene for the enzyme that causes rapid deterioration was knocked out, so the tomatoes last longer after picking and can be picked when ripe and tasty. Campbell Soup Company partly financed its development. But in response to public fear of biotech foods (or more scary-sounding generically altered food), they announced in 1993 that they wouldn't use it in their products.

One such gene is for a protein in the coat of a virus that infects and damages crops. It has been known that crops infected with a mild strain of a virus aren't susceptible to infection with a more damaging virus (like the example of cowpox infection in dairy maids conferring immunity to smallpox). It was found that one of the virus's proteins, alone, confers the same protection (the basis of some human vaccines).

Scientists could then cut out the gene for this viral protein, insert it into disarmed *Agrobacterium tumefaciens,* and let this bacterium do what it does naturally—insert the gene into plant DNA. This genetically altered plant can now make this viral protein for its own protection—it's "vaccinated" against the plant disease. (When we eat the plant with this "foreign protein," it's digested into its component amino acids.)

Mutations

Mutations are changes in the bases in DNA. The effect—or lack of an effect—depends on where and which bases are changed. An obvious impact of a mutation is its potential to change the instructions to make a protein. UUA codes for the amino acid leucine (see Table 10-1). If this changes to UUG, there's no effect (it's a "silent mutation")—UUG also codes for leucine. But if the UUA is changed to UAA, the protein can't be made—UAA means stop. Most mutations have relatively mild effects. In contrast, a mutation that results in the inability to make an enzyme needed to make ATP wouldn't even allow survival as an embryo. Also, many mutations occur in areas of DNA that aren't a part of our genes.

Mutations that occur in the genes of "germ cells" (cells holding the genetic material passed onto offspring, e.g., ova and sperm) are responsible for genetic diversity among species, and are a major factor in adaptation and evolution. They are also responsible for genetically based diseases.

Sickle Cell Anemia

Sickle cell anemia is caused by a single mutation (a change in a single base*) in the gene for hemoglobin (the oxygen-carrying protein in red blood cells). As a result, the amino acid valine (code GUU, GUC, GUA, or GUG) replaces glutamate (GAA or GAG) as the 6th amino acid in hemoglobin's chain of 146 amino acids. Valine (*the wrong amino acid*) is chemically different from glutamate. As a result, sickle cell hemoglobin has a "sticky" spot (valine at position #6) on its surface.

The sticky spot is exposed only when hemoglobin isn't carrying oxygen (oxygen changes hemoglobin's shape). Whenever oxygen falls in the blood, the hemoglobins stick together, forming long strands. This distorts the shape of red blood cells into a sickle, causing them to get trapped in small blood vessels. This causes severe pain by restricting the blood supply in the area, just as the narrowing of a coronary artery causes the pain of angina (Chap. 8). Interfering with blood flow not only damages organs, but also causes oxygen in blood to fall even more, causing more sickling. Also, sickled red blood cells are very fragile and break easily, resulting in fewer red blood cells (anemia).

Sickle cell anemia is a severe disease involving many organs. Steady improvements in treatment have extended survival to well beyond age 40. The gene for sickle cell anemia is found almost exclusively in blacks, and the gene is recessive, meaning that a person must get it from both parents to get the disease. The disease occurs in about 0.3% of blacks in this country. About 10% of blacks inherit the gene (*sickle cell trait*) from only one parent; they don't have the disease, but their red blood cells can sickle under certain circumstances of oxygen deprivation, such as vigorous exercise at high altitudes.

---

*Variation in a single base (nucleotide) at a precise point along our DNA is called a SNP (single nucleotide polymorphism), pronounced "snip." More than 99% of our DNA sequences are identical, and about 90% of the variations that make us unique individuals are our SNPs. Only a small portion of the millions of SNPs in human DNA have been identified, but the race is on. Unlike a single-SNP disease like sickle cell anemia, many diseases involve many SNPs. The National Center for Biotechnology Information maintains a SNP database (www.ncbi.nlm.nih.gov/snp). SNPs can not only predict our reactions to a drugs, etc., but can describe us, e.g., "This DNA is probably from a blond male of Danish heritage."

The prevalence of sickle cell trait in Africa suggests a selective advantage. Malaria is prevalent in Africa and is caused by a parasite that multiplies in red blood cells. Sickle cell trait protects against the most lethal form of malaria. The likely explanation for the prevalence of this mutation is that those who have it tend to survive malaria, enabling them to pass the mutation on to their descendants. This mutation was a mixed bag. It caused severe anemia, yet it gave people a better chance of surviving the most lethal form of malaria.*

In 2010, another "mixed bag" mutation was discovered that increases the risk of kidney disease and protects against sleeping sickness (trypanosomiasis) caused by tsetse flies infected with a particular parasite. These flies and parasite are found in sub-Saharan Africa. African-Americans have higher rates of kidney disease; about 30% of African-Americans carry this mutation.

Some mutations are much more one-sided. Mutations in certain genes cause cancer.† At the other extreme, there's a mutation that causes extremely high HDL-cholesterol (Chap. 8). This seems to increase longevity without any drawbacks. But genetic mutations that, say, extend life expectancy from age 75 to 95 don't tend to become widespread. In contrast, the mutation for sickle cell anemia helps children survive malaria, allowing them to make it to the childbearing years and pass on the mutation. "Longevity genes" could be propagated by letting men only over age 90 father children!

Spontaneous Mutations

The public tends to think of mutations as something caused by environmental insults. While these can certainly cause mutations, mutations also occur as copying errors. Each time a cell divides, the two strands of DNA separate, and copies of the original DNA are duplicated in the two new cells (Fig. 10-2).

A "spontaneous" mutation occurs if, for example, the wrong base is inserted in the process of making a matching strand—a copying error. In humans, copying errors are unusual because when our DNA is duplicated, the two strands are carefully checked to make sure that the bases are paired correctly. For a copying error to occur, it has to slip by the cell's diligent proofreader. But copying errors do slip by, and are more likely the more times something is copied, i.e., the more times a cell divides.

Spontaneous mutations are especially unusual in sperm and ova—DNA we pass on. As such, the number of mutations is used as an evolutionary clock. Molecular paleontologists compare DNA from animals to estimate when they branched apart from a common ancestor. They estimate how many mutations would have had to occur to account for the DNA differences between the animals and their common ancestor (e.g., 1000 mutations), estimate the rate of spontaneous mutations (e.g., 1 per 100 years), then estimate how long ago the animals branched apart [(1000 mutations)/(1 mutation/ 100 yrs) = 100,000 years].

Spontaneous mutations are common in microbes, allowing them to adapt easily. Suppose that disease-causing bacteria are flourishing in an environment that is then changed by introducing an antibiotic. If the antibiotic quickly kills all the bacteria, the assault is a success. If the antibiotic doesn't quite do its job (e.g., dose is too low or isn't taken long enough), the bacteria have an opportunity to adapt.

If even a single bacterium becomes resistant to the antibiotic because of a spontaneous mutation, that bacterium will flourish in the new environment and become the new, antibiotic-resistant strain. Such bacteria can then transfer thus antibiotic resistance to other bacteria.

Abortions following prenatal diagnosis of genetic diseases tend to lessen the perpetuation of a mutated gene. Some conditions tend to perpetuate

---

*Thalassemia is also a disease caused by a mutation that both protects against malaria and causes anemia. Worldwide, it's one of the most common inherited diseases. It's more common among those from Mediterranean areas, Africa, and Southeast Asia.

†These genes regulate normal growth of a cell. Harold Varmus and J. Michael Bishop won the Nobel prize in 1989 for discovering these genes and their connection to cancer.

mutations that would normally be kept in check by nature or social forces. When hemophilia was untreatable, only women passed on the mutation. They themselves didn't get hemophilia.* When a male inherited the mutation, he got hemophilia but didn't pass on the mutation because he usually died before he could reproduce or didn't marry because of his disease.

With an outside source of clotting factors, hemophiliacs can now live quite normal lives, including having children.† Men, in addition to women, now transmit the gene. If a man with hemophilia marries a woman who carries the gene (the odds of this are remote, but go up with inbreeding), all their children have a 50:50 chance of having hemophilia.

A woman with hemophilia carries the gene on both of her X-chromosomes. All her sons—regardless of the father—will have hemophilia, and all her daughters will be carriers.

The hope is that gene therapy will be able to cure not only genetic diseases, but genetic susceptibilities as well. Breast cancer is thought to involve several mutations. Women with a genetic susceptibility to breast cancer may have inherited at least one of those mutations (*breast-cancer genes*), giving them a head start. As yet, breast-cancer genes can't be corrected, but testing for them can be useful.

In 1992, the *Wall Street Journal* told of a woman with a strong family history of breast cancer. She so feared getting it that she scheduled surgery to remove her breasts. Her extended family happened to be part of a research project looking for breast-cancer genes, and the scientists were able to tell her that she hadn't inherited the one in her family.** She canceled her surgery.

Ames Test

Some mutations can cause cancer. Efforts to identify cancer-causing agents (carcinogens) often begin by screening substances to see if they are even capable of causing mutations. The Ames test does this.††

The test uses modified strains of bacteria—their cell walls have been modified to make it easier for substances to reach their DNA, and their DNA repair systems have been removed. Ground-up liver is also used, so that liver-altered forms of the substance will also be tested. (Some substances aren't carcinogens per se, but are changed into carcinogens in the body, typically by liver enzymes.) The test is done in a petri dish (the standard dish used to grow bacteria) with about a billion bacteria, the test substance, products of the test substance (from the action of liver enzymes), and a nutrient broth.

A key feature of this test is that the bacteria can't make the amino acid histidine. They can't grow (form colonies) in the petri dish because the nutrient broth is made without histidine. If the test substance (or one of its products) causes mutations, mutations of all sorts will occur in the billion bacteria. In a lottery of sorts, some of these mutations will enable some bacteria to make histidine. These bacteria will flourish, and many colonies of bacteria will appear within two days. This means that the test substance is capable of causing mutations—a *potential* carcinogen. The Ames test is extremely sensitive; many substances that are possible carcinogens may not actually be carcinogens in "real life."

This test has been used extensively to test chemicals already in use, as well as novel chemicals proposed for use. Besides testing to see if

---

*Genes for blood-clotting factors are on the X-chromosome. A male only has the X-chromosome from his mother (if he had gotten an X- instead of a Y-chromosome from his father, he would have been a she). If his X-chromosome carries the defective gene, he's born with hemophilia. Females have two X-chromosomes—one from each parent. If one of her X-chromosomes has the defective gene, she doesn't get hemophilia because the gene is normal in the other one—she has a back-up set of X-linked genes—but her children have a 50:50 chance of inheriting the defective one.

†When HIV-infected hemophiliacs want to have children, they want to impregnate their wives without infecting them. "Safe sex" presented a problem. Today, antiretroviral drugs can be used to lower the risk of infection.

**The scientists included Mary Claire King, who helped identify the children of the missing in Argentina, and Francis Collins, who helped find the cystic fibrosis gene and headed the Human Genome Project.

††Bruce Ames, a biochemistry professor at the University of California at Berkeley, devised this test.

a chemical is capable of causing mutations, the Ames test is also used to test the chemical's potency to do so. Highly mutagenic compounds will cause mutations at very low concentrations.

When a company requests approval for a new food additive, it must submit evidence that it's safe and effective. Prior to the introduction of the Ames test in 1973, a proposed additive was first tested on animals to see if it caused cancer. Now, it's first screened by the Ames test or a similar test before animal testing.

Summary

DNA is the genetic material of the cell. It's made of two long strands joined along their length by the pairing of the four bases found in DNA. The segments that hold the directions to make protein are called genes. The sequence of bases in these segments provides the directions to make all the proteins in the body and, as such, the directions to reproduce the entire body. Each gene provides directions to make a particular protein and occupies a precise location in DNA.

Protein is made by translating the sequence of bases in a gene into a corresponding sequence of amino acids: The cell makes a matching copy of the gene. The copy is messenger RNA, which then goes to a ribosome where the sequence of bases in messenger RNA is "read" in sets of 3.

Aside from the codes for "stop," each group of 3 bases is a code word for a specific amino acid. As the bases are read, transfer RNAs bring the corresponding amino acids to the ribosome, and the amino acids link together to make the protein.

Human DNA has about 22,000 genes, collectively called the human genome. The Human Genome Project aims to identify and locate each of these genes, to determine the entire sequence of the bases in our DNA, and to study the societal/ethical implications. This Project, DNA fingerprinting, identification of viruses, and many other applications of DNA analysis are made possible by PCR, the Polymerase Chain Reaction that greatly increases the amount of DNA available for analysis.

A virus—whether it causes chicken pox, the common cold, or herpes—is basically a short strand of RNA or DNA (the virus's genetic material) enclosed in a protein coat. The coat allows it to get through a cell's membrane (infect the cell). Once inside, the virus uses the cell's ribosomes, enzymes, amino acids, etc., to reproduce. It can't reproduce outside a cell.

Some viruses, such as HIV, are retroviruses. They carry special enzymes that enable them to incorporate their genetic material into the cell's DNA. In this way, the directions to make the retrovirus can become part of the cell's own genetic material.

One application of biotechnology is to make a particular protein in the laboratory by inserting the gene for that protein into DNA of bacteria or cell cultures. These modified cells serve as protein-making factories, and the protein can be made in large amounts. Human insulin is one of the proteins made this way.

Another application is to treat genetic diseases (diseases caused by defective genes) by gene therapy. One approach is to use a retrovirus to insert the normal version of the defective gene into the patient's cells.

Mutations are changes in the bases in DNA. They can be spontaneous errors in DNA duplication or can be caused by substances called mutagens. An obvious impact of a mutation is its potential to change the instructions to make a protein.

Mutations that occur in "germ cells" (cells holding the genetic material passed onto offspring, e.g., ova and sperm) are responsible for much of the genetic diversity among species, and are a major factor in adaptation and evolution. They are also responsible for genetically based diseases.

Although mutations don't necessarily cause cancer, most carcinogens (cancer-causing substances) do so by causing a mutation in a gene that regulates cell growth. The Ames test is a screening test used to evaluate a substance's capacity to cause mutations.

Chapter 11

Dietary Protein

A chicken in every pot.

A promise of prosperity, campaign ad
for Herbert Hoover, 1928

When we think of protein, most of us think of meat. Throughout human history, meat has been a luxury, a food of the rich, a food hungered for by the poor. Even today, most of the world's vegetarians aren't vegetarians by choice, but by the circumstances of poverty.

Protein is hard to discuss—it comes with more emotional baggage than other nutrients. Animal foods (meat, egg, milk) have the most protein and the highest quality protein. For some people, this brings up environmental or religious issues; for others, animal rights.

For nutritionists, the conflict is that for most of the world's population, protein is scarce. Small differences in a food's protein content, digestibility, etc., can be extremely important. Yet, these differences are trivial to most of us here. The amount of protein in the typical American diet far exceeds what we need, and much of our excesses of calories, fat, saturated fat, and cholesterol come from animal foods.

So, the various aspects of dietary protein are important, or unimportant, depending on the situation. We're reminded again that good nutrition aims for the middle ground—enough, but not too much—be it vitamins, fat, fiber, calories, or protein.

Evaluating Dietary Protein

To make protein, cells must have 20 kinds of amino acids. We can't make 9 of these, so we must get them in our diet. We also get the other 11 amino acids, or the material to make them, in our diet. For example, the amino acid alanine isn't needed in the diet. We can make it by taking the amino ($-NH_2$) off of an "extra" amino acid and adding it to the pyruvate made from glucose (Chap. 9).

Foods are evaluated for protein in two ways: (1) **Quality**: Is the food's content of amino acids similar to what we need? Proteins have different amounts of each amino acid. Corn protein, for example, has a lot of the amino acid leucine and very little tryptophan, compared to what we need. (2) **Amount**: How much **protein** is in the food?

Table 11-1: The 20 Kinds of Amino Acids Needed to Make Protein

9 Amino Acids Essential in the Diet:		
Histidine	Lysine	Threonine
Isoleucine	Methionine	Tryptophan
Leucine	Phenylalanine	Valine
11 Amino Acids Not Essential in the Diet (we can make these):		
Alanine	Cysteine	Proline
Arginine	Glutamate*	Serine
Asparagine	Glutamine	Tyrosine
Aspartate*		Glycine
*Aspartate and glutamate are also called aspartic acid and glutamic acid.		

Protein Quality

High-quality protein has an amino acid content that closely matches what we need. Animal foods generally have higher quality protein, e.g., the amino acid make-up of chicken meat is more in line with what we need. Other factors affect quality but are relatively minor. For example, a poorly digested food means a lower-quality protein, but we usually eat food in forms that are almost completely digested—we eat beans cooked, not raw.

Amino Acid Content

Virtually all proteins have all 20 amino acids*—the *standard 20* needed to make protein (Table 11-1). Any other amino acid in a protein is created <u>after</u> the protein is made on a ribosome (see Chap. 10). For example, the amino acid hydroxyproline is made by adding "a hydroxy" (-OH) to proline in collagen.†

Hydroxyproline can't be used to make protein; there isn't a genetic code for it, as there is for proline. Cells can use only the *standard 20,* no more or no less, to build muscle protein or any other protein, although ads for supplements may tout: *has 24 amino acids!*

Since we can make 11 of the 20, evaluation of amino acid content focuses on the other 9 (Table 11-1). The closer the proportions of the 9 amino acids in a protein match our protein, the higher its quality. In other words, cannibals eat the highest quality protein. (A supplement labeled, *has 9 amino acids,* probably wouldn't sell as well as the one touting 24. It might sell better if it were labeled, *has only the 9 amino acids required in the diet!*)

Among plant proteins, soybean is near the top in quality, and wheat and corn near the bottom. As shown in Figure 11-1, the content of essential amino acids in corn isn't a very good match to what we need.

Egg protein is the gold standard by which other proteins are measured. Protein in a hen's egg is evenly divided between white and yolk. (Eggs have only a small amount of carbohydrate; all of the fat, cholesterol, iron, and carotene/vitamin A is in the yolk.) The high quality of egg protein isn't surprising. After all, the egg represents the compact package of nutrients needed to make a bird!

Looking at an egg this way, it's no wonder that it's rich in cholesterol. It takes a lot of cells to form a chick, and cholesterol is an essential part of cell membranes. Cholesterol is a fancy molecule (Fig. 5-2), and making it takes a lot of energy. There isn't space to store much energy in an egg, so it makes sense to have a lot of ready-made cholesterol—and the correct amino acids in the right amounts.

---

*One that doesn't have all 20 is [the protein powder] gelatin. You may not want to know that that the gelatin used to make chiffon pie, Jell-O, etc., is usually extracted from [the collagen in] pig skin.

†Collagen is a protein that's abundant in animal tissue. Vitamin C is required to convert proline to hydroxyproline, making the collagen more stable. Many of the symptoms of the vitamin-C-deficiency disease scurvy (bleeding gums, etc.; see Chap. 1) are due to the instability of collagen in tissues.

Figure 11-1: Relative Proportions of Essential Amino Acids in Egg and Corn Protein

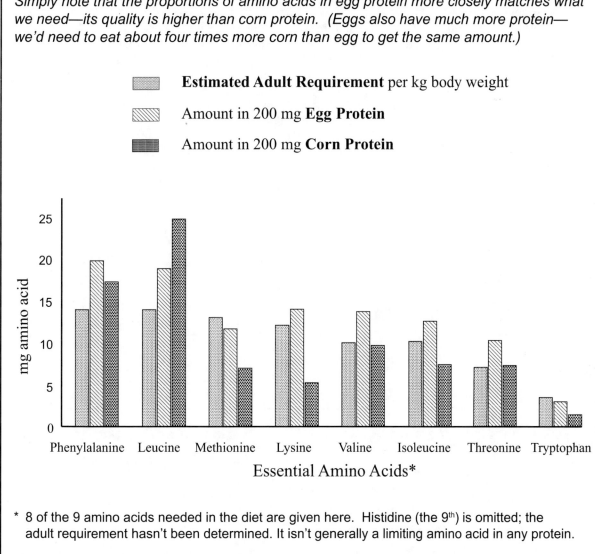

Simply note that the proportions of amino acids in egg protein more closely matches what we need—its quality is higher than corn protein. (Eggs also have much more protein—we'd need to eat about four times more corn than egg to get the same amount.)

Estimated Adult Requirement per kg body weight

Amount in 200 mg **Egg Protein**

Amount in 200 mg **Corn Protein**

* 8 of the 9 amino acids needed in the diet are given here. Histidine (the 9th) is omitted; the adult requirement hasn't been determined. It isn't generally a limiting amino acid in any protein.

Limiting Amino Acid

Since all 20 amino acids are needed to make protein, protein synthesis can't continue if even one is lacking (Fig. 11-2). One amino acid can't substitute for another. For example, lysine is the limiting amino acid in corn (Fig. 11-1). It's present in the lowest amount relative to our need, so it limits how much protein our cells can make from the amino acids in corn.

Complementing Proteins

Keep in mind that the above comparisons of protein quality are for single kinds of protein. In reality, we eat meals—a mix of proteins. The quality of plant proteins is enhanced when those with different limiting amino acids are eaten together (Fig. 11-2). An amino acid deficit of one protein is offset by the amino acid content of a different, complementary protein. This is what's meant by complementing proteins.

Many people throughout history have been vegetarians by circumstance, so it isn't surprising that plant foods have been combined "properly" long before the existence of amino acids was known. Lysine is the limiting amino acid in grain (e.g., corn, wheat, rice, oats, barley), whereas methionine is usually the limiting amino acid in legumes (e.g., soy, lima, garbanzo, pinto, kidney

Figure 11-2: Combining Proteins with Different Limiting Amino Acids

The letters represent amino acids. **R** represents the limiting amino acid (the one in short-est supply) in peanuts—**Mr. Peanut**. **T** is the limiting one in wheat—**Ms. Bread**. In making protein (spelling peanut), Mr. Peanut can make only one; the same for Ms. Bread. Joining forces (peanut butter sandwich), improves protein quality (they can spell protein 5 times).

beans—and peanuts, which are really legumes, not nuts).

Grain and legumes have different limiting amino acids, so eating them together provides higher quality protein. Grains are high methionine, low lysine.* Legumes are low methionine, high lysine. Grain-legume combos include tortillas and beans, falafel (chickpeas/garbanzo beans in pita bread), baked beans and bread, tofu (soybean curd) and rice, and a peanut butter sandwich. Also, there's nuts and seeds (e.g., sesame, pumpkin, sunflower) eaten with grains (e.g., stir-fried vegetables and cashew nuts over rice). Legumes and seeds also are a good mix, as in the Middle Eastern dish *hummus*, a chick pea-sesame seed combo. In a modern twist, Japanese scientists envision genetically complementing soy and rice proteins—inserting the gene for soybean protein into rice's DNA.

Amount of Dietary Protein

Besides essential amino acids, we need protein, in general. Now we're looking at the amount of protein, rather than its amino acid content (quality). Amount and quality are related—foods with the highest quality protein tend to have the most protein. Cooked lean beef, chicken, and fish are about 30% protein by weight, cooked soy-beans about 10%, and cooked grains like rice, pasta, oatmeal, about 5% or less.

Protein Requirements

How much protein do we need? We need to replace normal losses (maintain body tissues). For this, the need is based on normal body weight, with adjustments, if need be, for inadequate calories and for the dietary source of the protein. Children and pregnant or nursing women need additional protein. They're either adding body

*Lysine is sold as a feed additive. It's the limiting amino acid in grain, so adding it to the grain fed to animals improves growth (more meat for the same amount of feed). It's big business. In 1998, two former Archer-Daniels Midland Co. executives were indicted for criminal price-fixing of lysine.

tissue or "exporting" protein in breast milk. Some amino acids are required for purposes other than making protein, e.g., tryptophan is used to make the neurotransmitter serotonin (Chap. 15), but the amounts needed are small and are covered by a normal diet that meets protein requirements.

Effect of Inadequate Calories

Meeting energy needs is a higher priority for the body than meeting protein needs. If a diet is deficient in calories, the body "burns" amino acids for its calories, rather than use them to make protein. In other words, if we don't get enough calories, we need more protein because some of the protein is diverted for energy production (Chap. 9).

Low calories and low protein go hand-in-hand in many developing countries. Protein deficiency is made much worse by a calorie deficit. This creates a dilemma. Should the recommended protein intake be based on the average intake of calories, which is often inadequate, or should it be lower as if calories were adequate? (This isn't of much concern in this country, where diets are usually sufficient or excessive in calories and we have the luxury of recommending nutrients in amounts well above a minimum.)

As noted in Chapter 4, this is an important question because recommendations for protein intake are used in deciding food policies, and are used by other countries and world health organizations in providing aid. Protein-rich food (e.g., meat, egg, milk) costs much more than carbohydrate-rich food (e.g., rice, corn). Using protein-rich food to provide calories is an inefficient use of resources. When resources are limited, providing the least expensive form of calories must be considered along with providing adequate protein.

Effect of Dietary Source of Protein

Protein recommendations are higher when protein comes exclusively from plants. More is needed because of lower digestibility and quality. Proteins in whole grains, beans, and vegetables are about 80-85% digested, whereas animal proteins are about 95% digested. This difference is significant in diets with marginal amounts of protein.

When protein quality is low, extra protein is needed to provide adequate amounts of the essential amino acids. In Figure 11-2, the letter *T* represents the limiting amino acid in bread. Since the amino acids in bread come as a "package," eating more bread to get more *T* means eating more "extra letters" as well. These extra letters represent the extra protein needed to provide enough essential amino acids.

Because of its high quality, animal protein is especially valuable to growing children. Essential amino acids are a bigger part of animal protein than plant protein. An infant's need for essential amino acids is about 45% of the total protein requirement, whereas for adults it's only about 20%. It's no coincidence that breast milk is an infant's first and best food. Mother's milk is an easily digested, rich combination of nutrients (including essential amino acids) tailor-made for a baby.

Growing children need not only high-quality protein but, as noted earlier, also a lot of protein relative to their body weight. Animal foods (e.g., milk, eggs, meat) are not only more concentrated in protein than plant foods (e.g., beans, grain), but also have more fat—concentrated sources of calories are also scarce for many of the world's children.

Recommended Dietary Allowance (RDA)

As with other nutrients, the RDA for protein is generous, with a large margin of safety to meet the needs of virtually all healthy people in the U.S. (Table 11-2). The RDA is based on the typical diet—a mix of plant and animal proteins and enough calories.

As discussed in Chapter 4, there are several sets of RDA. Infants less than 6 months old grow fast, and their RDA is the highest at 1.0 gram of protein per pound body weight. The RDA of a man (or woman who isn't pregnant or nursing) is 0.36 g/lb. For perspective, the RDA for a 150-lb adult is 54 g protein. A McDonald's meal of a Big Mac, small fries, and a shake has about 40 g protein (and about 1100 calories).

The amount of protein in the typical American

Table 11-2: Recommended Dietary Allowance (RDA) for Protein

	Age	**RDA**
	years	g/lb*
Male and Female	0-0.5	1.00
	0.5-1	0.73
	1-3	0.55
	4-6	0.50
	7-14	0.45
Males	15-18	0.41
	19 and over	0.36
Females**	15 and over	0.36

* Grams protein per pound normal body weight per day, based on protein needs and composite quality of protein in the U.S. diet, e.g., RDA for a 150-lb adult is 54 g (150 X 0.36 = 54). For a rough estimate of adult RDA, divide normal body weight by 3. Recommended 25% more for **strict vegetarians** (plant foods only), e.g., if RDA is 40 g, add 10 g more.

During pregnancy, RDA is 10 g more. When **nursing, it's 15 g more for the first 6 months, 12 g more for the second 6 months.

diet is much higher than the RDA. So much so, in fact, that a dietary recommendation is to keep it from exceeding twice the RDA (Chap. 4). We eat a lot of meat and dairy products. Also, animal proteins are part of many of our favorite foods. Eggs are in cookies, cake, and pecan and lemon pie. We add milk or milk products to many foods —sour cream on baked potatoes, cream in coffee, milk in pumpkin pie with whipped cream on top, ice cream above split bananas and below hot fudge, milk over our cereal, cheese on pizza and in burritos.

Protein Requirements of Athletes

Do athletes need more protein? Yes and no. Yes, when they're building muscle or if their athletic endeavors make them sweat profusely (some nitrogen is lost in sweat, which protein in the diet replaces). No, they typically don't need

more. Chances are, their diet already provides much more than they need. Not only is the typical American diet high in protein, but athletes eat a lot more food to meet their higher calorie needs. When people eat more, they take in more of all nutrients, protein included.

Whatever more an athlete needs, it isn't much. Protein RDA even for fast-growing and active teenage boys (age 15-18) is only 0.41 g/lb (vs. 0.36 g/lb for a grown man). As stated by the RDA committee, "In view of the margin of safety in the RDA, no increment is added for work or training." In other words, the RDA is generous enough to cover any added protein needs of athletes. Keep in mind that protein itself isn't the best source of energy (Chap. 9). Carbohydrate is a better and less expensive source.*

Believing that something helps, even if it doesn't, has great psychological value. Many athletes take expensive amino acid supplements in hopes of increasing their athletic prowess. *Free amino acids* have more allure than *ordinary protein,* although ordinary protein is rapidly broken down to amino acids in the digestive tract.

Use of amino acid supplements by athletes is relatively new, so long-term effects, if any, aren't known. Excessive protein (amino acids) does increase water loss through urine, which can raise the risk of dehydration. People taking amino acid supplements should keep in mind that fat-free sources of protein foods like cooked egg whites† and nonfat milk are much cheaper and more likely to have a more balanced amino acid

---

*Carbohydrate, unlike protein, doesn't carry the liability of aminos (this liability will be discussed shortly), and, unlike fat, it isn't wholly dependent on oxygen for energy production.

†Routinely eating lots of raw egg whites (e.g., 8 raw eggs a day "a la Rocky the boxer") can cause a biotin (a B-vitamin) deficiency. Avidin, a protein in egg white, binds to biotin in food and keeps biotin from being absorbed. This doesn't happen with cooked egg whites; heat inactivates (denatures) avidin. Before biotin was identified, it was described as a dietary factor protective against raw-egg-white injury in rats.

content (although sometimes the supplements are simply "pre-digested" egg or milk protein).

Protein Deficiency

Protein deficiency is common in populations that don't have rich sources of protein (e.g., meat, eggs, or legumes). When there are only very dilute sources, it's hard to get enough, even if there's plenty of food. Diets that consist entirely of low-protein plant foods can meet calorie needs without meeting protein needs.

Protein and calorie deficiencies commonly occur together. Without enough calories, amino acids are used for energy instead of being used to make protein. When adults are protein deficient, they look emaciated from a loss of body tissue— there isn't enough protein to maintain it. Protein deficiency is much more serious in children.

The most striking result in young children is growth retardation. There isn't enough protein to sustain growth, and children don't grow to their genetic potential. Because bigger bodies need more protein, stunted growth is a form of environmental adaptation—smaller people need less protein (and fewer calories). If the diet improves dramatically (e.g., moving to a more developed country), the next generation often grows dramatically taller— an adaptation to a more bountiful environment.

Severe protein deficiency hampers the synthesis of a wide variety of proteins. For example, less albumin (a protein in blood-plasma; Chap. 7) is made. Albumin holds water (like all our proteins) and is important in fluid balance. When albumin is too low, some of the fluid normally held in plasma by albumin, flows out of blood vessels into surrounding tissue. As a result, the tissue swells (edema), and the child looks "puffy," especially in the face and belly.

The children also tend to be anemic (hemoglobin is a protein) and prone to infection (antibodies are protein). If their hair is normally black, it may have light bands of orange, because they can't make enough pigment to darken it (the pigment melanin is made from the amino

acid tyrosine). Brain growth is also hampered, often starting before birth with a malnourished mother. To make matters worse, protein-calorie malnutrition is often complicated by other nutrient deficiencies and by infectious diseases.

Breast-feeding is extremely important in developing countries where malnutrition and poor sanitation are common. Breast milk often is the only regular source of high-quality protein (and other essential nutrients) available to an infant. Infants often develop protein-calorie malnutrition when displaced at the breast by a newborn sibling. When a nursing mother is malnourished, she makes less milk, but the milk she does make is fairly normal in composition.

Aggressive marketing of infant formula in developing countries has come under attack for good reason. Mothers everywhere want their children to be as healthy and happy as those pictured in the ads. When poverty-stricken mothers are given free samples of infant formula, they can't afford to buy more. Meanwhile, if they stopped breast-feeding while using the free samples, their milk production may have stopped.

To make matters worse, the mothers often greatly over-dilute the formula (thus diluting the nutrients) to make it go further. Unsanitary water added to the formula can cause diarrhea, a major cause of infant death in these countries. Sometimes, when the formula is gone (or there was none to begin with), liquids of poor nutritional quality that look like milk (e.g., rice water) are used in the baby bottle. World health organizations are doing what they can to encourage breast-feeding in developing countries.

Excess Dietary Protein

What happens to excess amino acids when you eat more protein than you need? Amino acids themselves aren't stored in the body. The amino part ($-NH_2$) comes off, and what remains must be dispensed with. It can, for example, be used for ATP production or stored as fat (Fig. 9-2, 9-3).

The amino ($-NH_2$) that's taken off is a liability. It can be converted to ammonia (NH_3), which is toxic even in fairly low concentrations. To prevent this toxic effect, aminos are used to make urea* (NH_2-CO-NH_2), which can be tolerated at much higher levels. The urea is excreted in the urine. (We, of course, make urea even without excessive protein intake, since body proteins are continually broken down and replenished. This replenishment is provided for in our protein requirement.)

Urea excretion requires water, so we make more urine (*urinate more*) when we eat excessive amounts of protein. So eating a lot of protein raises the body's need for water (and we feel more thirsty). Chronically excessive protein (or amino acid supplement) intake may possibly be damaging to the kidneys. This has been shown in animal experiments, but whether this is a cause for concern in humans is uncertain.

Interestingly, not all animals use urea to get rid of aminos. Birds make uric acid instead. Unhatched chicks are stuck inside an egg, so they can't get rid of urea. Mother hens can't "urinate" for them (as our mothers did for us). Unlike urea, uric acid forms crystals at low concentrations.†

This "removes" it from the liquid surrounding the developing chick. (Similarly, you can take sugar out of sugar-water by getting the sugar to crystallize.)

Freshwater fish don't need to make urea or uric acid. They can get rid of their excess aminos directly as ammonia. It's diluted to low, harmless concentrations by the vast amount of water that surrounds the fish.

Moderation in Protein Intake

Populations at both ends of the spectrum of protein intake—those deficient and those with an overabundance—can benefit from a change. Foods rich in high-quality protein are often rich in saturated fats and cholesterol and are high in calories. Meat, milk, and egg also have no fiber. The typical American diet can generally be improved by smaller amounts of foods high in fat and calories, whereas these foods can "cure" malnutrition in impoverished countries.

Grains, vegetables, and fruit are lower in protein (in amount and quality), cholesterol-free, usually low in fat and calories, and rich in fiber (Table 11-3). As discussed in earlier chapters, the typical American diet can be improved by more of these foods. In contrast, much of the malnutrition in developing countries stems from diets with only these foods.

Many native diets are traditionally moderate in protein. Animal foods are not the center of the meal,

"Of course he was cut down in his prime. Don't you get it? We're all cut down in our prime."

---

*Urea is made mostly in the liver. A diseased liver (e.g., cirrhosis) can have trouble making urea. The resulting rise in ammonia is thought to play a role in the personality changes, impaired consciousness, and coma that can occur with severe liver disease. Alcohol abuse is the major cause of cirrhosis in this country. In parts of Asia and Africa, chronic infection with hepatitis-B virus is the major cause.

†Humans make some uric acid. In gout, uric acid crystals form in and near joints and tendons because of high uric acid. The crystals cause pain and disability. About 95% of people with gout are men. Uric acid levels are lower in premenopausal women; levels rise after menopause.

Table 11-3: Calories, Protein, Fat, Fiber in Food

	Calories	Protein*	Fat*	Fiber*
Animal foods:				
3 oz grilled hamburger patty	245	20	18	0
3 oz grilled chicken breast	135	25	3	0
3 oz tuna, canned in water	100	22	1	0
1 ½ (3 oz) frankfurters	285	10	26	0
2 boiled eggs	150	12	10	0
1 cup low-fat (2%) milk	120	8	5	0
1 cup low-fat yogurt	145	12	4	0
1 cup ice cream	265	5	15	0
1-oz slice cheddar cheese	115	7	9	0
McDonald's Big Mac	560	26	31	3
Slice of small pepperoni pizza	210	10	10	1
2-oz Snickers candy bar	275	5	14	1
Plant foods:†				
1 cup cooked soybeans**	310	30	16	11
1 cup cooked pinto beans**	195	12	1	14
1 cup cooked oatmeal	145	6	2	4
1 cup cooked brown rice	215	5	2	4
1 cup cooked cassava††	195	6	0	2
1 cup cooked carrots	70	2	0	5
1 cup cooked zucchini	40	2	0	3
1 baked potato	135	3	0	3
1 bagel	150	6	1	1
1 banana	105	1	1	3
1 apple	80	0	0	4
¼ cup peanut butter**	380	16	32	4

* Protein fat, and fiber are in grams. For perspective, the protein RDA for a 150-lb man or woman is 54 grams.

† Calories in low-fat plant food vary mostly by water content.

** Soybeans pinto beans, and peanuts are legumes, which are high-protein plant foods.

†† Cassava (manioc) is a staple food in some tropical countries; most Americans eat it only as the tapioca in tapioca pudding.

We too can eat meals that are moderate in protein by having smaller portions of meat (e.g., thinner hamburger patties in thicker buns) or "diluting" our meat course with other foods (e.g., barbecued spareribs served with many side dishes such as bread, baked beans, rice, green salad, corn-on-the-cob, fruit salad, relish tray, so we eat fewer spareribs).

Environmental concerns are another good reason to eat less meat. Most of our meat is mass produced, which affects water supply. It's been estimated that it takes 7000 pounds of water to grow the 7 pounds of feed grain it takes to produce 1 pound of beef. Cattle ranches and hog farms also produce huge amounts of waste—and foul odors—that can make life miserable and contaminate drinking water of people living nearby. Eating less meat—eating more foods lower on the food chain instead—benefits both our health and the environment.

as they are in the American diet. Rather, they're often just an ingredient in the main course—Chinese stir-fried broccoli with shrimp, the dish from India of lentils and vegetables mixed with small cubes of cheese, and the Middle Eastern dish of couscous (crushed grain) topped with vegetables mixed with meat.

Vegetarian Diets

As noted earlier, many of the vegetarians throughout the world aren't vegetarians by choice. They would eat animal food if it were available and/or affordable. They suffer from the many ills of poverty, and their strictly vegetarian diet typically is a poor one.

In this country, most vegetarians are among the more affluent, and have a readily available variety of food rich in protein (e.g., beans) and calories (e.g., nuts, salad oils). Moreover, many are lacto-ovo-vegetarians (include milk and egg) rather than vegans (plant food only). Milk and egg are not only rich sources of high-quality protein, but have other important nutrients, e.g., milk is a good source of the B-vitamin riboflavin, which is often low in strictly vegetarian diets.

The RDA for protein assumes a mixed diet of plant and animal foods. So for the vegan, the recommended intake is about 25% higher. For adults, combining proteins can be rather casual, e.g., tortillas at lunch and beans at dinner. But young children should combine plant proteins at the same meal. They have a greater need for high-quality protein.

As long as vegan diets include a variety of nutritious foods and are adequate in calories, protein generally isn't a nutritional concern. But some other nutrients tend to be low. As discussed in Chapter 7, vitamin B_{12} can be lacking, since it's found naturally only in animal foods. Vegans can meet their needs by eating foods like B_{12}-fortified soy milk and fortified cereal, or by taking a vitamin pill.

Two other vitamins —riboflavin and vitamin D—tend to be low in vegans, since dairy foods are the main source in the American diet. For riboflavin, vegans should include lots of dark-green leafy vegetables and whole or enriched grains. Vitamin D isn't found in plant foods, but it isn't needed in the diet if the body makes enough through adequate skin exposure to sunshine. Riboflavin and vitamin D are also found in fortified cereals and can be taken as vitamin pills.

Vegan diets tend to be low in calcium, iron, and zinc. One problem can be the form of the mineral. For example, non-heme iron is poorly absorbed as compared to heme iron (Chap. 7), and iron in plant foods is non-heme iron. Also, high-fiber diets can hamper mineral absorption. For example, whole grains have phytic acid, and spinach and sesame seeds have oxalic acid. Both of these acids bind minerals and impede their absorption.

Good non-animal sources of calcium include fortified soy milk and soybean curd (tofu) processed with calcium sulfate. Iron in the diet can be increased by cooking (acid foods especially) in iron cookware and eating fortified cereals. Eating vitamin C-rich foods in the same meal increases

"Tit for tat, I suppose. He was a vegetarian."

the amount of iron absorbed from plant foods. Plant sources of zinc include legumes, whole grains, nuts, and tofu.

Strictly vegetarian diets can be nutritious when one is knowledgeable about nutrition and foods. People who choose to become vegans as adults (or choose this for their young children) need to take the time and care to acquire and use this knowledge. Pregnant or nursing women must take extra-special care to see that they meet their nutrient needs.

Infants born of vegan mothers and fed only their mother's breast milk have suffered nerve damage from B_{12} deficiency (Chap. 7). Some children on vegan diets have developed bone deformations from vitamin D deficiency.

Infants and toddlers are at higher risk of developing nutrient deficiencies on vegan diets for many of the same reasons given for protein and calorie deficiencies in developing countries. They need more calories and nutrients, including protein, in proportion to their body weight, and need higher-quality protein. Growth retardation is often the first sign of malnutrition.

Lacto- and lacto-ovo-vegetarian diets are generally adequate in nutrients, except for iron and zinc. Milk is a good source of B_{12}, riboflavin, and calcium, and is usually fortified with vitamin D. But milk and eggs are low in iron and zinc.

Good diets of all kinds tend to be those that include a variety of foods. Vegetarian diets exclude an entire group of food, so variety is all the more important. Vegetarian diets can be very healthy—but not necessarily. Some people eat a lot of cheese pizzas, ice cream, soft drinks, french fries, pastries, candy, etc., and call themselves vegetarians because they don't eat meat. There are more than a few "vegetarians" who don't like vegetables!

Summary

We need 20 kinds of amino acids to make protein. Our bodies can make 11 of them; the other 9 must come from the diet. An evaluation of dietary protein focuses on the quality and amount of protein in the diet. Protein quality focuses on the 9 amino acids essential in the diet, and is based on how closely the proportion of these amino acids matches that needed by the body. Animal protein is generally the highest in quality, with egg protein as the gold standard. Also, animal foods generally have more protein than do plant foods.

Relative to our own needs, a plant protein is low in one of the essential amino acids. This "low" amino acid is called a limiting amino acid, because its relative scarcity limits our ability to make our own proteins. This limitation can be overcome by complementing proteins, which simply means eating, together, plant proteins that have a different limiting amino acid. For example, strict vegetarians (vegans) can improve the quality of the protein in their diet by eating grains and legumes together.

The body also needs a certain amount of protein for normal growth and maintenance of body tissues. The amount an individual needs varies with several factors, but the most important ones are whether the person is growing and how big he or she is in terms of lean body mass. More protein is needed in the diet when it's from plant sources because of its lower quality and because plant foods are a bit less digestible. For these reasons, vegans are advised to add 25% to the "regular" protein RDA.

Extra amino acids aren't stored by the body. Instead, the amino part comes off, and the rest of the molecule goes for ATP production or for storage as fat. To avoid accumulating the discarded aminos as toxic ammonia, the body makes urea, which is excreted in the urine. A large excess of dietary protein means making lots of urea. This can have a dehydrating effect, since water is lost in getting rid of urea through the urine.

Protein deficiency is most common in infants and children in developing countries. Compared to adults, they need higher-quality protein and more protein per body weight, because of their fast growth. Animal foods are scarce in these countries. Even when people in these countries get enough calories, they may not get enough protein, simply because their foods are so "dilute" in protein.

Often, protein and calorie deficiencies occur together, which makes protein deficiency even worse. When calorie needs aren't met, the body uses some of the dietary protein as a source of calories, rather than using it to meet protein needs. The effects of protein-calorie malnutrition include stunted growth, anemia, and impaired immunity.

World health organizations encourage mothers in developing countries to breast-feed. A malnourished mother makes less milk, but the milk she does make has high-quality protein, and is the best food for her child. For many of these children, breast-feeding is the difference between health and sickness or death. Aggressive marketing of infant formula in these countries has been heavily criticized.

In marked contrast to that in developing countries, the typical American diet includes an abundance of high-quality protein, because it's so rich in animal foods. Such a diet also tends to be high in fat, cholesterol, and calories. Also, the mass production of animals uses much more fresh water than does growing a comparable amount of plant food, and the huge amount of animal waste can lower the quality of air and drinking water of those living nearby. A prudent diet is one which lies between the extremes—a diet that includes only moderate amounts of animal foods and an abundance and variety of plant foods.

Chapter 12

Cancer

Cancer is a disease of DNA.

James D. Watson, Nobel laureate, co-discoverer of DNA structure

Don't Smoke!

The Health Professions

ancer is second only to heart disease as a leading cause of death in the U.S. For those under age 65, it's our leading cause of death.

Trends in Cancer Rates

Be wary of how statistics are presented. Cancer deaths have been rising, but this is due to more lung cancer and more old people (cancer is more common in older people). Cancer rates must be age-adjusted when comparing one time period with another, just as prices are adjusted for inflation. Ideally, we would also adjust for changes in socioeconomic status, ethnic make-up, etc., but this is hard to do.

The age-adjusted cancer death rate had been rising because of lung cancer (Fig. 1-2). Excluding lung cancer, this rate has fallen over the last 60 years. Our leading cause of death from cancer is lung cancer. In 1930, it was cancer of the stomach for men, and of the uterus and stomach for women (Table 12-1).

What about occurrence rates? Are they going up? This is a harder question. Whereas all deaths

are recorded, we don't have a national office that records every occurrence of cancer.

Occurrence rates are estimates based on sample populations. Most of the data go back to only 1973, when the National Cancer Institute began a program to gather data from selected areas of the country, representing about 10-15% of our population. These limited data are the main source of information on occurrence rates, survival times, etc.

The rates are based on the number of new cases diagnosed and reported in the sample population. If you get cancer in 2009 but it isn't diagnosed until 2011, it's counted as occurring in 2011, since only the diagnosis date can be pinpointed. If it isn't diagnosed or reported, it isn't counted at all. Thus, there can seem to be changes in occurrence when, in fact, the changes are related to diagnosis, e.g., when former First Lady Betty Ford got breast cancer, women became more aware of it, more got checked, and more were diagnosed that year.

Likewise, when screening is promoted or when new tests detect cancer earlier, the rate will seem to rise, and cancer will seem to be occurring at a younger age.

Table 12-1: Cancer Death Rates in 1930-2007

Cancer Deaths/100,000 males or females, age-adjusted to the population in 2000.			
	1930	**1960**	**1990**	**2007**
Males				
Lung & Bronchus	4	44	90	66
Prostate	18	29	39	24
Colon & Rectum	23	33	31	21
Stomach	46	22	9	5
Females				
Lung & Bronchus	3	7	37	40
Breast	30	31	33	23
Colon & Rectum	27	29	21	14
Uterus	36	19	7	6
Stomach	35	12	4	3

American Cancer Society: Cancer Facts and Figures - 2011

Brain tumors now can be diagnosed by imaging techniques, raising both its reported occurrence and its listing as a cause of death. In the past, some brain tumors could be diagnosed only by going into the brain. If you died of an undiagnosed tumor and an autopsy wasn't done, the cause was often listed as a stroke (the most likely cause of death involving the brain). If a man is cured of colon cancer at age 50 and gets prostate cancer at age 70, two occurrences of cancer are counted for the one person. In contrast, death—as the saying goes—is one to a customer.

Whereas all deaths from cancer are included in cancer death rates, some highly curable cancers are excluded from some occurrence rates. For example, more non-melanoma skin cancer is diagnosed in the U.S. than the combined total of lung, colon, breast, and prostate cancer, but it usually doesn't spread and is easy to remove.

In contrast, melanoma (skin cancer from pigmented cells, e.g., mole) spreads fast. There is much less time to find and remove it. The 5-year survival is 98% if it hasn't spread, 62% if it has spread regionally, but only 16% if it has spread further. Thus, when occurrence rates are compared, *skin cancer* includes only melanoma.*

The fast rise in breast and prostate cancer diagnoses in the mid-1980s (Fig. 12-1) doesn't necessarily mean that there's been such a rise in their actual occurrence. Diagnosis rates are based on the number of people in the population, not on the number examined.

If 10 in a population of 1000 are screened for breast or prostate cancer and 1 is found to have cancer (1 diagnosis/10 screened), the diagnosis rate is 1/1000. If, the next year, 20 get screened and 2 are found to have cancer (1/10), the rate has now doubled to 2/1000 simply because 20 instead of 10 were examined. More diligent reporting, more sensitive tests, and more insurance companies paying for routine screening can also raise diagnosis rates. To get a best estimate of changes in occurrence rates, the entire population would have to be screened every year by the same method.

When breast self-exams and mammograms are promoted with increasing success, the diagnosis rate goes up, regardless of whether actual occurrence goes up. Similarly, the diagnosis of prostate cancer has gone up dramatically with the promotion of screening via prostate-specific antigen (PSA) blood tests and digital rectal exams (finger in rectum to feel the prostate gland). When new screening tests become available, those in higher socioeconomic groups usually get tested first and in greater numbers, e.g., women with more education get more mammograms. This can distort diagnosis rates.

*2011 estimates of melanoma in U.S.: 70,230 cases, 8,790 deaths. Melanoma has been rising for 30+ years in young, fair-skinned adults. It seemed for awhile to stop rising, but this was because insurance began providing more coverage when it was treated outside a hospital—more cases treated this way and fewer reports of melanoma. When this underreporting was corrected, the occurrence rate continued its upward course.

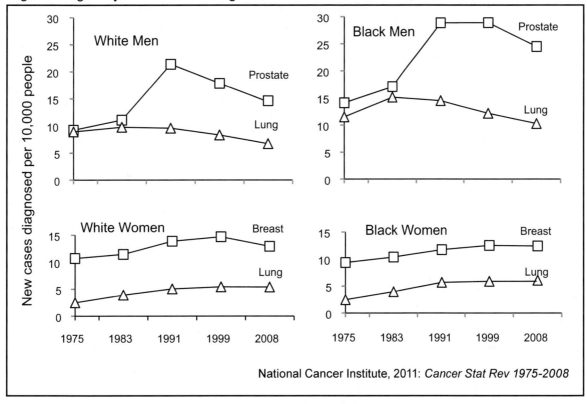

Fig 12-1: Age-Adjusted Cancer Diagnosis Rates 1975-2008

National Cancer Institute, 2011: *Cancer Stat Rev 1975-2008*

Current Cancer Statistics

Death Rates

In the U.S., **lung cancer is the most common cause of death from cancer** in both men and women (Tables 12-1, Table 12-2, Fig. 12-2). It's responsible for about 1 of 3 cancer deaths in men and 1 of 4 in women.

In looking at deaths from various causes, keep in mind that if we don't die of one thing, we eventually die of something else. If fewer die of heart attacks, other causes fill the gap. Prostate cancer is very common in elderly men. The longer a man lives, the more likely he is to get it. Fewer middle-aged men dying of heart attacks is partly responsible for more men (middle-aged men living longer) dying of prostate cancer.

Diagnosis Rates

In men, cancer is diagnosed most often in the prostate gland; in women, the breast. Lung is next (Table 12-2, Fig. 12-3). Note that death rates for lung cancer are much higher than diagnosis rates

(Table 12-2). More women get breast cancer, but more die of lung cancer. Only 16% of all lung cancer patients live five or more years after diagnosis because only 15% of lung cancers are found before they have spread. In contrast, breast cancer is detected much earlier, and the survival and cure rates are much higher; when found before it has spread, 5-year survival is 98%.

Figures 12-2 and 12-3 show how cancer rates differ by age, gender, and race. The 2002-2006 U.S. cancer deaths for Hispanic males were highest for lung—22% of their cancer deaths, prostate 13%, colon 10%; Hispanic females were highest for breast 15%, lung 14%, colon 10%. For Asian-Americans, males were highest for lung 27%, liver 11%, colon 10%; females were highest for lung 19%, breast 13%, colon 11%

We get hints of what causes cancer and how to prevent it by comparing people from different countries (Fig. 12-4), occupations, etc. An 18th century London doctor Percival Pott noted that chimney sweeps (boys who clean chimneys) tended to get nasal and scrotum cancer. He postulated that

Figure 12-2: Cancer Death Rates (2003-2007) Ages 30-69

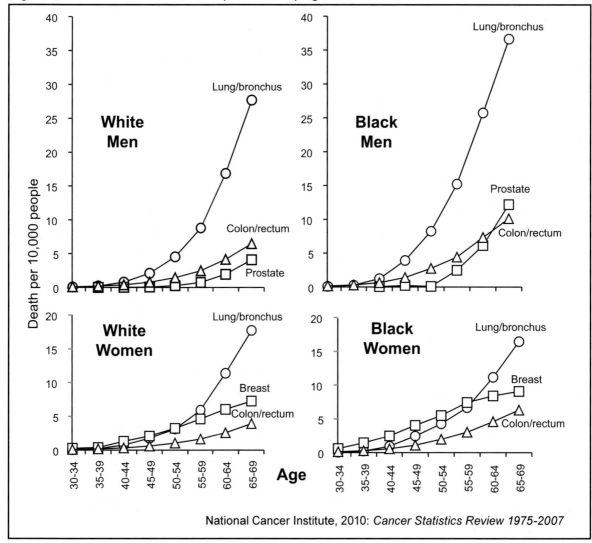

National Cancer Institute, 2010: *Cancer Statistics Review 1975-2007*

there was a cancer-causing substance in soot. A chimney sweep worked naked and not only got soot in his nose but "accumulated soot on the scrotum." There was no proof that the soot caused the cancer, but the limited information was enough to recommend ways to prevent it.

Scientists noted that nuns have less cervical cancer and more breast cancer and looked for causes related to ways in which nuns differ from other women. We know now that a sexually transmitted virus can cause cervical cancer, and that hormonal changes of childbearing lower the risk of breast cancer. Scientists have used this information to develop a vaccine to prevent cervical cancer, and to look for drugs to lower the risk of breast cancer, e.g., birth control pills that also help prevent breast cancer.

Biology of Cancer

Cancer is an uncontrolled growth of cells that can lead to death. Cancer can invade surrounding tissue and spread to vital organs. A tumor (*an abnormal growth of cells that forms a lump*) that spreads is called malignant (*evil*). The word *cancer* comes from the Latin word meaning *crab*—its threatening claws extended outwards. Benign (*good*) tumors don't have this capacity to spread.

What makes a cell suddenly divide wildly and invade other tissues? From basic research into how normal cells work, genes that control cell growth have been identified. Mutations in several such genes may be needed for cancer to develop, causing a cell to grow out of control—like a car

Table 12-2: 2011 Estimated Cancers

	% of All Cancers in Males		% of All Cancers in Females	
	Deaths	Diagnoses*	Deaths	Diagnoses*
Lung/bronchus	28	14	26	14
Breast	<1	<1	15	30
Prostate	11	29	-	-
Colon/rectum	8	9	9	9
Pancreas	6	3	7	3
Ovary	-	-	6	3
Lymphoma	3	4	4	4
Leukemia	4	3	3	2
Uterus	-	-	3	6
Bladder	4	6	2	2
Kidney	3	5	2	3
Liver	4	2	2	1
Melanoma	2	5	1	4

*New cases diagnosed

American Cancer Society: *Cancer Facts & Figures - 2011*

when the accelerator is stuck or the brakes are gone. Substances that cause these mutations are called **carcinogens.**

How cancer develops is very complex. Some examples:

• Carcinogens have to reach a cell's DNA to do damage. A cell's sturdiness can make a difference. Irritating or damaging a tissue can make it more vulnerable, e.g., drinking an excess of alcohol raises the risk of cancer in the esophagus and liver. Also, when tissues are damaged, cells usually divide to replace the damaged cells. More cell division means more chances for mutations from DNA-copying errors (Chap. 10).

Other features of cells affect whether a cancer-causing agent can reach the DNA. Skin cancer is rare in Blacks because their skin has so much melanin, a brown/black pigment. Melanin is a natural sunblock that absorbs the ultraviolet light that can damage DNA (genetic differences in skin color vary with exposure to ultraviolet radiation in sunlight during evolution—more exposure/darker skin). *Getting a suntan* is a protective response—skin makes more mela-

nin to protect its DNA. Albinos can't make melanin and are very vulnerable to skin cancer. Melanoma is a cancer of melanin-making cells.

• If a cell's DNA *has* been made cancerous by a carcinogen, it won't "become cancer" if the damage is repaired or the cell is destroyed. Cells routinely repair DNA damage, but repair processes can be defective or overwhelmed. People with the genetic disease *xeroderma pigmentosum* ("no pigment in skin") lack the protective melanin in their skin plus defective DNA repair, making them very susceptible to skin cancer. Many die before age 30 from its spread. Defects in DNA repair have also been implicated in more common cancers (e.g., some forms of colon cancer).

Our immune system routinely destroys damaged cells. So, a deficient immune system makes us more susceptible to cancer, as happens in AIDS (Acquired *Immunodeficiency* Syndrome) or in taking immunosuppressive drugs to prevent rejection of an organ transplant. We probably "get cancer" often, but develop it only occasionally. Although we accumulate more mutations as we get older, cancer is more common in the elderly partly because many body systems—immune system included—deteriorate in old age.

• Some viruses can cause cancer. The first one shown to cause cancer was one that causes tumors in chickens. Peyton Rous won the Nobel prize in 1966 for this discovery. A retrovirus (Chap. 10) could carry a cancer-causing gene and insert it into a cell's DNA. One such retrovirus causes a rare form of leukemia, and is similar in many ways to HIV (also a retrovirus). Human papillomavirus, which isn't a retrovirus, is sexually transmitted and can cause cervical cancer.

Figure 12-3: Cancer Diagnosis Rates (2004-2008), Ages 30-69

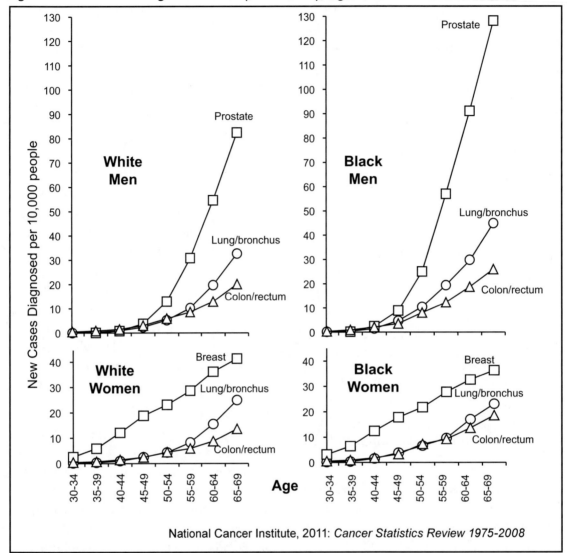

National Cancer Institute, 2011: *Cancer Statistics Review 1975-2008*

• Substances linked with cancer often can't be neatly categorized as carcinogens. Some aren't carcinogens per se, but can change into carcinogens in the body. Conversely, the body can disarm some carcinogens. Some substances are carcinogens only when paired with another substance (co-carcinogens). Some carcinogens are found in nature together with substances that protect against cancer.

Possible interactions between diet and colon cancer were discussed in Chapter 6: Dietary fat stimulates bile secretion, and some breakdown products of bile can act as carcinogens. Other substances in the diet, like calcium, can combine with some of these breakdown products and make them harmless. Different diets, encouraging growth of different bacteria in the colon, can change—for better or worse—conditions for developing colon cancer. The villains can be sly.

Assessing Risk

Causes of most cancers are very hard to pinpoint. Many environmental and genetic factors interact throughout a lifetime. As noted earlier, scientists often start by looking for links, e.g., cancer is less common among people who are physically active. If cause-and-effect relationships are plausible, scientists explore the links in laboratory experiments and clinical trials.

Fig 12-4: U.S. Cancer Death Rate vs. World Average (age standardized)

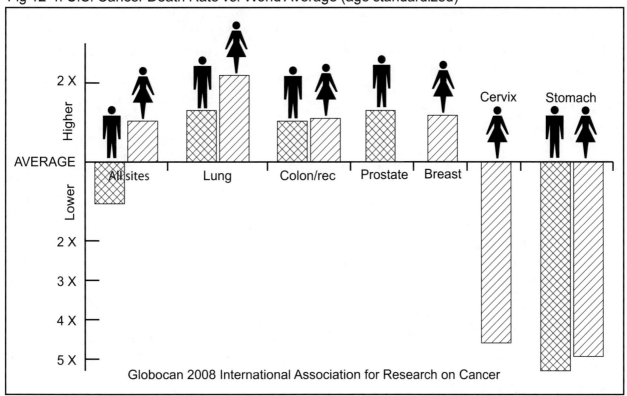

Globocan 2008 International Association for Research on Cancer

Direct Contact—Breathing, Eating, Drinking, Chewing

We'd expect eating or breathing carcinogens to have the most effect on the mouth, throat, esophagus, stomach, and lungs. There's overwhelming evidence that smoking and tobacco are the main cause of cancer at all these sites except the stomach. We might expect that dietary carcinogens cause stomach cancer. If so, counting stomach cancers might be a way to estimate the amount and potency of carcinogens in our diet.

Stomach cancer and its relationships to diet and to *H. pylori* were discussed in Chapter 4. Stomach cancer has fallen steadily in this country for decades (Table 12-1); we now have one of the lowest rates in the world (Fig 12-4).

Smoking includes not only tobacco, but marijuana (people who smoke only marijuana often don't think of themselves as smokers). Most of us know that smoking causes lung cancer, but many of us don't know that smokeless tobacco (chewing tobacco, snuff/dip) also causes cancer. Users

not only get more cancer in the mouth and throat, but become addicted to the nicotine that enters the bloodstream through the tissues in the mouth.

The Center for Disease Control and Prevention found that 1 of 6 males in 12th grade was using smokeless tobacco in 2009. An estimated one-third of professional and college baseball players use it. Its use in younger baseball players is alarming. Even chewing gum packaged in shreds to imitate chewing tobacco (*Big League Chew*) is popular among Little League players.

It's not proof of cause-and-effect, but baseball legend Babe Ruth, who drank, smoked, and was a heavy user of smokeless tobacco, died of oral cancer at age 53. Fellow Hall-of-Famer Honus Wagner was so opposed to smoking that he wouldn't give his permission to tobacco companies for a baseball card (cards had cigarette ads on the back and came in packages of cigarettes). Wagner was born 21 years before Ruth, but lived (to age 81) until 7 years after Ruth's death. One tobacco company had already started printing his cards, but most of them were successfully recalled.

Wagner's rare card is the "king of baseball cards." Hockey great Wayne Gretzky and a partner bought one in 1991 for $451,000. In 1996, it sold for $640,500. In 2007, it sold for $2.35 million.

There are many carcinogens in smoke and tobacco. For simplicity, they're grouped here into tar (the solids in smoke) and nitrosamines. Smoking is thought to cause about 90% of lung cancers in men, 80% of lung cancers in women, and 30% of all cancer deaths. Breathing smoke around smokers (secondhand smoke) can also cause lung cancer. Relative to smoking and tobacco, carcinogens in food don't cause much cancer by direct contact. But there are food substances that aren't carcinogens themselves (e.g., alcohol) but can, by direct contact, make tissue more susceptible.

• **Tar**: What carcinogens in tar and soot did to the nose and scrotum of a chimney sweep is similar to what happens in the respiratory system of smokers. The description *he smokes like a chimney* is fitting. It matters a lot, of course, what people smoke, how often and how long, if the cigarettes are filtered, etc.

Smoking 3 or 4 marijuana cigarettes is estimated to damage lungs about as much as more than 20 tobacco cigarettes. Most marijuana smokers smoke only a few, but breathe in the unfiltered smoke more deeply, in larger amounts, and hold it in longer. They also smoke the marijuana cigarette to a shorter length (less filtering by the cigarette itself).

Smoke has carcinogens; so does food prepared by smoking (e.g., smoked fish). Food cooked over a grill can also be "smoked" by smoke from dripping fat. Eating a lot of smoked food may raise the risk of cancer in the esophagus and stomach. We're advised to eat smoked food only in moderate amounts.

• **Nitrosamines** form when nitrite (NO_2) combines with substances called amines (amines are natural components of food and tobacco). Nitrosamines are very potent carcinogens in lab animals, are found in cigarette smoke and smokeless tobacco and snuff, and are thought to raise the risk of cancer in tissues they contact. Nitrosamines in food are thought to raise the risk of stomach cancer.

Most of the nitrosamines in our diet come directly or indirectly from nitrite-cured meat—bacon, frankfurters, ham, bologna, pepperoni, pastrami, sausages, corned beef, etc. Nitrite is added to preserve meat and prevent botulism, gives meat a distinctive flavor that people like, and combines with the meat's myoglobin (Chap. 9) to form nitrosomyoglobin, giving meat a distinctive red/pink color (otherwise, it

"And while 'Nature-Bran' may contain carcinogens, they're all natural carcinogens."

can look gray). Nitrosamines can form in food during cooking or in the acid conditions of the stomach. Until recently (when malting methods were modified), our main dietary source of nitrosamines was beer.

Vitamin C (*ascorbate*) is sometimes added to nitrite-cured meats to lessen nitrosamine formation. We can also do this by eating vitamin-C-rich foods at the same time as nitrite-cured meats—orange juice with breakfast bacon, bacon/lettuce/tomato sandwich, corned beef and cabbage, sausage and sauerkraut, etc. (orange juice, tomatoes, and cabbage all have vitamin C). Nitrite occurs naturally in saliva, but at much lower concentration than nitrite-cured meat. We're advised to eat vitamin-C-rich fruits and vegetables, and only moderate amounts of nitrite-cured foods.

• **Alcohol**, especially in concentrated forms like martinis, can irritate or damage tissues it contacts as it is swallowed, making them more vulnerable to cancer. It's hard to sort out direct effects of alcohol since it is consumed as beer, wine, whiskey, etc., which have other substances that might also raise risk. But there is ample evidence that alcohol (especially when combined with smoking and smokeless tobacco) raises the risk of cancer in the mouth, throat, esophagus, and stomach. The advice is that if you drink, drink in moderation.

• **Salt**: High salt intake along with eating lots of salt-cured, smoke-cured, and pickled food is linked with a higher risk of stomach cancer. It's hard to sort out specific effects of salt, since these foods may also contain nitrosamines. High salt intake can irritate and damage the stomach lining (as can *H. pylori* bacteria), and might thus raise the stomach's vulnerability to carcinogens. We're advised to eat salt and salt-cured foods only in moderation.

Cancer at Remote Sites

Once what we breathe, eat, and drink are absorbed, it's hard to track their effects. They contact cells throughout the body and can be changed by the multitude of substances they encounter. It's like trying to track quick-change artists entering the subway at rush hour.

Bladder and liver cancer aren't our biggest cancers, but many of the cancer-causing agents in what we breathe, eat, and drink have been tracked there. Like cancer of direct-contact sites discussed earlier, bladder and liver cancer can reflect carcinogens in what we ingest and inhale.

Not much is known about causes of colon, breast, and prostate cancer, but these cancers have been linked to obesity and diets that are high in fat—especially animal fat. But keep in mind that high-fat diets also tend to be high in protein and calories, and low in vegetables, fruit, and whole grains. Obesity is also more common in populations with high-fat diets. Thus, any specific effect of obesity or a dietary component is hard to pinpoint.

Proof of a link isn't proof that one causes the other, but animal studies have shown that tumors occur more often with high-fat diets, and that diets low in protein and calories suppress the development of tumors. We're advised to maintain a healthy weight and eat a diet generous in plant foods and moderate in fat and protein (Chap. 4). Exploring the intricacies of how diet affects the risk of cancer is an active area of research.

Bladder Cancer

If a water-soluble substance can't be used or broken down in the body, one of the only ways we can get rid of it is via the urine.* Any cancer-causing substance in the urine raises the risk of bladder cancer because urine is stored there. The cancer is more common in men than women. Evidence suggests that most bladder cancer in this country is caused by smoking and

---

*Analyzing urine is useful: Glucose suggests diabetes; it gets into urine when blood-glucose is abnormally high. Cotinine (a breakdown product of nicotine) is used to gauge a nonsmoker's exposure to tobacco smoke. Protein indicates a kidney problem—kidneys aren't doing their job of keeping protein out of urine.

occupational exposures to carcinogens. Smoking is the biggest risk factor; it's estimated to cause about 47% of bladder cancer deaths in men, and about 37% in women.

If smoking causes bladder cancer, why hasn't its rate gone up along with that of lung cancer? It could be that more carcinogens in urine from smoking have been offset by less carcinogens from occupational exposures and diet. The rise in lung cancer and the fall in stomach cancer have occurred together (Table 12-1).

People who work in jobs that expose them to carcinogens (e.g., making or working with dyes, rubber, and leather) have a higher risk of bladder cancer. Occupational exposures are thought to cause about 20-35 % of bladder cancers in men. Carcinogens can be absorbed through skin and lungs.

It's not known whether the artificial sweetener saccharin causes bladder cancer in humans (huge doses can cause bladder cancer in rats). If it did, we would have expected bladder cancers to rise with widespread consumption of saccharin in diet drinks, but age-adjusted occurrence and death rates have stayed quite steady. Even if saccharin does cause human bladder cancer, it would be hard to prove. This cancer is not very common, and other variables (e.g., smoking, diet) can't be controlled as in animal studies. Saccharin has no calories—we absorb it but do not have the enzymes to break it down (Chap. 3). Saccharin is left intact to be excreted in urine.

Liver Cancer

The liver is especially vulnerable to toxic substances. It is hit with high levels of dietary substances because it is the first organ the blood encounters after leaving the digestive tract (Fig. 7-1). Also, many toxins are metabolized there. It is the main organ that breaks down alcohol, and is where many substances are altered,

e.g., carcinogens are sometimes changed into innocuous substances and vice versa (recall that liver enzymes are an important part of the Ames test; Chap. 10). Many fat-soluble substances (including fat-soluble carcinogens) concentrate in the liver, e.g., it stores more than 90% of the body's vitamin A (a fat-soluble vitamin).* (Only water-soluble substances are excreted in urine.)

Excessive alcohol consumption is a major risk factor for liver cancer, especially when combined with smoking or chewing tobacco (Mickey Mantle had these combined risk factors and died of liver cancer). But in developing countries, other liver toxins play a bigger role.

Aflatoxins are potent carcinogens thought to be a major cause of liver cancer in developing countries (aflatoxins are fat-soluble and accumulate in the liver). They're made by common molds *Aspergillus flavus* and *Aspergillus parasiticus* and are natural contaminants of cottonseed, cereal grains, and peanuts, and are particularly found in improperly stored crops of peanuts and corn.

The Food and Drug Administration (FDA) has set the maximum permissible level of aflatoxin at 20 parts per billion (ppb) in our food. It's illegal to dilute a heavily contaminated batch of grain with a less contaminated batch to get below 20 ppb. As an extra measure of safety for infants and children, less is allowed in milk (0.5 ppb). Aflatoxin can get in the fat in milk, cheese, meat, etc., when contaminated grain is fed to the animals.†

Large amounts of aflatoxins have caused acute poisoning in countries like Thailand, India, Philippines, Uganda, Laos, China, and Taiwan. Places in the world where crops are heavily contaminated with aflatoxins are also places where liver cancer is common. In these areas, long-term risk of liver cancer takes a back seat to the immediate problem of food scarcity.

A complicating factor is that areas in the world where food is highly contaminated with

---

*Many people take self-prescribed vitamin A supplements. Acute symptoms of toxicity include nausea, headache, blurred vision, and peeling skin. Arctic explorers have suffered from vitamin A toxicity from just a single meal that included seal or polar bear liver (exceptionally high in A).

†In 1989, many dairies had to dump milk (e.g., 400,000 lbs by Michigan farmers) contaminated as a result of the 1988 drought-induced aflatoxin infection of corn crops in the Midwest.

aflatoxins are the same areas where infection with hepatitis B virus is common. Hepatitis B itself can cause liver cancer, particularly among those eating aflatoxin-contaminated food. It's hard to separate out the effect of aflatoxin alone. A worldwide vaccination program against hepatitis B in high-risk populations is helping prevent liver cancer, and is much more cost-effective than lessening aflatoxin contamination in developing countries.

Breast Cancer

Fewer women die of breast cancer than of heart disease or lung cancer, and breast cancer is most common in older women, but it still affects many women under age 65 (Fig. 12-3). Genetic susceptibility is thought to play a part in 10-25% of breast cancers; some of these genes have been identified. A woman's reproductive history affects her risk, presumably through the timing and duration of various female hormones.*

Breast cancer is more common in women with more education and higher socioeconomic status, presumably because they have children later and in fewer numbers, live longer (die less of other causes), and are more likely to get the regular mammograms that increase diagnoses. But their death rate from breast cancer is not higher, presumably because it is caught earlier and they have more access to medical care.

Genetic and reproductive histories don't account for the wide variation in the frequency of breast cancer throughout the world. Diet is thought to play a role. Evidence that a high-fat diet raises the risk of breast cancer comes from comparing countries (those with high-fat diets have more breast cancer), studying immigrants (increased rates with immigration from Asia and Eastern Europe—low-fat diets and low breast-cancer rates—to the U.S.), and animal studies (those fed a high-fat diet have more mammary/breast tumors).

Studies comparing Japan and the U.S. are especially noteworthy. Both countries are comparable in industrialization and good statistical record-keeping, yet have far different rates of breast cancer. Globocan 2008 gives the age-adjusted death rate (breast-cancer deaths/100,000 women) as 15 in the U.S. and 9 in Japan. If genetics were the determining factor, Japanese Americans would be expected to have rates similar to those of their racial counterparts in Japan. But they have higher rates (though not as high as Caucasian Americans), suggesting an environmental influence.

In looking at dietary links, it's hard to know if it's something in the diet or something lacking in the diet. A diet high in one thing tends to be low in something else. Also, ethnic diets vary in seasoning, methods of preparation and storage, and predominant foods. For example, substances in soybeans (prominent in the Japanese diet) might protect against breast cancer.

We do know that as Japan's diet has become more Americanized (McDonald's, Kentucky Fried Chicken, Mrs. Field's Cookies, etc.), it has become much higher in fat, and breast cancer and obesity have become more common. Rates of stomach cancer are falling simultaneously (a high-fat diet is associated with less stomach cancer).

Studies of high-fat diets and breast cancer are difficult. To get control and experimental groups that are comparable in race, religion, socioeconomic level, etc., it is often necessary to recruit women from the same population. When this is done, fat intake is often similar. Also, fat intakes assessed at the time of the study may not be as important as fat intake at a younger age, and people tend to under-report things they don't think people approve of.

Also keep in mind that breast cancer is strongly influenced by the timing and duration of female sex hormones,† and a high-fat diet

---

*Higher risk with early age of first menstruation, late menopause, no children, having the first child at an older age—all of these involve long stretches of uninterrupted, high estrogen levels. (There's also a higher risk when breasts are exposed to radiation during childhood.)

†In Japan, postmenopausal hormone replacement therapy is unusual, and birth-control pills weren't approved until 1999, when approval of Viagra (for male impotence) forced the issue.

can have indirect effects. It can raise the risk of becoming overweight, which can mean earlier onset of menstruation (a risk factor) and more estrogen (a risk factor) from more body fat.

It appears that a high-fat diet, per se, doesn't increase the risk of breast cancer, but large studies, such as a prospective study of more than 90,000 premenopausal women enrolled in the Nurses Health Study II, suggest that a high animal-fat intake in premenopausal women raises the risk of breast cancer.

Alcohol also seems to raise the risk of breast cancer. Animal studies indicate that alcohol is capable of raising the risk of cancer, in general, by increasing the activation of potential carcinogens (e.g., it raises the activity of some liver enzymes that can make some substances potentially carcinogenic) and by suppressing DNA repair (e.g., alcohol can lower the activity of an enzyme that repairs DNA damage).

Human studies also show that alcohol increases estrogen in premenopausal women and in post-menopausal women on hormone-replacement therapy. Postmenopausal women who drink moderate amounts of alcohol (about 1 drink/day) have a lower death rate than women who don't drink at all or drink excessively (a link, not proof of cause-and-effect). Heart disease rises dramatically after menopause (Chap. 9), and alcohol and hormone replacement therapy seems to decrease heart-disease deaths more than it increases breast-cancer deaths. On balance, it seems that an increase in breast cancer risk with alcohol is more of a concern for women at lower risk of heart disease (premenopausal women and postmenopausal women who take estrogen).

Prostate Cancer

Less is known about prostate cancer than breast cancer, but as in breast cancer, it is linked to sex hormones (high testosterone), increasing age, and a high animal-fat diet. Also, like breast cancer, the death rate is higher in the U.S. than in Japan. Globocan 2008 gives the age-adjusted prostate cancer rate (deaths/100,000 men) as 5 in Japan and 10 in the U.S.

African-American men have extremely high rates (Fig. 12-1, 12-2)—about the highest in the world. Uncovering the reasons could tell us a lot about what causes prostate cancer and how to prevent it. One intriguing theory is that inadequate vitamin D might be a factor. African-Americans have more of the skin pigment melanin, which lessens sun-induced vitamin D production in the skin (Chap. 14). They also get less sun exposure than men in Africa. Also, many of them avoid milk (vitamin D fortified) because of lactose intolerance.

As mentioned earlier, a high-fat diet has been linked to prostate cancer. Men with a diet high in animal fat have about a 2-fold higher risk. Eating cooked tomato products is linked to a lower risk, possibly due to lycopene, a red carotenoid in tomatoes (carotenoids will be discussed shortly). It's ironic that in the typical American diet, we eat most of our tomato products along with fat, e.g., pizza, catsup on fries, salsa with tortilla chips.

Testicular Cancer

Cancer of the testicals is not very common, but is discussed here because it is most common in young men, ages 20-44 (most cancers are more common with increasing age). The cause is unknown. The only known risk factor is undescended testes at birth, which occurs in about 1% of males (ask your mom!) and typically is surgically corrected at about age one. Also, testicular cancer is much more common in whites than blacks.

When Lance Armstrong was diagnosed with advanced testicular cancer in 1996 at age 25, he was one of the best bicycle racers in the world. His recovery (with only about a 1% chance of recurrence) is a testament to both him and modern medicine. He was treated with surgery and intensive chemotherapy (after storing his sperm). He not only made a remarkable recovery from the cancer, but in 1999 he won the grueling 2,288-mile Tour de France (followed by 6 more wins) and had a child (his wife was artificially inseminated from his stored sperm).

Treatment

When cancer is localized, removing it is a straightforward cure. Once cancer cells have spread, whole-body methods to destroy cancer cells are used—it is hard to know where the cancer has gone. Radiation and chemotherapy also affect normal cells (hence, side effects). Even these methods came about only as we learned how normal cells work.

Learning the details of how cells divide, scientists devise strategies to interfere with the rapid cell division that characterizes cancer. Fluoro*uracil* is an anticancer drug. DNA production (needed for cell division) requires the base *uracil* (U). Fluorouracil competes with uracil, thus hampering the process.

Folate (a B-vitamin) is needed for cell division. Methotrexate hampers cell division by interfering with folate's job, and is effective in treating such cancers as leukemia and cancers of the breast, ovaries, and bladder. But methotrexate hampers cell division in general, causing side effects where rapid cell division is normal. Side effects include anemia, gastrointestinal disturbances, and hair loss. The goal of chemotherapy with methotrexate (and similar drugs) is to give a high enough dose to kill cancer cells without damaging normal cells too severely.

For decades, scientists have been trying to devise ways to selectively destroy cancer cells—"magic bullets" that leave healthy cells alone. New ways to treat cancer have come from advances in immunology and biotechnology. One example is the TIL-cell therapy discussed in Chapter 10. Another is one in which cancer cells taken from the patient are grown in the lab until there is enough to make a personalized vaccine. In response to the vaccine, the body makes antibodies specific for the patient's cancer cells; stray cancer cells are caught in a "search-and-destroy mission." Both treatments are still in an experimental stage, aren't always successful, and are tremendously expensive (treatment material is made specifically for each individual patient by highly trained personnel).

Survival Rates

How early cancer is detected and treated is the single most important factor in whether it is curable. Thus, the location of cancer markedly affects survival. Non-melanoma skin cancer is highly curable, not only because it doesn't spread fast, but also because it can be detected (and excised) promptly (left untreated, it can be fatal, like other cancers). Even though melanoma skin cancer spreads fast, overall 5-year survival rate is 91% because it can be detected and treated relatively early.

If a cancer can't be easily seen or felt, the next best thing is for it to produce early signs that prompt a visit to a doctor. Blood in urine can be a sign of bladder cancer, and blood in stool can be a sign of colon, rectal, or anal cancer. But the signs don't necessarily mean cancer, e.g., blood in

stool can be from a bleeding ulcer in the digestive tract, blood in urine can be from a urinary tract infection, most lumps in the breast aren't cancer.

Big advances in survival have been made with methods to detect cancer at its earliest stages. Introduction of the Pap test* as a way to screen for early stages of uterine/cervical cancer led to dramatically fewer deaths from this cancer (Table 12-1). Most cervical cancers are caused by sexual transmission of human papillomavirus. In 2006, a vaccine (Gardasil) was approved for prevention of this infection.

Cancers with the lowest survival rates are at sites that aren't easily examined, or don't usually produce symptoms until the cancer has spread. Warning signs of lung cancer are a persistent cough, sputum streaked with blood, chest pains, and recurring attacks of pneumonia or bronchitis. But some of these symptoms are just a more severe form of "normal" in heavy smokers, so lung cancer is usually found late. The 5-year survival is 16%.

Cancer of the ovary is typically "silent," so it usually is not found until it has spread. If detected early, 5-year survival is 94%; if found late, it's 28%. Pancreatic cancer is particularly grim (smoking is a major risk factor); it is usually detected at an advanced stage. One-year survival is 18%; at 5 years it's 6%.

The American Cancer Society recommends regular checkups to screen for various cancers (see Appendix A-6 for sources of more detailed information). At what ages and how often people should be screened varies for different cancers and different family and personal histories. You can do some screening on your own.

Women are advised to examine their breasts monthly for lumps (for premenopausal women, the best time is at the end of menstruation when breasts are the smallest). Men can feel for lumps in their testicals; this can be done conveniently while showering

You can examine your skin for changes, especially changes in moles or nodules or the appearance of new ones. ABCD is for warning signs of melanoma: A for asymmetry—one half of the mole isn't the same shape as the other half. B for border irregularity—edges are ragged, notched, or blurred. C for color—not uniform or is intensely black. D for diameter—wider than 6 millimeters (about 1/4 inch) and/or has grown suddenly or steadily.

Prevention

Continual news reports of substances that can cause cancer leave us with the fear that we are inescapably surrounded by carcinogens. In fact, we are, and nature is a major contributor. Sunshine can cause skin cancer; naturally occurring radiation in the air can cause lung cancer; and there are natural substances in food that can cause cancer.

It's no surprise that nature has also given us good defenses, e.g., melanin in skin, DNA-repair mechanisms, a powerful immune system. After all, if our image of cavemen is correct, we evolved in a hostile environment with little clothing to protect us from the sun, few ways of preserving food, and only an open fire for cooking.

For all the worry about environmental causes of cancer, most are related to personal choice. (Pollution is not a major cause in this country, as is popularly believed.) For example, we can avoid tobacco and excesses of alcohol, eat a good diet, and avoid sunburn.† Clearly, if you have one risk factor, it's all the more important to avoid other risk factors. If you smoke plus breathe in asbestos fibers or radon, you raise the risk of lung cancer even more. What if you add to that, smoking, heavy alcohol consumption, and a poor diet?

Also, we may choose to take some risks because they are exceeded by benefits. Many women are willing to trade possible small increases in risk of breast cancer for the benefits of having a first child at an older age, having fewer children,

---

*Physician George Nicolas Papanicolaou (1883-1962) devised this painless test. A few cells from the cervix and part of the vagina surrounding the cervix are removed with a swab and examined under a microscope.

†A hypothesis about the alarming rise in skin cancer is that we are exposed to more ultraviolet radiation because of a decreasing ozone layer between us and the sun.

hormone replacement therapy after menopause, etc. Besides, such women typically have more education and higher socioeconomic status—both very closely linked to better health—and hormone replacement therapy lowers the risk of osteoporosis.

Geographical clusters of cancers are alarming and should certainly be investigated, but keep in mind that they may have little to do with environmental toxins. A striking example is a cluster of cancer in our nation's capital. In 2003-2007, Washington D.C. (many African-Americans living in poverty) had an age-adjusted cancer death rate of 26 per 10,000 men, in contrast to Utah (many Mormons) with a rate of 16.

Don't forget that smoking is the single most common cause of cancer in this country, causing about 30% of all cancer deaths, and is a major risk factor for heart disease, emphysema, and chronic bronchitis. White-collar workers are the best educated as to the dangers of smoking, so tobacco companies focus on other groups, e.g., fewer ads in "white-collar" *U.S. News and World Report* and more in "blue-collar" *Popular Mechanics.*

U.S. tobacco companies spend about $3 billion a year to recruit new smokers and make smoking more socially acceptable. Blacks and Hispanics are main targets in the U.S. The companies also promote their products in areas of the world where malnutrition, infectious disease, and inadequate health care are prevalent. In some developing countries, tobacco use is now higher than it ever was in the U.S.

Diet and Cancer

Follow the dietary advice for good health discussed in Chapter 4. Healthy bodies are more resistant to damage and infection. The emphasis in cancer prevention is to eat a diet rich in vegetables and fruit. Such a diet tends to be low in fat and rich in fiber, vitamins, and minerals.

Many plant foods also have non-nutrient substances that may be protective. Cabbage-family (cruciferous*) vegetables have substances shown in animal studies to protect against cancer. In human studies, eating more of these vegetables is linked to a lower risk of colon and rectal cancer. Substances in soybeans are being studied for possible protection against breast and prostate cancer.

Diets rich in plant foods also tend to be rich in carotene and vitamins C and E—all can act as antioxidants to protect against cell damage. The need for C and E is covered in the Recommended Dietary Allowance (RDA). There's no RDA for carotene; we're simply advised to eat a daily serving of a carotene-rich fruit or vegetable.

Carotenes/Carotenoids

Carotenoids are a group of several hundred bright yellow, orange, and red pigments made in plants. They are in fruits, vegetables, flowers, and foliage, and give fall leaves their beautiful colors. About 20 of these carotenoids can be converted to vitamin A in the body. For simplicity, the various carotenoids that have vitamin A value will be referred to collectively as carotene or carotenes.† In food composition tables, carotenes are given vitamin A values, even if the food doesn't have any actual vitamin A, because eating carotene-containing foods can meet our vitamin A needs.

Carotenes are found in yellow-orange fruits and vegetables (they were first isolated from carrots in 1931, giving carotene its name), and also in dark-green vegetables (the green color of chlorophyll masks the yellow-orange color of carotenes). Carotenes are made only by plants but are found in animal tissue when animals eat carotene-rich plants. Poultry and egg producers routinely add carotenes (e.g., from alfalfa or corn) to poultry feed so the egg yolk and chicken skin will be more attractive to the consumer. Carotene is also added to margarine (otherwise, it would be white).

---

*Cruciferous comes from the Latin *crux,* meaning *cross* (as in crucifix); some vegetables in this plant family have flowers that form the pattern of a cross. Cruciferous vegetables include cabbage, broccoli, cauliflower, turnips, brussels sprouts, radishes, kale, and kohlrabi.

†Some carotenes provide more vitamin A than others. (Vitamin A, itself, isn't made by plants; it is found exclusively in animal products.) Beta-carotene is one of the most common carotenes in food. Its chemical structure is almost identical to 2 molecules of vitamin A linked together.

Like vitamin A, carotene is fat-soluble. But unlike vitamin A, it is not toxic when eaten in large amounts. This is because carotene itself is not toxic, and the body stores excesses rather than converting it to vitamin A. The skin of people who eat a lot of carotene (e.g., drink carrot juice) looks yellow-orange because carotene, as a fat-soluble substance, colors the fat under the skin.*

Some foods rich in carotene: in ½ cup cooked portions: canned pumpkin (2700 RE†), carrots (1915), sweet potatoes (1285), spinach (735), kale (480), broccoli (110). In various portions: ½ cantaloupe (860), 1 mango (805), 1 hot chili pepper (485), 3 apricots (275), 1 cup romaine lettuce (105), 1 avocado (105), 1 nectarine (100), 5 prunes (95), 1 tangerine (75), and 10 sprigs of parsley (50).

Carotene-rich food seems to protect against cancer. To say it another way, diets low in carotene-rich food seem to raise the risk of cancer. The Daily Food Guide says to eat a daily serving of a fruit or vegetable rich in carotene (Chap. 4). This doesn't mean you have to eat it each and every day. If you "pig out" on pumpkin pie and sweet potato on Thanksgiving, you may store enough carotene for months (it's fat-soluble).

Scientists measure nutrients precisely, but we need to think only in terms of portions of foods. Keep in mind that food has more than single nutrients. Broccoli, for example, is a cruciferous vegetable that is rich in vitamin C, fiber, carotene, and B-vitamins.

Since the body can convert carotenes to vitamin A, it's hard to separate the effects of carotenes from those of vitamin A in human studies.** But carotenes have an advantage, since vitamin A can act only as vitamin A, whereas carotene can also act as an antioxidant (some carotenoids without vitamin A value can also act as antioxidants).

Vitamin A helps maintain epithelial tissue (tissue that covers the internal and external surfaces of the body, e.g., skin and tissue lining the respiratory and digestive tracts). Thus, it is no surprise that diets low in carotene/vitamin A have been linked to higher risk of cancer—especially lung and esophageal cancer.

Studies showing protective effects of specific nutrients shouldn't be interpreted to mean that we need supplements. Part of the reason we self-prescribe supplements so readily is because we hear, for example, that a study shows that people with more carotene in their blood (i.e., who eat more foods rich in carotene) have less cancer. We forget that a link isn't proof of cause-and-effect. Carotene can be a marker for a diet rich in fruits and vegetables and a healthier lifestyle; those who eat more fruits and vegetables may smoke less, exercise more, live in cleaner air, etc. Also, many people resort to supplements because they aren't sure what carotene is, what foods have it, or whether it's helpful only in pills.

In 1747, when James Lind showed that lemons and limes protected against scurvy (Chap. 1), we didn't know what it was in lemons and limes that did this. Finding that it was vitamin C did not mean that we needed to take supplements. Rather, it allowed us to choose to eat any of a variety of foods having vitamin C (kiwi, green peppers, strawberries, etc.). When we want more of a particular nutrient, a sensible thing to do is to eat more of the foods that are rich in that nutrient.

If it were found that x milligrams of carotene protects against cancer, chances are that diets in line with dietary advice given in Chapter 4 provide enough. If not, the experts will revise the recommendations. The advantage to sticking to food as a source of carotene is that such food

---

*Some carotenoids are sold as suntan pills. These aren't usually carotene; they're selected for their brown-orange color (tan) rather than for vitamin A value. Tanning pills containing the carotenoid canthaxantin are illegal, although they are sometimes sold via mail-order or in health-food stores. Canthaxantin can cause problems by accumulating in the liver.

†These values are for Retinol (vitamin A) Equivalents (RE), which is a measure of carotene's potential conversion to vitamin A in the body. Thus, RE values given for plant foods give an estimate of carotene. The RDA for women is 700 RE; it's 900 RE for men (Appendix A-4).

**Cats can't convert carotene to vitamin A, so are useful in studying specific effects of carotene. This also means that cats must get their A from meat or milk (vitamin A occurs naturally only in animal foods). Vegetarian cats wouldn't make it in the wild!

is also rich in other healthful substances. In fact, most double-blind studies of carotene pills found that the pills did not lower the risk of cancer (and in some studies increased the risk). Unlike the vitamin-C-deficiency-disease scurvy, the diet-cancer relationship is very complex.

Carcinogens

As will be discussed in Chapter 16, there are many carcinogens that are normal components of food, many of which could technically be called pesticides. After all, a plant's chemical resistance to pests must have been crucial to a plant's survival in evolution (plants don't have fangs or claws and can't run). Also, note that we usually don't eat the seeds (the plant's next generation). If we do swallow the seeds, they're often undigested and exit surrounded by "fertilizer" (human manure). Seeds often are bitter, and often contain toxins.*

Many natural carcinogens have been identified, especially in plants. They're so prevalent in food, we really can't avoid them. There's little doubt that the benefits of eating fruits, vegetables, and grains far exceed the risks from the natural carcinogens in them. Any risk from residual pesticides sprayed on food crops may be relatively trivial.

A bigger concern is people may buy fewer fruits and vegetables because of fear of pesticides and higher prices. Unwarranted restrictions on effective and inexpensive pesticides raise the price of the very fruits and vegetables that are thought to reduce the risk of cancer. While it is important not to downplay the presence of natural and man-made carcinogens in our food, the danger should not be exaggerated, either.

Summary

The U.S. rate of cancer deaths has been rising because of more lung cancer and more elderly in the population. The most common sites of cancer have changed, and the age-adjusted rate of cancer deaths over the past 60 years has risen slightly. But there's a falling trend when death from lung cancer is excluded. Lung cancer is the leading cause of death from cancer and is mainly due to smoking.

Trends in the occurrence of cancer are much harder to assess than trends in cancer deaths. The reasons are many, but the most prominent one is that occurrence rates are based on the recorded rates of diagnosis in only about 10-15% of the population (deaths and causes of death are recorded for the entire population). Trends in cancer rates can be misleading, e.g., cancer rates go up when progress is made against other causes of death such as heart disease, and when smaller cancers are detected by improved testing.

Cancer is an uncontrolled growth of cells that can have fatal consequences. It's typically caused by inherited or acquired mutations in genes that control cell growth. Substances that cause such mutations are called carcinogens.

Efforts to determine which substances are carcinogens begin with screening tests such as the Ames test (which uses special bacteria to see if the test substance can cause mutations), discussed in Chapter 10. This is followed by animal testing. Animal test data are often challenged on the degree to which they can be extended to humans. We depend on animal studies together with population studies to evaluate human cancer risk.

Because of the complex biology of cancer and the complexity of our heredity and environment, it's hard to isolate contributing factors and determine the degree to which each plays a role. In most cases, the best we can do is determine what factors are linked with cancer, and do what we can to lower risk. For example, causes of most colon, breast, and prostate cancers aren't known. But these cancers are linked with a diet high in fat, protein, and calories, and low in fiber. Thus, we're advised that changing to a diet lower in fat, protein, and calories, and higher in fiber might possibly lower our risk of these cancers.

---

*Apricot pits have cyanide (the poison used in the Jonestown mass-suicide in Guyana). Laetrile is an apricot-pit extract touted as a cancer cure. Promoters call it vitamin B_{17}, but there's no such vitamin. Due to public pressure, scientists did a controlled (and costly) study of laetrile in cancer patients; it did not help. (Vitamin C in megadoses was similarly tested on cancer patients in response to public pressure; it did not help either.)

The natural world surrounds us with cancer-causing agents, including ultraviolet light, radioactive materials found naturally in soil, and substances found naturally in food. But we are not defenseless. As examples, we have melanin in our skin, DNA repair mechanisms, and a very sophisticated immune system.

We can also choose to avoid major risk factors such as smoking. Smoking is the cause of most lung cancers and the cause of other cancers as well. We can eat a lot of vegetables and fruit. These foods seem to be particularly protective against cancer. They not only tend to be high in fiber and low in fat and calories, but also contain a variety of substances that may protect against cancer.

Chapter 13

Energy Requirements

I think the devil will not have me damned, lest the oil that's in me should set hell on fire.

Sir John Falstaff in Shakespeare's *The Merry Wives of Windsor*

Cells constantly use a lot of energy and can not afford to run out. Even the thinnest of us keeps an ample back-up supply of fuel as fat.

As discussed in Chapter 3, energy in food and energy use in the body are measured in calories. Food calories are measured by burning the food and measuring the heat. Calories we use ("burn") are measured either directly by measuring the heat we generate, or indirectly by measuring the oxygen we use.*

We release the energy in food via the reactions of metabolism (Chap. 9). We capture about 40% of the energy as ATP. The rest (60%) is released as heat. A 40% fuel efficiency may not sound high, but even a well-tuned car uses gas at less than 30% efficiency.

In cold weather, the generated heat is useful in heating our bodies or heating the car. But hot weather can be a problem. We instinctively avoid overheating our bodies by being less active (less heat made) and by wearing less clothing (more heat lost). When the car engine is overheating, we do try to stop the car (less heat made), but most of us don't think of turning on the car's heater (more heat lost), though this would help.

How many calories do we need? Simply the number of calories needed to maintain a healthy weight. This answer is, of course, deceptively simple. Energy requirements of adults include that needed for:

- **Basal metabolism**: Maintain normal body functions (breathe, pump blood, maintain tissues, etc.)—what it takes to sustain life. Except for the extremely active, it makes up the biggest part of our energy need.
- **Physical activity**: Moving!
- **Energy expended upon eating**: Incorporating food into the body (digestion, etc.).

*It usually doesn't matter whether we use glucose or fat as fuel. But endurance athletes try to use glucose sparingly, since they fatigue when their muscles run out (Chap. 9). They can gauge their "fuel mix" by measuring how much carbon dioxide they make, relative to how much oxygen they use. As shown in Fig. 9-2, if only fat is used, it's $16CO_2/23O_2=0.7$; if only glucose is used, it's $6CO_2/6O_2=1.0$; "mixed fuels" fall between 0.7 and 1.0. By this method, it's been shown that caffeine taken an hour before an endurance event spares the use of glucose (caffeine raises fatty acids in blood) and delays the onset of fatigue.

Basal Metabolism

The amount of gas your car uses idling at a stop light can be likened to how much fuel your body "burns" for basal metabolism. It's the calories you use when you haven't eaten for several hours (you're done "processing" food) and are lying down in a comfortable setting, relaxed and awake. (You need less energy when asleep. But when you're awake, it's easier to make this measurement, e.g., wearing a gas mask to measure how much oxygen—thus how many calories—you're using.)

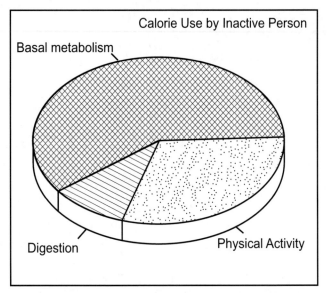

Basal metabolism makes up the bulk of our caloric requirement. This is contrary to the popular belief that most of the calories we use each day is for physical activity. If you're sedentary, basal metabolism makes up about two thirds of your energy requirement. It's about half of your energy requirement if you're extremely active—a laborer, football player in training, etc.

Except for pregnant or nursing women,* the calories adults need for **basal metabolism depends mostly on body size and body composition**. A football lineman has a very high basal metabolism. He's not only big, he has less fat and more lean tissue than most of us. It takes more energy to maintain lean tissue. Figure 13-1 shows how basal metabolism goes up with higher body weight and lower body fat.

Another factor, not taken into account in Figure 13-1, is **body surface area** (basically, the amount of skin you have—not counting wrinkles). At the same body weight and composition, someone tall and thin has more body surface area and a higher basal metabolism than someone short and wide. A bigger surface area means more body heat is lost, requiring a higher basal metabolism to maintain body temperature.

Think of a cup of hot coffee—it cools faster in a tall, thin cup than a short, squatty one. Or note that when you're cold, you curl into a ball—reduce heat loss by reducing the exposed body surface area. When you're hot, you sprawl out to dissipate body heat. Amputees feel warmer than we do because they don't lose heat as fast (arms and legs have a lot of surface area relative to their weight).

Factors that affect body size and composition affect basal metabolism. Women generally have a lower basal metabolism than men; they're usually smaller and have a higher percent body fat. Thus, **gender** affects basic energy needs.

Age

Basal metabolism goes up as we grow in size from infancy to adulthood. But if we look at the calories needed *per pound* of body weight, it's highest in infancy. One reason is that growth is greatest during infancy. Another reason is that the brain makes up a large portion of an infant's body, and the brain uses a lot of energy compared to other organs.† The brain uses about 45% of a 20-pound infant's basal metabolism, but it's only about 20% for a 155-pound man.

---

*Pregnancy and breastfeeding raise basal metabolism. The RDA (Recommended Dietary Allowance) for pregnancy is an added 300 calories per day during the 2nd and 3rd trimesters. Extra calories aren't usually allotted during the 1st trimester unless the woman is undernourished at the start of pregnancy. The RDA for a nursing mother is an added 500 calories per day.

†You might think: If the brain needs so much energy, I must really burn a lot of calories when studying. No such luck. Your brain is very active whether studying or not, so studying doesn't significantly raise its energy use. But if you're tense, pace the floor, chew pencils, or shake your leg while studying, these accompanying activities do burn calories.

Figure 13-1: Basal Metabolism in Adults

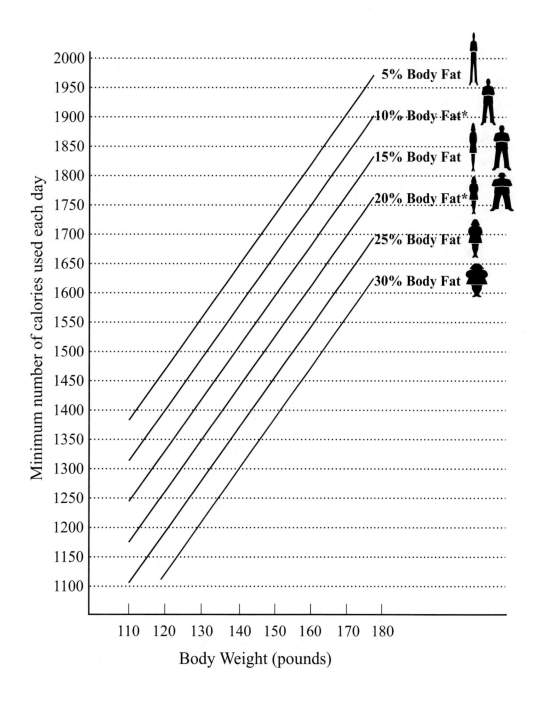

Estimated calories used per day for 16 hours rest and 8 hours sleep are given on the left. The graph is simply to show how basal metabolism is related to body weight and body composition. There's a lot of person-to-person variation.

*Normal % body fat is about 10% for young men and about 20% for young women.

Starting at about age 30, basal metabolism falls about 2 to 3 % per decade, mostly from loss of lean tissue. At a given body weight, the amount of lean tissue falls and the amount of fat goes up (people incorrectly say *muscle is turning into fat*). This loss of lean tissue is thought to be partly from an age-related fall in growth hormone.*

In practical terms, this means that even if we keep the same weight and physical activity, we need fewer calories as we age because of the decrease in lean body mass. Thus, if we continue to eat the same number of calories and don't become more active, we gain weight. Americans gain about 20 pounds, on average, between age 25 and 45. But part of this weight gain is attributed to a decline in physical activity that often occurs during this time (physical activity uses calories *and* helps maintain muscle mass).

"You've established a 20% growth rate."

Hormones

Female hormones fluctuate and affect basal metabolism. Basal metabolism starts to rise around the time of ovulation and peaks just before or at the beginning of menstruation. Then it falls and stays at that lower level until mid-cycle when ovulation occurs again. This fluctuation in basal metabolism is reflected in a fluctuation of body temperature. Thus, a woman can find out when she ovulates by taking her temperature before getting out of bed every morning to look for the rise in body heat (from an increase in basal metabolism) associated with ovulation. (Remember, a higher basal metabolism uses more calories. The more calories you use, the more heat you produce. Think of how warm you get when you exercise— it's from using so many calories.)

A woman's appetite often reflects these changes during the menstrual cycle. Many find they're hungrier and eat more during the last part of the menstrual cycle, and their appetite lessens and they eat less when menstruation begins. Body water also fluctuates during the cycle, generally paralleling the fluctuation in basal metabolism. Thus, women shouldn't be unduly concerned with increased appetite and weight late in the cycle. The increased hunger is from an increased use of calories, and the extra water will be lost early in the cycle.

Sex hormones can also affect basal metabolism indirectly. The male sex hormone testosterone promotes an increase in muscle mass, and more energy is then needed to maintain this added tissue.

---

*In one study, growth hormone given for 6 months to 21 older men (ages 61-81), who were selected for their very low levels, resulted in more lean tissue, less body fat, and increases in skin thickness by amounts comparable to that lost during 10-20 years of aging. Studies like this are now possible because of the availability of human growth hormone made by biotech (Chap. 10).

Thyroid Hormone

The hormone that has the biggest effect on basal metabolism is thyroid hormone (thyroxine), made by the thyroid gland. Either an excess or a deficiency of thyroid hormone causes ill effects, and our body has an elaborate system for keeping levels within a narrow range. Excess amounts raise basal metabolism—much like a car with its idle set too high—and inadequate amounts lower it.

Iodine is an essential part of thyroid hormone, and iodine concentrates in the thyroid gland for making the hormone. * If there isn't enough iodine in the diet, the gland can't make enough hormone, and it enlarges in its attempt to make more.† This enlarges the neck, because the gland is there. An enlarged thyroid gland from a lack of iodine is called **simple goiter.** Until 1924, when iodized salt (iodine added to salt) was introduced, simple goiter was common in this country. During World War I, the neck sizes of the men drafted from all parts of the U.S. reflected the geographical distribution of goiter.

The effect of simple goiter depends on the extent of the iodine deficiency and when it occurs. Severe deficiency during fetal life can cause physical and mental retardation (cretinism), whereas a slightly enlarged thyroid gland may be the only noticeable effect of a mild deficiency that occurs as an adult. Intermediate symptoms include sluggish mental activity and weight gain and puffiness due to abnormal retention of water in tissues. Iodine deficiency is still a worldwide problem, especially in developing countries. Worldwide, an estimated 1.6 billion people don't get enough iodine. In inland China, hundreds of thousands of people are mentally retarded from iodine deficiency.

Seafood is the most consistent source of iodine (sea water is rich in iodine). As long ago as 3000 B.C., the Chinese used burnt sea sponge to successfully treat simple goiter, even though they didn't know what caused it. Sea sponge has iodine, which, as a mineral, isn't destroyed when the sponge is burned.

Inland, the iodine in food reflects the amount in the soil. As might be expected, goiter was least common in areas next to the sea, not only because seafood is available, but because soil next to the sea is rich in iodine. In fact, one method used today to combat iodine deficiency in some countries is to put iodine in the water used to irrigate food crops.

In the American diet, the main sources of iodine are iodized salt, dairy foods, and processed foods. Dairy foods and many processed foods contain iodine from residual iodine-containing disinfectants used to clean milking machines, storage tanks, processing equipment, etc., and some of the iodine gets into the processed food.

In the 1970s, scientists were concerned that we might be getting excessive iodine from these inadvertent sources. As a result, these iodine-containing compounds are used less. This source of iodine has been declining since 1982, and our average intake is now considered to be ample but not excessive.

Goiter, by definition, is simply an enlargement of the thyroid gland. The gland not only enlarges in its attempt to make more hormone when there isn't enough, but it can also enlarge from making excessive amounts. Once the thyroid becomes enlarged, for whatever reason, it doesn't shrink back to a normal size after the cause is corrected.

There are many causes of goiter. Worldwide, iodine deficiency is the most common cause. There are also other dietary causes of goiter. Ironically, large excesses of iodine can hamper the production of thyroid hormone and cause

---

*Radioactive iodine is released and falls out of nuclear accidents like that in Chornobyl in 1986. The World Health Organization recommends that [non-radioactive] iodine pills be available to children living near nuclear power plants, to take in case of an accident. Taking an iodine pill before exposure saturates the thyroid gland, so that very little radioactive iodine will be taken up (moderate excesses of iodine, radioactive or not, are excreted in the urine). Children are especially vulnerable. There's now an epidemic of thyroid cancer among children in Belarus (just north of Chornobyl).

†When thyroid hormone is low, a hormone called thyroid-stimulating hormone stimulates the thyroid to make more. When there's a shortage of iodine, the thyroid simply can't make enough hormone. Prolonged stimulation by thyroid-stimulating hormone causes the gland to enlarge.

goiter (another example of too much or too little as a problem). In Japan, some people get goiter from regularly eating large amounts of iodine-rich seaweed.

Another dietary cause of goiter is eating a lot of foods that contain anti-thyroid-hormone substances called **goitrogens**. This can lower thyroid hormone and cause goiter. Goitrogens act in different ways. Some interfere with production of the hormone; others cause excessive loss.

Goitrogens are found naturally in a wide variety of foods, e.g., cabbage, cassava, turnips, soybeans, and peanuts. There are also some synthetic goitrogens, such as the antibiotic tetracycline, sulfa drugs, and industrial PCBs (polychlorinated biphenyls). Goitrogens only cause goiter when people ingest excessively large amounts over a long time.

Goitrogen-induced goiter is found where goitrogen-containing food is a large part of the diet, e.g., cassava in some tropical countries. But goiter doesn't always develop with a high goitrogen intake if the diet is ample in iodine. In many countries, the key factor is the relative amounts of goitrogens and iodine in the diet.

There are interesting variations in this balance between dietary iodine and goitrogens. Two neighboring communities in Venezuela were found to have a 10-fold difference in the occurrence of goiter. Both communities got very little iodine, and it appeared that a higher amount of dietary goitrogens was the determining factor.

Excessive thyroid hormone: There are no known dietary causes of excessive thyroid hormone. Iodine deficiency or an excessive amount of iodine or goitrogens causes too little rather than too much hormone. The causes of excessive hormone production (hyperthyroidism) aren't well understood, but the most common types may be due to a dysfunction in the immune system.

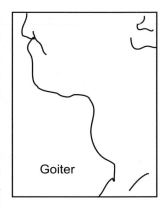

Goiter

As mentioned earlier, excess thyroid hormone speeds metabolism, like a car with its idle set too high. Symptoms include nervousness, sweating, hypersensitivity to heat, rapid heartbeat, and fatigue (*hyper* is slang for *high-strung* or *keyed-up,* and aptly describes the revved up state of *hyper*thyroidism).

Basal metabolism can double or triple (*a car uses more gas when its idle is set too high*), and despite a bigger appetite, weight loss is typical.* To treat hyperthyroidism, part or all of the thyroid gland is removed by surgery or destroyed by giving radioactive iodine. Thereafter, thyroid-hormone pills are taken to achieve normal levels.

Miscellaneous Factors

Scientists measure basal metabolism under standardized conditions (e.g., lying relaxed in a comfortable environment), because many factors can alter the amount of energy used, even when a person is resting. Some examples:

Fever: The higher body heat of a fever causes metabolic reactions to speed up—just as heat speeds up chemical reactions in the laboratory or kitchen. For every 1°F rise in body temperature, basal metabolism goes up about 7%. This means that if you're lying in bed with a fever of 103°F, your calorie need would be about 30% higher.

Prolonged Food Deprivation: Basal metabolism falls when adults don't get enough calories for a prolonged period. This adaptation is good in a famine—it lets you live longer. But dieters are unhappy with this. They're purposely subjecting themselves to prolonged food deprivation in trying to lose weight. In children, famine

---

*Former First Lady Barbara Bush lost 18 lbs in 3 months without even trying (she said she should have known something was wrong!) due to Graves' disease, a common type of hyperthyroidism (George Bush was found to have it also). It seems that receptors on the thyroid gland for thyroid-stimulating hormone (see earlier footnote) are mistakenly seen as foreign, and the body makes antibodies against them. These antibodies are unusual in that they themselves stimulate the thyroid gland, causing excessive hormone production. The prolonged stimulation causes the gland to enlarge (goiter). Protruding eyes, like hers, is a common symptom.

doesn't lower basal metabolism. Instead, growth is stunted, an adaptation to prolonged food deprivation. Smaller bodies need fewer calories and nutrients.

When people undergo repeated cycles of feast and famine, their basal metabolism falls faster during famine. This adaptation is helpful to the many people worldwide who involuntarily cycle between feast and famine. But for the many regular dieters in this country, this is disheartening.

Mental State: Being excited, nervous, upset, stressed, etc., uses calories. Hormones like adrenalin—the "fight or flight" hormone—speed the rate of metabolism. Also, things like increased muscle tension uses calories, and we have a lot of muscle that we can "make tense." On the other hand, meditation or self-hypnosis can lower energy needs by about 15% (blood pressure falls, breathing is slower, etc.). Meditation is, in essence, the opposite of tenseness.

Environmental Temperature: Greater or lesser loss of body heat affects our energy needs. When we're in comfortable surroundings, it doesn't take as much energy to maintain normal body temperature. But even at a comfortable temperature, we differ in how much body heat we lose. As noted earlier, body shape—body surface area—makes a difference. Body fat also matters, because fat is stored mainly in a layer just under the skin and is a good insulator. A lean person loses more body heat than a fat person of the same weight—just as hot coffee cools faster in a paper cup than in a styrofoam cup.

In fact, getting rid of excess body heat is often a problem for obese people in hot weather or during even moderate exercise. Their body shape and insulation minimize heat loss. In contrast, the lean and skinny physique of marathon runners maximizes heat loss, which can be crucial to winning in warm weather. Recall that heat is a byproduct of ATP production. In running a marathon, a lot of ATP and heat is generated over an extended time. Runners need to get rid of excess heat as fast as possible to avoid heat prostration.

If we're too cold or too hot, it takes more calories to maintain normal body temperature. Like a house with a thermostat, the heater or air conditioner goes on if it's too cold or too hot, and both appliances use energy. One of the functions of the circulatory system is to distribute body heat (Chap. 7). By blood going in or out of capillaries in the skin, more or less blood contacts the cooler body surface and the body can adjust the amount of heat lost.

We sweat when hot. Evaporation of sweat cools the skin and the blood in the skin's capillaries. (When hot—or embarrassed—capillaries in our facial skin fill up and our face "turns red.") Dry weather or a breeze evaporates sweat faster, and we feel cooler. (A cool breeze is actually a cool*ing* breeze.) We feel hotter when the weather is hot and humid, because the humidity slows the rate of evaporation.

We shiver when cold. Blood moves out of the capillaries in our skin to minimize heat loss. We get goose bumps, meant to stand our once-abundant body hair on end—a thicker and warmer fur coat. We take action ourselves—put on more clothes (insulation) and wrap our arms across our chest or curling up in a ball to lessen the body surface exposed to the cold.

Interestingly, there's a special type of fat called *brown fat* that, unlike regular fat, is geared to produce heat.* We have it in only small amounts and in specific parts of the body, like around the neck and kidneys. Brown fat cells have lots of mitochondria and have a rich blood supply, both of which give them their distinctive brown color.

They work like miniature heaters that burn fat in response to cold-exposure. Blood picks up the heat as it circulates through brown fat and then circulates that heat to the rest of the body. It appears that we're born with a limited amount of

---

*The other more abundant and familiar type of fat (white fat) is mostly in a layer under the skin. The main function of this fat is storage of "excess calories" as triglycerides (which are white). When ATP energy is needed, fat cells release fat into the blood, so that other cells can use it to make ATP. In essence, white fat is for ATP production at other sites, and brown fat is for "on site" heat production

brown fat, which lessens thereafter, unless we're chronically exposed to a severely cold climate—"use it or lose it?" Complete loss of brown fat has been reported in adults and children who have died of cold-exposure.

Smoking: Smoking raises basal metabolism, one reason why people often gain weight when they quit (smoking is far worse for health than being moderately overweight). Concern with this weight gain can make it even harder to quit smoking; it's already very hard because of nicotine addiction. In this country, women have a harder time quitting. This may be due to the greater emphasis they put on thinness (also, depression is more common in women, and nicotine may help alleviate depression).

Physical Activity

While we can't make drastic changes in basal metabolism, it goes without saying that we can make big changes in physical activity. In fact, during adulthood (except for pregnancy and lactation), being more active is virtually the only way we can use substantially more calories under normal circumstances. It's important to keep several points in mind when discussing the calories used in various types of activities:

• Calories used for various activities are often given as specific numbers (e.g., 100 calories for walking a mile). This can be misleading. Calories used for a weight-bearing exercise like walking, depends not only on how far we walk, but on how much we weigh (i.e., how much weight is moved).

Calories used when walking is also affected by other factors: speed, walking surface (e.g., sand or pavement, uphill, downhill, or flat), distribution of body weight, physical fitness, etc. In non-weight-bearing exercise, other factors (e.g., buoyancy in water when swimming) make a difference.

A 120-lb person uses about 70 calories walking a mile in 20 minutes, but someone 200 lbs uses about 105 calories walking that same mile. (Good reason to carry an infant in a baby carrier—or books in a back-pack—if you're looking to use more calories.) This also means that if you lose weight, you use fewer calories for that same walk-unless you balance your weight loss with an infant of the same weight, or add a counterbalancing number of books to your backpack.

• It's important to distinguish between calories used during an activity and calories that the activity itself uses. There's a difference. Energy used *during* exercise includes calories used

"When I was your age, I had to walk 6 feet, change the channel by hand, and then walk the 6 feet back."

Table 13-1: Calories Used per Minute for Activities of a 140-lb Person

Calories/minute*	
1	Sitting while reading, knitting, talking, etc.
2	Typing, writing, driving, laboratory work, playing cards or a clarinet
3	Walking 2 miles per hour (mph), washing dishes, cooking, carpentry
4	Walking 3 mph, washing the car, housecleaning, playing ping pong
5	Swimming leisurely, plastering a wall, dancing a waltz
6	Downhill skiing, playing tennis, climbing stairs, bicycling 6 mph
7	Sawing logs with a handsaw, mowing the lawn with a hand-mower
8	Pitching bales of hay, playing football, digging a pit
9	Cross-country skiing, playing basketball, dancing the polka
10	Running 6 mph, strenuous swimming, snowshoeing in soft snow
11	Jumping rope (125 times/minute), playing racquetball
12	Running 7 mph

* Estimated caloric cost of the activity per minute = calories used/minute above that used when resting. At rest, a 140-lb man (10% body fat) uses about 1.1 cal/minute, and a 140-lb woman (20% body fat) uses about 1.0 cal/minute. When sleeping, calories used is about 10% less than when resting.

for the activity *and* the calories used for basal metabolism. For example, Sue (140 lb) walks 1½ miles in a half hour, and uses about 150 calories during that time—about 120 for walking and about 30 for basal metabolism. In business terms, it's 150 gross, 120 net. Someone "selling exercise" is more likely to use the 150-calorie number.

- People vary a lot in how many calories they use in an activity (e.g., playing tennis). Even in sleeping, some people lie still the entire night, whereas others toss and turn. In listening to a lecture, some people sit on the edge of their seats, using more calories than others who are almost asleep—or actually are!

Table 13-1 gives a rough estimate of the energy cost of a few activities (net caloric cost)f that activity) for someone weighing 140 pounds. Keep in mind that when an activity is strenuous, it's hard to sustain—we have stop to catch our breath. Weightlifting, for example, is very hard work. In an hour spent working out at a gym, a lot of it may be spent resting between lifts and strolling from one piece of equipment to the next. We tend to overestimate our physical activity (and underestimate how much we eat).

Generally, you can estimate the calories spent per day on physical activity as a percent of basal metabolism:

- **Sedentary** (mostly sitting, typing, etc.; no routine, strenuous activity) = **50%** (If 1400 cal for basal metabolism, energy for physical activity = 0.50 X 1400 = 700 cal)
- **Lightly active** (laboratory work, cooking, etc.; no routine, strenuous activity) = **60%**
- **Moderately active** (carpentry, housework, etc.; very little sitting) = **70%**
- **Very active** (unskilled labor, dancing, running; very little sitting) = **80%**
- **Strenuously active** (professional football players/strenuous training, etc.) = >**80%**

Energy Expended Upon Eating

The energy expended as a result of eating is not completely understood. We do know it takes energy to digest food and absorb and assimilate nutrients into the body, e.g., replenish liver glycogen, convert "extra calories" to body fat. This energy use is highest during the first 2 hours after eating and then subsides (this is why basal metabolism is measured several hours after eating). An analogy is the processing of supplies delivered to a manufacturing plant. When supplies arrive, the plant expends energy to open boxes, distribute supplies, discard or recycle packaging, etc.

Composition of the diet has some effect on energy expenditure (protein the most, carbohydrate less, fat the least). But the composition of our diet is a mixed one (i.e, not pure protein, carbohydrate, or fat), and the energy used is about 5-10% of calories consumed, regardless of the composition of the diet. This means that if we take in 2000 calories, we pay a tax—or get a discount—of about 100-200 calories.

We can feel warm after eating because of this increased energy expenditure. In fact, we can use this to our advantage when we're out camping in cold weather. By eating before climbing into the sleeping bag, we feel warmer and find it easier to sleep.

Adaptations For Survival

Survival of any species depends on surviving to the reproductive period. We act instinctively, and don't die easily of cold exposure or heat prostration. When cold, we're more apt to feel like eating, and are virtually compelled to exercise by shivering and perhaps stomping our feet or jumping up and down. When hot, we don't feel like exercising and aren't as hungry. This is good, since we get warm from exercise and eating.

Our ability to maintain body temperature in extreme climates has literally allowed us to inhabit the ends of the earth. Note that people from extremely hot climates (e.g., Africans) tend to

"May I remind you that 99 percent of all species that ever existed are today extinct."

be tall and lean (more surface area and less fat-insulation), whereas those from extremely cold climates (e.g., Eskimos) tend to be shorter and have more body fat.

An immediate threat to survival anywhere is starvation. So the body minimizes calorie use when food is scarce and efficiently stores calories when food is abundant. In a famine, basal metabolism falls, and we feel weak and minimize our physical activity—including sex (pregnancy uses a lot of calories, and there's even less food with children to feed). If a woman's fat stores become extremely low—whether because she's starving, a marathon runner, a ballet dancer, or has anorexia nervosa—she may become less fertile and stop menstruating.

For many women in developing countries, fat stores are crucial in providing the energy needed to carry a pregnancy to term. During pregnancy, they also need to store fat to provide energy needed for breast-feeding. Too often, this isn't possible, and they can't make much milk. A dilemma for nutritionists working for world-health agencies is how to distribute limited food aid—more food for the mother, so she can breast-feed her baby, or more food for the baby directly.

Even today in some parts of the world, obesity in young women is encouraged for child-bearing reasons. In the Sahara where famine is still a threat, obesity signifies wealth and is considered sexually attractive in women. Some brides-to-be are forced to drink several quarts of camel's milk daily until they become obese. During a famine, their large store of body fat helps provide the calories needed for a successful pregnancy.

Obesity

When food is abundant, extra energy is readily stored as body fat. Foods high in fat and sugar (concentrated sources of calories) are especially appealing. In a famine, obese people live the longest. There are genetic tendencies toward obesity, and these are perpetuated in famines because the obese are more likely to survive to have children. Ill effects of obesity usually don't occur until after the prime childbearing years.

Ironically, our wealth and development provide us with both an abundance of calories and less of a need for them. We're continually encouraged to eat. Food's nearby (*refrigerator, vending machines, 7-11 stores*) and appealing (*donuts, pizza, Mrs. Field's Cookies*). There are constant reminders (*TV commercials, magazine ads, driving by McDonald's*) and "eating occasions" (*coffee breaks, birthdays, Thanksgiving, baseball games, movies*). Food's easy to prepare (*frozen dinners, microwave ovens*) and convenient to eat, even while walking (*ice cream cones, candy bars*) or driving (*dashboard dining*).

We're often hard-pressed to find ways of using the extra calories that we so easily store as fat. We have automatic garage-door openers, electric can openers, power lawnmowers, cars with automatic transmissions and power steering, push-button phones, light-touch keyboards, food processors, and remote controls for the TV and VCR. With an abundance of food and a dearth of exercise, not only do we grow to our genetic potential in height, but it's easy to grow to our genetic potential in width as well.

Our situation is really an aberration, relative to the rest of the world's population and human history. Physiologically, we've adapted to a scarcity of food, and have an elaborate system to maintain the fat stores that have been essential to human survival. The size of our fat stores is simply a matter of energy balance. When we use more calories than we take in, we burn body fat to make up the difference—the size of our fat stores goes down. To bring it back up, we have to eat more or use less. Early man used a lot of calories, and using less wasn't really an option. Survival depended on searching for food, building shelter, running from predators. What worked was a compelling urge to eat when fat stores fell.

Obesity was rare. There was a lot of exercise and not enough food. Besides, obesity hampered an escape from predators—harder to run fast and harder to hide behind a tree. Our genetic heritage includes only modest physiological controls to limit the amount of fat we store. We weren't even given an urge to jog around the block when we get too fat.

The Urge to Eat

Hunger is the discomfort we feel when we haven't had eaten for a while. We feel weak and get hunger pangs (stomach contractions) that become stronger and more frequent and even painful, the longer we go without eating—the body's message to eat becomes more urgent. "Tightening your belt" (a colloquialism for *being more frugal in hard times*) temporarily helps relieve hunger pangs, as does drinking cold water or alcohol, smoking, and tasting food without swallowing it.

Appetite is the desire for food, a much more positive sensation than hunger. We don't have to be hungry to have an appetite (*I'm stuffed, but did you say chocolate?*). You might say that appetite has more to do with external cues. Overweight people are, in fact, more responsive to external cues—a dish of candy on the table, the clock showing that it's lunchtime, magazine and TV ads for food and drink, donuts next to the office coffeepot. Studies also show when overweight people have unlimited access to a drab formula-drink as a sole source of calories, they tend to lose weight, whereas those of normal weight tend to maintain theirs.

Satiety is the satisfaction of hunger or appetite. There are feeding, drinking, and satiety centers in the brain. We know this from animal studies in which those areas of the brain are electrically stimulated. So when it's said, *you can lead a horse to water, but you can't get him to drink,* it's not quite true. Stimulate the drinking center, and the horse will drink.

Normal stimulation of these control centers is complex. As soon as we start eating, signals are relayed to the brain from various parts of the digestive tract—starting with the tongue—and we stop eating. Well, we're supposed to, anyway. Unfortunately, not many of us stop eating at two thirds of a Big Mac, even if we're full. We override internal signals. In fact, the huge increase in the portion size of so many foods is partly to blame for our epidemic of obesity. Instead of "super-sizing," we need to downsize.

"Oh, Ma'am—I wouldn't bother him while he's eating."

What about long-term controls? Our weight stays remarkably steady over decades, much to the dismay of those who struggle to lose weight only to put it back on again. In the early 1950s, rat studies suggested that something circulates to the brain to signal how much body fat is stored, and food intake changes accordingly. By destroying the brain's satiety center, a rat would eat voraciously and become obese. A side section of the rat's skin was then joined to that of a normal-weight rat, so substances in their tissue fluids could pass between them. The obese rat would keep eating, but the normal rat would stop eating to the point of starvation if it wasn't separated from its obese partner. It was hypothesized that the huge fat stores sent out huge amounts of a hormone—an urgent message to stop eating that only rats with an intact satiety center can respond to.

In the early 1970s, scientists found two strains of mice that are obese due to recessive genes* called *ob* and *db*. They become obese by over-eating, but for different reasons, as shown by connecting them by skin to normal-weight mice. A normal-weight mouse connected to an obese ob/ob mouse ate normally. But the obese mouse ate less and lost weight, indicating that its signal-receiving function was OK—it responded to the normal amount of hormone coming from the normal-weight mouse. It was concluded that ob/ob mice are unable to make the hormone—they cannot send a "fat storage is full" signal even when they're obese.

In contrast, a normal-weight mouse connected to an obese db/db mouse stopped eating, and the obese mouse kept over-eating, suggesting that the obese mouse made plenty of hormone but could not respond to it. In other words, db/db mice get fat because they can't respond to the

---

*A recessive gene is one that must be inherited from both parents for the trait to appear. Blue eyes, for example, is a recessive trait. The parents could have brown eyes with one gene each for blue and brown eyes.

hormone, whereas ob/ob mice get fat because they can't make the hormone.

The advent of DNA technology resulted in a flurry of more detailed information. In 1994, the gene for this hormone (a protein) was found. The hormone is called *leptin* and is made in fat cells. In 1995, it was shown that leptin was made in proportion to the amount of body fat, and that administering biotech-made leptin to the ob/ob mouse "cured" the obesity. This caused a tremendous amount of excitement, especially among drug companies who see huge dollar signs next to such drugs.

The db/db mice were found to have a defect in the gene for a membrane protein called leptin receptor. Thousands of obese people have been screened for ob and db mutations. It seems to be rare, and the resulting obesity seems to occur where there's a lot of intermarriage.* Like the mice, they're of normal weight at birth and become severely obese by overeating.

"Yes, Billy, but Mr. Phillips pushes legal drugs."

The few who have such mutations include a pair of obese cousins who have a deletion of a single base (a *G*) in the leptin gene's base sequence, resulting in little or no leptin production. In 1998, there was a report of 3 severely obese sisters whose defect in the leptin-receptor gene results in a shortened amino acid chain that doesn't allow the signaling of the leptin message.

Of course, the hope was that low leptin levels were common, so that obesity might be successfully treated with leptin, just as we treat insulin-deficient diabetes with insulin. It appears that most obese people make plenty of leptin, but have less of a response to it—leptin resistance, perhaps

analogous to the insulin resistance of diabetics who are obese and make plenty of insulin. Leptin is now being tested for its effectiveness in treating obesity, to be used much like insulin is used to treat insulin-resistant diabetes-using more insulin to try and break through the resistance.

A wide variety of "anti-obesity" drugs are now in the pipeline. A major concern is that such drugs can become so popular that their use spreads beyond those for whom the drugs were intended and tested. Even if serious side effects are rare, they can occur in substantial numbers if there are huge numbers of people taking them. And when people take them to lose weight for cosmetic rather than health reasons, the risk/benefit ratio goes up. Another concern is that there will be less resolve to eat better and exercise more, both of which are extremely important for health in people, overweight or not.

*When there's a rare, recessive gene in a family, intermarriage makes it more likely that someone will inherit the 2 copies of that gene needed for the trait (in this case, obesity) to occur.

We're not likely to find more "magic pills" like the vitamin C pill that cures scurvy—a safe pill that provides an immediate cure. Today, our major ailments are much more complex, as are the pills used to treat them. For all that we know about how the body works, down to the kinetics of various enzymes and the single base-changes in our DNA that can cause disease, there's so much we don't know. The weight-loss drug dexfenfluramine (Redux) was approved by the FDA in 1996 and was withdrawn in 1997 because, besides raising brain-serotonin levels (Chap. 15) to curb appetite, it unexpectedly caused serious heart-valve problems in some people.

One drug being investigated is an "uncoupler" that occurs naturally in brown fat. It disrupts the tight coupling of ATP production to the burning of body fuel (Chap. 9), so that more heat is made instead—a way of getting rid of body fat without having to exercise more or eat less. Fortunately, drugs are more thoroughly tested today than in the 1930s, when an uncoupler used for weight loss was so effective that the heat produced could exceed the body's capacity to get rid of it and cause death (oops!). Some uncouplers are found naturally in plants, which raises concern about their possible use as dietary supplements, which, unlike drugs, don't have to be proven safe or effective before being sold.

We already know that leptin can affect fertility —ob/ob and db/db mice can't reproduce (they're born of parents who carry only one copy of the recessive gene). That a hormone made by fat stores would affect fertility really isn't surprising. Recall the observation that when body fat gets too low,

fertility falls. Pregnancy and nursing use a lot of calories, a wasteful use of calories in a famine, when survival of fetuses and infants is especially precarious. The body is sensitive to signals of starvation—from a rise in ketone levels (Chap. 8) to a fall in leptin levels—and reacts to protect itself.

Genes vs. Environment

For all the discussion about genes, the environment is the cause of the obesity epidemic in the U.S. The prevalence of obesity has gone from about 14% of our adult population in 1980 to about 22% today—too short a time for genetic changes to be the culprit. The increase in obesity and also the "merely overweight" has occurred across all ethnic, socioeconomic, and age groups.

This isn't to say that genetics doesn't play a big part. It does. At the least, we've all inherited a compelling urge to eat when hungry. And part of human diversity is the range of genetic influences on disease, e.g., the extra-long lifespan of those with genetically high HDL-levels and the extra-short one of those with the genetically high LDL-levels of familial hypercholesterolemia (Chap. 8). But even at these extremes, environment can hasten or delay disease.

Most of us fall between the extremes. For us, environment (diet, exercise, smoking, drinking, stress, medication, etc.) makes a huge difference. Even normal-weight rats, when given cookies instead of food pellets will overeat. Pets of overweight families tend to be overweight, and we know that's not genetic!

The cause of obesity is excess calories—from not burning enough or eating too many. So the remedy is "simply" to get more exercise and eat less. Needless to say, this is very difficult, and much more difficult for some than others. If you're inclined to overeat and underexercise, make it harder to do so. "Store" your chips and candy at the store, so you need to go there to buy it each time you want some. Tell the neighbor kid to come by at 7 PM every evening and you'll go running together. Store your cans of soft drinks in the cupboard, so you either have to drink it warm, wait for it to cool, or (horrors!) go to all the trouble of getting a glass, filling it with ice, pouring the drink, and returning the glass to the kitchen. Small changes add up to help you lose weight, just as they can cause you to gain it.

Chronic diseases, including obesity, develop over many years, involve many genetic and environmental factors, and aren't easy to cure. Even small changes in dietary and living habits can dramatically prevent or delay our most common diseases. Fortunately, there doesn't have to be a different set of guidelines for each condition, e.g., a good diet and regular exercise lowers the risk of heart disease, cancer, osteoporosis, and obesity.

Summary

The energy our cells need comes from the food we eat. Food energy is measured in calories. The body releases food energy (*burns calories*) through the various reactions of metabolism. Unless we're pregnant, nursing, or growing, our total energy requirement is the sum of what we need for: (a) basal metabolism, (b) physical activity, and (c) incorporation of food into the body.

Basal metabolism is what's needed for the body to function at its most basic level (breathing, maintaining tissues, etc.). It's measured under standard conditions—when a person is lying down, hasn't eaten for several hours, is relaxed, comfortable, and awake.

Basal metabolism accounts for about two thirds of the total calorie requirement of sedentary people and about half the requirement of "strenuous athletes." Aside from genetic variations, basal metabolism varies mainly with body size and composition. A large body needs more energy to maintain the greater mass, and lean tissue uses more energy, since it's more metabolically active.

Women have lower basal metabolism than men because they're smaller and have proportionately less lean tissue. During pregnancy and nursing, calorie needs go up to provide for the fetus and the making of breast milk. Relative to body weight, infants have the highest resting metabolism, due to their rapid growth. Basal metabolism falls as growth slows and also falls as we age, since aging causes a reduction in lean body mass.

Some hormones, especially thyroid hormone (thyroxine), affect resting metabolism. Basal metabolism falls if there isn't enough thyroid hormone. This causes symptoms like sluggish mental activity, weight gain, and water retention. Iodine is a vital component of thyroid hormone. Without it, the thyroid can't make enough hormone.

Goiter—an enlargement of the thyroid gland —has many causes, but the most common cause, worldwide, is a deficiency of iodine in the diet. Excessive thyroid hormone is also possible, but there are no known dietary causes. Excess thyroid hormone raises basal metabolism (*speeds metabolism*). This can cause nervousness, sweating, rapid heartbeat, fatigue, and weight loss.

Part of our basal metabolism is for maintaining normal body temperature. We always lose some heat to our surroundings. A tall, thin person loses more than a shorter, wider person of the same weight, and thus has a higher basal metabolism. A thin person has more skin surface and less fat as insulation—an advantage in endurance events where heat generated by the prolonged activity must be dissipated rapidly to avoid prostration.

Physical activity can use a lot of energy, and gives us the most control of our energy needs. The amount of energy expended in a given activity is largely dependent on body weight. The more a person weighs, the more energy it takes to move. Calories needed for physical activity can be estimated as a percent of what you need for basal metabolism (since this also reflects body weight).

Digestion, absorption, and assimilation of food into the body uses about 5-10% of the calories we eat. This can make us feel warm after we eat.

The body is well-adapted. For more efficient regulation of body temperature, people from hot climates tend to be thinner, and people from cold climates tend to be fatter. When food is scarce, basal metabolism falls, and we tend to be less physically active. Those who store more calories as fat when food is plentiful survive longer in a famine.

Obesity is epidemic in the U.S. We have an abundance of appealing food combined with less physical effort needed for routine activities. Our genetic heritage includes a compelling urge to eat when body fat falls, an adaptation to food scarcity that's frustrating to people trying to lose weight.

There are genetic forms of obesity, where the genes dominate, but for most us, obesity is caused by a more even mix of genes and environment. The cause of obesity is an excess of calories from not burning enough and/or eating too many, so the difficult remedy is to do the "unnatural"—exercise more and eat less.

Many recent discoveries, including that of the hormone leptin made by fat cells, raise the hope that there will soon be more effective drugs to treat obesity.

Chapter 14

Musculoskeletal System

Use strengthens, disuse debilitates.

Hippocrates (460-377 B.C.)

Get off your duff!

Mom and Dad

Watching the agility and accuracy of a star quarterback, we marvel at what a skeleton and a set of muscles can do. We tend to forget about their other functions. Without a skull and ribs, think of the brain, lung, and heart damage the quarterback would suffer when sacked. And remember that his endeavors—and life itself—depend on the regular contractions of the heart and respiratory muscles.

Muscle

Muscles make up about 45% of normal body weight in men and about 35% in women. There are various kinds, such as the cardiac muscle that contracts the heart, and the smooth muscles of blood vessels that contract or relax to alter the body's distribution of blood. Most of our muscles are skeletal muscles—the ones attached by tendons to our skeleton.

We think of muscles as protein, but protein holds about three times its weight in water (Chap. 5). So muscle is mostly water-about 70% water

and about 20% protein; the rest is fat and a bit of minerals and carbohydrate (glycogen). The exact content varies from person to person and muscle to muscle-much like the variation in different cuts of beef.

A muscle is made up of thousands of individual muscle cells. In addition to the standard cell parts, muscle cells have special proteins that enable the muscle to contract (Fig. 14-1). Skeletal muscle cells are long and cylindrical, so they're called muscle fibers. They're bunched together by thin wrappings of connective tissue. You can see the layout in meat. Carving tough meat across the fibers—cutting "across the grain"—makes it easier to chew.

The male sex hormone testosterone promotes muscle growth. Thus, boys become more muscular at puberty, and men are more muscular than women. Women also make testosterone, but their levels are about 20-30 times lower. But people vary a lot—men at the low end have testosterone levels near those of women at the high end.

Figure 14-1: Skeletal Muscle Contraction

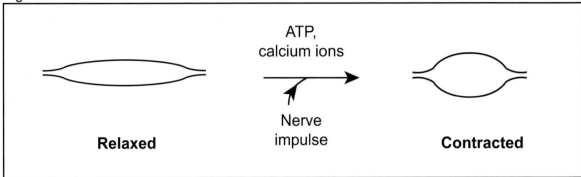

As discussed in Chapter 9, there are different kinds of muscle fibers. Red fibers are geared for endurance and aerobic (oxygen-requiring) metabolism—they have more mitochondria (for oxygen-requiring metabolism), myoglobin (red, oxygen-carrying molecules), and fat droplets (main fuel for an endurance event). White fibers are more suited for bursts of activity (weight-lifting, sprinting)—geared toward making ATP energy faster and without oxygen (anaerobic metabolism), using glucose as fuel.

Most of us have muscles with red and white fibers in about equal amounts. Elite strength-and-power athletes have proportionately more white fibers in the relevant muscles; elite endurance athletes have more red. Training can enhance the aerobic (and possibly anaerobic) capacity of both kinds of fibers, but the proportion of each seems to be genetic.

Exercise

The number of muscle cells in a muscle also seems to be genetic. Thus, when we exercise or stop exercising, the size—rather than the number of cells—changes. When we regularly exercise a muscle, more of the contraction proteins are made, and the cell thickens and becomes stronger. A muscle's strength is generally proportional to its size.

As food, the tenderest meat comes from the least-exercised muscles. The muscle that lies along an animal's back isn't used much; it's narrow and tender (e.g., pork tenderloin). In contrast, shoulder muscles are used a lot (exercised) and become thicker—and tougher (e.g., pork shoulder). Other things affect tenderness (e.g., marbling with fat) but, in general, the most tender meat comes from the least exercised muscles and the youngest animals (e.g., veal, roast suckling pig).

Muscle size adapts rapidly to use or disuse. Even the need to pull against gravity helps maintain muscle. Astronauts exercise regularly on space voyages, since weightlessness can cause rapid muscle loss. Anyone who has ever had an arm or a leg in a cast has seen the marked contrast in muscle size between the limb just out of a cast and the other one. Likewise, the forearm of the arm that swings a tennis racket is much more muscular than the opposite one. Body builders add bulk to specific muscles by exercising them. And as they know all too well, this bulk is quickly lost when they quit working out. (Use it or lose it!)

Building muscles means you need a little more protein in your diet, an amount easily met by a normal diet (Chap. 11). Contrary to what ads in magazines for body builders would have you believe, protein or amino acid supplements don't in themselves increase muscle mass.

Anabolic Steroids

Anabolic steroids are used by some athletes to build muscle and strength; they're often simply called steroids. This can be confusing, since there are many hormones (e.g., estrogen, corticosteroids) that, technically, are steroids (i.e., hormones made from chole*sterol*), but have far different effects.

Anabolic steroids were first developed to treat patients with muscle-wasting diseases. Athletes take them at much higher doses than are prescribed for medical purposes. Their use to enhance athletic performance is generally illegal in the United States and in international competition.

Ben Johnson was stripped of a 1988 Olympic gold medal and his world record in the 100-meter dash when he tested positive for stanozolol. In 1990, Randy Barnes (a world record-holder in the shot put) was suspended from competition for 2 years for testing positive for methyltestosterone, and suspended again in 1998 for testing positive for androstenedione. Androstenedione is banned by the Olympics, the National Football League, and the National College Athletic Association. Mark McGwire's use of it when he broke Roger Maris's home run record in 1998 was legal—the steroid wasn't banned then in professional baseball and was sold legally without a prescription in the U.S. as a dietary supplement.

Because anabolic steroids are similar to testosterone, the body reacts by making less testosterone (shrunken testicles is a side effect). Low testosterone does not prove the use of these drugs, but provides supporting evidence.

"First of all, we found steroids in your urine."

Anabolic steroids are constructed to retain or enhance testosterone's growth-promoting effects on muscle while minimizing its other effects. Studies done on athletes in what was then East Germany clearly show that anabolic steroids taken in large doses during training promote increased muscle mass and strength. This was confirmed in a double-blind study in the U.S. Keep in mind that the dose matters. Steroids sold as dietary supplements advertised as "effective and without side effects" are usually one or the other—effective (effective dose) *or* without side effects (ineffective dose).

Some side effects of anabolic steroids are relatively mild (e.g., acne, lower-pitch voice, increased body hair, lower sex drive); others are serious. One of the more worrisome is the effect on the liver. There's substantial evidence that anabolic steroids raise the risk of liver damage and liver cancer. Also, HDL-(*good*)-cholesterol is made in the liver, and anabolic steroids lower it to extremely low levels—a risk factor for heart disease. It's ironic that a higher HDL is a benefit of physical fitness, and this benefit is more than canceled by taking steroids.

Another very worrisome side effect is a severe psychiatric reaction of anger and hostility (*'roid rage*) that occurs in some steroid users. Of those taking large doses, major depression or mania occurs in about 1 out of 5, and psychosis occurs in about 1 out of 10. Steroids may have a role in the growing problem of some athletes' violent behavior.

Steroid use has spread beyond the fraternity of elite athletes. Some men are using them to build muscle simply for looks. A substantial number of athletes—male and female—are using them as early as junior high school; unfortunately, most school districts can't afford a screening program in their athletic programs.

Growth Hormone

Some athletes now use human growth hormone made by biotechnology (in addition to or in place of anabolic steroids) to build muscle. Because the human growth hormone made by biotechnology is identical to that made by the body, its illegal use by athletes isn't easily caught. But the very high cost of human growth hormone limits its use among athletes.

Side effects from using large doses for athletic purposes are hard to establish, since athletes are trying to conceal their use, but anecdotal reports of abnormal bone growth are consistent with what we'd expect. We know the problems caused by excessive production of growth hormone. In childhood, it accelerates bone growth, resulting in gigantism, characterized by gigantic height and sexual immaturity. When excessive production begins in adulthood (acromegaly), it causes the feet, hands, and the lower jaw to grow. There are other problems such as thickening (and sometimes darkening) of the skin. Nearly all women with this disease develop menstrual irregularities, and about a third of the men become impotent.

Aging

Starting at about age 30, we gradually lose muscle protein, and the amount of fat in muscle increases. This age-related change is thought to be partly due to less growth hormone. Now that it can be made by biotechnology, growth hormone replacement therapy might be used in treating the elderly for loss of muscle protein (Chap. 13).

The fall in muscle protein leads to the weaker muscle strength seen with aging. But note that a physically fit 80-year-old can be stronger, more agile, and have more endurance than a sedentary 30-year-old. Mavis Lindgren at age 81 ran the marathon (26.2 miles) in 4 hours and 34 minutes, winning her the world's record for the 70-81-year-old age group. There aren't many sedentary 30-year-olds that can maintain a pace of 5.7 miles per hour for 4½ hours.

Muscle Contraction

Nerve cells usually provide the stimulus for muscle contraction, as when we walk or when we jerk our hand back from a hot pan. But heart muscle is stimulated rhythmically by pacemaker cells in the heart tissue itself. When these pace-

makers don't work right because of disease or damage from a heart attack, normal rhythm can be restored by implanting an artificial pacemaker. (When its owner dies, an artificial pacemaker can be recycled to patients in less affluent countries.)

To contract, muscle cells need energy (ATP) and certain minerals (e.g., calcium ions) (Fig. 14-1). ATP is made in breaking down glucose and fat (Chap. 9). We think of muscular contraction as moving, but it's also needed just to maintain normal muscle tone, using some of the energy used in resting metabolism. Muscle cells contract asynchronously to sustain a tightness in the muscle—a tightness needed to maintain posture. Without muscle tone, your head would slump onto your chest.

Many athletes take protein or amino acid supplements because of a common misconception that protein is what fuels muscle contraction. Some amino acids are used for fuel when glycogen is depleted in endurance events, but the extra need for protein is modest and easily met by a normal diet (protein needs of athletes were discussed in Chap. 11). Athlete or not, almost all of the energy needed for muscle activity comes from the ATP generated by the metabolism of glucose and fat.

Bone

We tend to think of our bones as dry—a Halloween skeleton-chalky, dead tissue. But bone is well supplied with blood, and minerals constantly move in and out. Some bones contain red marrow, which makes red blood cells, some white blood cells, and platelets. The skeleton is very much alive.

Besides its use as support, protection, movement, and blood-cell production, bone is a mineral reserve. About 99% of the body's calcium, 85% of the body's phosphorus, and 60% of the body's magnesium are in bone. These minerals are crucial to body chemistry. Without calcium, blood can't clot, muscle can't contract, and a nerve cell can't send its message. Phosphorus is a key part of ATP (adenosine tri*phosphate), and* magnesium is needed to regenerate ATP. Very small amounts of calcium, phosphorus, and magnesium are needed for these uses, but their presence is crucial, and the body is assured of never running out. Bone minerals are readily mobilized to make up for any shortfall.

Bone is about 30% protein (collagen) and about 70% minerals. It's sort of like reinforced concrete—protein for tensile strength, and minerals for compressional strength. Taking out the minerals is a popular experiment in a child's science class: Put a chicken bone in vinegar; the acid (acetic acid in vinegar) dissolves the minerals; after a few weeks, only the protein is left—demonstrated by bending the bone in half.*

When a bone is said to be dense, it's dense with minerals. Bones aren't really solid. The outside is smooth and compact, but the inside is porous, much like styrofoam. It's well engineered. The outer hardness of a leg bone provides the strength of a tube (a tube is almost as strong as a solid rod of the same diameter). The porous inside adds strength without adding much weight. The protein gives it some flexibility.

Stimulated by growth hormone, bone grows fast during childhood and adolescence. Bone density increases until about age 30, but most of that density is acquired before age 20. Generally speaking, bone density stays the same from age 30 to 50 and then falls. A key factor in the development of osteoporosis is the amount of bone a person has in early adulthood when bone mass reaches its peak (peak *bone density).*

In dwarfism, the pituitary gland doesn't make enough growth hormone during childhood, and the person is abnormally short. Growth hormone (a protein) used to be extracted from human pituitary glands, and the limited supply was

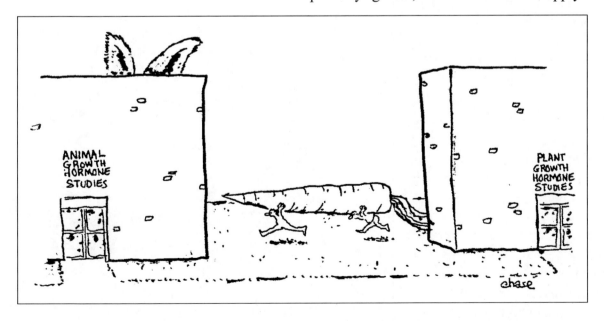

*When soup bones are boiled, collagen dissolves, forming gelatin. This is why soup stock gels when refrigerated. Gelatin (for Jell-O, etc.) is typically made by extracting it from pig skin.

used to treat children with dwarfism. Some of them came down, many years later, with a fatal brain disease caused by an infectious agent in the extracted glands. Production of human growth hormone by biotechnology eliminates this risk and makes more hormone available.

Now, some parents request this hormone for their children to make them taller, even though the children are of normal height and have normal amounts of growth hormone. Treatment takes about 6-8 years, and costs about $20,000 per year. The hormone isn't officially approved for this use, but is legitimately available by prescription, since it's approved for the treatment of dwarfism.

Bone Nutrients

Vitamin D

Many nutrients are important in bone development and maintenance, but the focus is on vitamin D and calcium, since these play the biggest roles. Vitamin D is called the sunshine vitamin—it can be made in skin by the action of ultraviolet (UV) light from the sun (or a sunlamp). UV light converts a vitamin D precursor (made in the body from cholesterol) into D. This occurs in other animals as well.

Chickens running around the farmyard make enough vitamin D from sun exposure. After inexpensive sources were found, D could be added to the diet of domesticated animals (including pets), and they could be raised entirely indoors. Foods like eggs and poultry became more plentiful and inexpensive, improving the diets of many people.

One might argue that vitamin D isn't really a vitamin, since we can make what we need if we get enough sun. But without enough sun, D is needed in the diet.

It's hard to say how much sun is enough. The amount of UV radiation that reaches the skin varies with time of day, latitude, cloud cover, air pollution, clothing style and custom, and amount of sunscreen put on the skin. Also, those with lighter skin need less exposure, and the production in the skin is less efficient in the elderly.

For a young person with fair skin living in a clear, sunny climate, just a few minutes outdoors each day (e.g., walking around campus) can be enough. But an elderly person with dark skin living in a smoggy, cold climate may need hours of exposure. Because of the uncertainty of sun exposure, there are Recommended Dietary Allowances (RDAs) for vitamin D.

Once vitamin D is made in the skin or taken in from the diet, its chemical structure is altered in the kidney and liver to an activated form of D. Thus, people with liver or kidney disease may have symptoms of a deficiency, even if they get enough. They can be prescribed the activated version.

Vitamin D is needed for bone to grow correctly. It is needed to absorb calcium from the intestine and to mineralize bone (D turns on the gene for a calcium-binding protein used to take in calcium). Without enough D, bones aren't fully mineralized, making them weak and easily bent. Severe deficiency of D causes *osteomalacia* when

"Would you mind stepping out of the light?.
I've got a solar-powered pacemaker."

it occurs in adults, and *rickets* when it occurs in children. A child with rickets has bowed legs from the weight of the body pressing down on the developing leg bones.

The bone deformities can cause serious problems. Bent rib bones can cause a permanent "sunken chest" in children, making them more prone to lung disease. A permanently narrowed pelvic bone in girls can be a problem in childbirth. Osteomalacia (severe D deficiency in adults) can cause painful fractures, especially in the spine and pelvis.

Rickets and osteomalacia were common in industrialized cities during the 17th century. Buildings that lined the narrow streets and the heavy soot in the air blocked the sun. The diet was also poor in vitamin D. Rickets was so common that it was thought to be normal. Before vitamin D (and its relationship to rickets) was discovered, it was found that codliver oil (rich in D) could prevent and cure rickets. In the 19th century, many a mother forced her children to swallow a squirt of smelly cod-liver oil every day.

Today, vitamin D deficiency is relatively uncommon. In tropical countries, the deficiency rarely occurs, regardless of diet, unless people completely avoid the sun. In the practice of *purdah* by some cultures, women cover themselves head to toe whenever they go outdoors. This puts them at risk unless they get vitamin D in their diet.

Vitamin D is found naturally in such foods as egg yolk, butter, and fish, and is added to foods such as margarine, milk, and some ready-to-eat breakfast cereals. Two cups of vitamin-D-fortified milk (or foods with an equivalent amount of milk) for adults ages 19-50 and 4 cups for those 51-70 years old will, alone, provide the RDA for vitamin D. It would take the vitamin D in 6 cups of milk to meet the RDA of those over age 70.

Virtually all the milk sold (or made into milk products) in this country is fortified with vitamins D and A. Thus, adults who have the recommended amounts of milk or milk products generally should not take vitamin D supplements.

Those who don't drink much milk may need supplements, depending on their sun exposure and how much D they get from other foods. Babies who aren't exposed to the sun and are exclusively breast-fed for a long time should be given a supplement. ("Natural" milk— human and cow's milk alike—has very little D; infant formula is fortified with D.) But anyone taking vitamin D supplements should be warned against taking doses higher than the RDA. Excessive amounts can be very toxic—especially in young children.

Toxic amounts mostly come from large doses taken as supplements (D isn't made in toxic amounts by sun exposure). Toxicity can occur at only 4-10 times the RDA, and can cause damaging calcium deposits in soft tissues and irreversible damage to the kidneys and cardiovascular system.

Vitamin D deficiency may become more common among those who don't consume milk or milk products, as more people avoid the sun for fear of skin cancer and eat less butter, margarine, and egg yolks in trying to lower dietary fat and cholesterol. Dietary sources of D are particularly important for African-Americans who live in industrialized cities in the northern United States. The majority of them are lactose intolerant, and may avoid milk for this reason. However, as mentioned in Chapter 6, many people with lactose intolerance can avoid symptoms by consuming milk or milk products in small doses and with meals.

It takes more sun exposure to form D in the skin of African Americans because their skin has a lot of melanin (a brown/black pigment)—a natural sunblock against sun's UV light (Chap. 12). This situation is made worse by limited sun

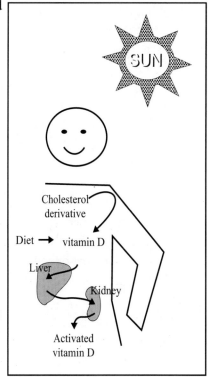

Cholesterol derivative

Diet → vitamin D

Liver

Kidney

Activated vitamin D

exposure due to air pollution and by less skin exposure during the cold seasons.

For much of history, Africans had strong and prolonged sun exposure because they lived at latitudes near the equator. They made ample D in their skin, while their large amounts of melanin protected them from the sun's damaging effects (e.g., skin cancer). In contrast, Eskimos had little exposure to the sun, because of heavy clothing and living at an extremely northern latitude. But they weren't dependent on sun exposure for D. Their diet was rich in oils from seafood (e.g., fatty fish, seals)—oils that are rich in D.

Calcium

The Halloween skeleton is chalky indeed. Both chalk (limestone) and the skeleton are rich in calcium. Calcium exists in nature only in combination with other elements. In chalk, it's calcium carbonate ($CaCO_3$). In bone, it's mainly hydroxyapatite [$Ca_{10}(PO_4)_6(OH)_2$].

Bone is a calcium reserve. Calcium is kept at a constant level in the blood. When it goes up, one hormone (calcitonin) takes calcium out of blood and deposits it in bone. When it falls, another hormone (parathormone) draws calcium out of bone.

Problems occur when blood-calcium goes outside of its narrow range. For example, nerve cells become more sensitive with an abnormal drop in blood-calcium. This can cause a rapid stimulation of muscle nerves, such that the muscle cramps or "freezes" in contraction.

Some popular health books falsely attribute this to a deficiency of calcium in the diet. In fact, dietary calcium doesn't ordinarily alter blood-calcium. About 99% of the body's calcium is in bone, and this calcium is easily mobilized to make up for any shortfall in the blood. Abnormal blood-calcium is usually from a problem with either vitamin D or one of the hormones that control the movement of calcium in and out of bone.

Bone is constantly altered throughout life, with calcium continually moving in and out of bone to be deposited where it's needed. Small difference in the rate in which calcium moves in or out of bone can have a big effect on bone density. Stress on a bone stimulates calcium to move in, making the bone denser. Less stress on a bone (as when people become disabled or when astronauts escape the pull of gravity) causes calcium loss.

During childhood, bone grows slower if the diet is deficient in calcium. If this persists through puberty, children stay shorter. This could be an adaptation to an inadequate diet, since less calcium is needed to maintain a shorter skeleton. The adaptation is temporary—if the next generation has a good diet, the children will grow to their full genetic potential. In Japan, nutrition improved right after World War II, and the children then grew several inches taller than their parents.

Severe calcium deficiency causes rickets in children. Although vitamin D is needed to properly mineralize bone, it can't do so if there isn't enough calcium. So the outcome (rickets) is the same, whether it's D or calcium that's deficient. (Vitamin D deficiency is the most common cause of rickets.)

The main source of calcium in the U.S. diet is milk. It's an especially good source because the vitamin D, protein, and lactose in the milk promote calcium absorption. In the U.S., calcium intake generally is related to the amount of milk or milk products in the diet.

"Yes?"

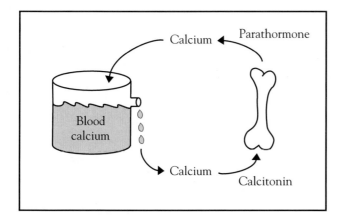

Some ethnic foods have a fair amount of calcium. Traditional Mexican corn tortillas are rich in calcium. Corn itself isn't rich in calcium, but it's soaked in limewater (a solution of calcium oxide) before being ground to make the tortillas. This calcium-fortified cornmeal is called *masa harina.*

Traditional soybean curd (*tofu*) is made rich in calcium by processing in a calcium-rich solution (some brands of "organic tofu" aren't made this way). Sesame seeds are rich in calcium, and a paste of ground sesame seeds is the main ingredient in *halvah,* a Turkish confection. Sesame paste is also added to Middle-Eastern dishes such as *hummus.* Bones (e.g., in canned sardines and salmon, or calcium leached from bones boiled in an acidic liquid) also provide calcium.

Where do adult animals get their calcium? Calcium-rich antlers are shed onto the forest floor where small animals eat them. When animals need lots of calcium but eat only low-calcium foods, they eat huge amounts, e.g., cows spend virtually all their waking hours munching on grass or hay.

The amount of calcium that's absorbed in the intestine varies. Spinach has a fair amount of calcium, but also has lots of oxalic acid, which binds to calcium and prevents its absorption. In contrast, vitamin D promotes calcium absorption. Absorption goes up as a long-term adaptation to a low-calcium diet and during early childhood, pregnancy, and breast-feeding. Absorption goes

down in the elderly. This variability in absorption is taken into account in setting the recommended amounts of dietary calcium.

It's important to get enough calcium, especially during childhood, adolescence, and early adulthood, when bone is growing and becoming more dense. Although the calcium recommendations are the same for both sexes, most people over age 11 don't get enough. Females are particularly low; they drink less milk and eat less food than males the same age. The more we eat, the more nutrients we take in.

Try to get your calcium from a good diet. Calcium supplements can cause constipation and interfere with the absorption of other essential minerals (e.g., iron). Supplements vary in the amount of calcium (Chap. 3). To be effective, the supplement must dissolve in the stomach (Chap. 6 tells how to test for this). Taking ground-up bone (*bone meal*) isn't advised, since it can be contaminated with lead or other toxic elements. Bone meal may be more "natural," but it also can be naturally contaminated.

Bone takes in lead (withdraws it from blood), which lessens lead's toxic effects. Bone also takes in strontium-90, a radioactive element present in fallout from nuclear explosions. Strontium is chemically similar to calcium (both atoms have 2 electrons in their outer shell; Chap. 3), so the body handles it like calcium and stores it in bone. Since blood cells are made in bone marrow, radioactive strontium-90 in the bone raises the risk of leukemia (cancer of white blood cells). In a radioactive fallout, ingesting lots of calcium lessens the amount of strontium-90 absorbed from contaminated food-calcium and strontium compete for attachment to the calcium-binding protein that brings them in from the intestine.

Vitamin C

Vitamin C (ascorbic acid) is needed to make the protein collagen, a component of bone and connective tissue (e.g., in skin and gums).*

*Collagen has hydroxyproline, an unusual amino acid made by adding an -OH (hydroxy) to the proline that's already part of collagen's amino acid chain. (Proline, but not hydroxyproline, is 1 of the 20 amino acids needed to make protein.) Vitamin C is needed to convert proline to hydroxyproline, so a deficiency interferes with the formation and maintenance of bone and connective tissue.

Delayed wound healing (collagen is a part of scar tissue), bleeding gums, and loose teeth are classic signs of scurvy (severe C deficiency). Keep in mind that these symptoms don't necessarily indicate a vitamin C deficiency. The most common cause of bleeding gums and loose teeth is periodontal disease caused by poor dental hygiene.

Foods like citrus fruits, strawberries, broccoli, red and green peppers, and tomatoes are rich sources of C. Potatoes have only modest amounts, but we eat so much of them (e.g., french fries) that they're a major source. Vitamin C is also added to many foods, especially fruit-flavored drinks.

The RDA for vitamin C is generous and, like other vitamins, it doesn't need to be met every day. The average intake from food alone is above the RDA in men, women, and children. In addition, about a third of the adults in this country take vitamin C supplements. Deficiencies occur mainly in people who eat little or no fruits or vegetables—like the sailors who went to sea and got scurvy (Chap. 1). Such a diet is most common in alcoholics and elderly men who live alone.

Although vitamin C is important in functions like wound healing and immunity, amounts in excess of the RDA doesn't enhance these functions. Enough is simply enough. For example, a deficiency of C may raise one's risk of cancer (Chap. 12), making it wise to meet one's RDA. But the idea that taking even more provides additional protection isn't supported by controlled studies.*

Phosphorus

About 85% of the body's phosphorus (P) is in bone, mainly as hydroxyapatite [$Ca_{10}(PO_4)_6(OH)_2$]. The other 15% is found throughout the body in the lecithin that makes up our cell membranes (Chap. 5, 9) and in DNA, RNA, ATP, etc.

Phosphorus is widespread in food. Meat, milk, fish, grains, and nuts are rich sources. Even diet soft drinks have a fair amount. A deficiency is unlikely under ordinary circumstances, but it's

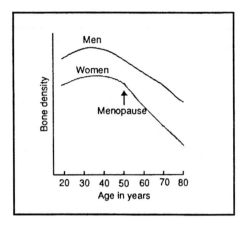

been seen in premature babies fed only breast milk. Breast milk has enough phosphorus for full-term babies, but not enough for premature ones. Thus, premature babies can need supplemental phosphorus for proper bone mineralization.

Phosphorus deficiency can also occur with long-term use of antacids made of aluminum hydroxide, which can combine with dietary phosphorus and prevent its absorption from the intestine. Phosphorus deficiency can cause bone loss, weakness, and pain.

Osteoporosis

Osteoporosis literally means porous bones. Bone is normally porous (styrofoam-like), but the pores get bigger (become lace-like) as minerals are lost. In aging, the amount of collagen in bone also falls, making it more brittle. Bones become so porous and brittle (especially in the wrist, spine, and hip) that they're easily fractured.

A key factor in developing osteoporosis is one's peak bone mass—the density (calcium content) of bone in early adulthood, when bone mass reaches its peak. The higher the peak density, the less likely osteoporosis will occur later.

Osteoporosis is especially common in white, thin, elderly women. After age 50, wrist fractures are more common, usually from extending the arm to break a fall. Wrist fractures aren't usually serious, but can indicate underlying osteoporosis.

---

*It's been suggested that megadoses of C (1 gram or more—more than 16 times the RDA) prevent the common cold and cures cancer, but this has not been seen in double-blind studies (which adjust for placebo effects; Chap. 2). The only evidence for benefit is that huge doses may slightly lessen the severity of a cold, but even this is not a consistent finding in controlled studies.

Fractures of the spinal vertebrae, which tend to occur after about age 55, are often painless, though some people suffer severe pain and disability. Outward signs of these fractures are a loss of height and the stoop of old age—often called *dowager's hump.*

Fractures of the hip are the most serious and the most common in women over age 70. Many die within a year from complications (e.g., pneumonia), or are so disabled that they can no longer live independently.

Although osteoporosis can be detected to some extent by losses in height, it's usually brought to medical attention by a fracture. A puzzling aspect of osteoporosis is that the amount of bone loss isn't necessarily related to the amount of pain or disability. One person may have compression fractures of the vertebrae and severe loss of bone density yet not suffer pain or disability, while someone else may have much less bone loss and experience debilitating pain.

Osteoporosis has been hard to study because it is detectable by X-ray only after much mineral loss. Most studies of changes in bone mass compare people of different ages within a population (cross-sectional study) rather than following the same people as they age (longitudinal study). Longitudinal studies give better information (Chap. 2).

Another complicating factor is that bone isn't lost evenly throughout the skeleton or even throughout a single bone. Certain bones are often studied because of convenience, cost, etc. The wrist may be easier to study than the spine, but what one sees in the wrist may not reflect what's happening in the spine or hip. How osteoporosis develops is an active area of research, and there are now more sophisticated methods of measuring bone loss, e.g., dual-energy X-ray absorptiometry.

Risk Factors

Looking at all the ads for calcium supplements, you'd think that osteoporosis was simply caused by a low-calcium diet. In fact, osteoporosis is a very complex disease brought about by an interplay of many factors. Some of these are:

Gender: Women are at higher risk. They have smaller bones, lower peak bone mass, accelerated bone loss at menopause, and live longer. Also, bone density increases most during fast growth, and growth slows for girls in their early teens, whereas it doesn't slow for boys until their late teens. In other words, boys have more years of rapidly increasing bone density.

Both the male hormone testosterone and the female hormone estrogen help preserve bone mass. There's a rapid fall in estrogen for women at menopause. Aging men have a small and gradual fall in testosterone and a rise in estrogen (which may contribute to their "mellowing" as they age).

Family history: Genes affect bone density and bone size and thus affect risk. Having a parent, grandmother, etc., with osteoporosis raises risk. But it may not all be genetics. Families also share food and exercise habits.

Race: Osteoporosis is more common in Whites and Asians than in Blacks, presumably because of racial differences in bone density. Blacks have denser bones (even though their calcium intake is lower), and Black women have about half as many hip fractures as White women. Those with very light skin (e.g., those with naturally blond or red hair) also have higher risk. There are not as much data on osteoporosis in racial subgroups (e.g., Hispanics), but they're being collected.

Physical activity: Normal physical activity preserves bone mass; prolonged inactivity causes bone loss. The importance of stress on bone is most dramatically demonstrated by the rapid bone loss during space travel, when astronauts escape the pull of gravity.

The greatest effect on bone mass occurs in going from minimal to moderate physical activity. Stress-bearing exercise (e.g., running) offers additional help in strengthening bone. But as with muscles, the effects are very specific, e.g., bone density is higher in the playing arm of a tennis player than in the other arm.

We sometimes need to be reminded that *getting exercise* doesn't necessarily mean we have to take up a sport or work out. Vigorously scrubbing the bathroom or using a manual lawn mower is also good exercise. It should be noted that women who engage in strenuous exercise to the point of amenorrhea (stoppage of menstruation) can lose bone mass (remember moderation). Amenorrhea has some of the same characteristics as menopause.

Body weight: Being overweight lessens risk. The extra weight puts more stress on bones, thereby protecting bone density, and extra body fat provides more cushioning for a bone in a fall. (For those anxious to find health benefits of being overweight, another is less risk of tuberculosis—another is you live longer in a famine.)

Also, fat cells make some estrogen and become an important source when ovary-produced estrogen falls at menopause. Extreme thinness to the point of amenorrhea in premenopausal women (many ballerinas and women with anorexia nervosa have this problem) can cause bone loss because of insufficient estrogen.

Smoking seems to raise the risk for both men and women. The reason isn't entirely clear, but part of the reason for women who smoke is that they have an earlier menopause, resulting in accelerated bone loss at an earlier age. Also, smokers tend to weigh less. As noted earlier, a heavier body weight and more fat tissue offer some protection.

Alcohol: Osteoporosis is more common among alcoholics. Alcoholics tend to have poor diets. Alcohol can also lessen nutrient absorption by damaging the intestinal lining. Also, being tipsy raises the risk of falling—and fractures.

Dietary calcium: It's important, of course, to meet your dietary requirement. As said earlier, most people over age 11 don't. Ads and magazine articles encouraging more calcium in the diet are mostly directed at women, but adolescents should be the main focus. Adequate calcium intake during childhood and early adulthood is crucial for attaining high peak bone mass.

Other nutrients can potentially affect risk, mainly by affecting calcium absorption and losses. Protein taken in high doses as a dietary supplement dramatically increases the loss of calcium in the urine. Smaller amounts are lost when the protein is from food. One reason could be that foods high in protein also tend to be high in phosphorus, which seems to help prevent the loss of calcium.

Lest one think that excessive phosphorus is helpful, it should be noted that a high intake of phosphorus reduces calcium absorption in the intestine. So, it seems that there is neither loss nor gain in bone calcium when a diet is high in phosphorus and adequate in calcium. But these conclusions are based on studies of adults, and there's some concern that excessive phosphorus may have a detrimental effect on bone growth.

This is of particular concern for growing girls, since their diets tend to be high in phosphorus and low in calcium. Studies in young animals show that a diet that's both high in phosphorus and low in calcium promotes bone loss. An important group to study in this regard are growing girls who are thin, small-boned, sedentary, fair-skinned,

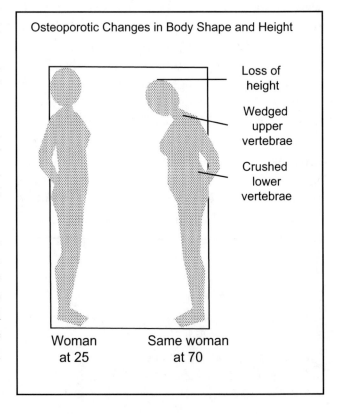

Osteoporotic Changes in Body Shape and Height

Loss of height

Wedged upper vertebrae

Crushed lower vertebrae

Woman at 25   Same woman at 70

continually dieting, and who consume very little milk or milk products.

A high-sodium diet combined with a low-calcium diet can also contribute to osteoporosis. Excess sodium is excreted in the urine, and the sodium pulls some calcium out with it, making the calcium deficiency even worse.

Prevention

As can be seen from the risk factors, the best that children and adults can do is eat a good diet (Chap. 4), get a moderate amount of exercise, and not smoke. The aim is to achieve high peak bone mass, and to slow bone loss during aging.

Many new preventive therapies are being evaluated to retard bone loss in postmenopausal women, but estrogen-replacement therapy starting at menopause is the most effective one available now. Estrogen therapy starting at menopause reduces the number of hip and wrist fractures by about half.

As with all medications, possible side effects of estrogen-replacement therapy is a concern, a major one being estrogen-related cancers. Estrogen used to be given alone (*unopposed estrogen*), and this raised the risk of cancer in the lining of the uterus (endometrial cancer).* Now, estrogen is given together with another hormone (progestogen) that greatly lessens—and possibly eliminates—the higher risk of this cancer.

Estrogen therapy lasting more than 10 years seems to raise the risk of breast cancer. Studies have been inconsistent, as is common in studies looking for small effects in differing circumstances. A problem is that only recently have women been randomly assigned to control and experimental groups. In most studies, postmenopausal women who chose to take hormones have been compared with those who didn't take them, and the two groups differ in many other ways (Chap. 2).

The best a woman can do upon approaching menopause is to discuss the available therapies with her physician in terms of her own risks and the potential benefits and risk of various therapies. Not all women are suitable for hormone-replacement therapy, including those who are many years past menopause and have already lost a lot of bone, those who have had breast cancer, and those with certain health problems such as liver disease or very high blood pressure.

Several drugs that maximize the benefits and minimize the risks of hormone replacement therapy (e.g., lower the risk of both osteoporosis and breast cancer) are now being developed. Non-hormonal drugs such as slow-release fluoride and bisphosphonates (e.g., etidronate, alendronate) are also used to prevent and treat osteoporosis. Fluoride hardens bone, much like it hardens tooth enamel. Bisphosphonates reduce bone loss. Also, don't overlook common sense in preventing the falls that can fracture bone, e.g., installing handrails, strengthening muscles, and wearing good eyeglasses.

Periodontal Disease

Periodontal disease is an infection of the tissues that surround a tooth *(perio* = around; *dontal* = tooth). In function, teeth are a part of the digestive system (tooth decay was discussed in Chap. 6). But in structure, teeth are more like bone—a skeleton does have teeth. Altogether, we form 52 teeth: 20 baby teeth and 32 permanent teeth.

Tooth enamel—the outer layer—is almost entirely mineral, and is the hardest part (Fig. 14-2). The dentin underneath, like bone, is about 70% mineral and 30% protein. The center of the tooth is full of the pulp which contains nerves and blood vessels that enter and exit through the root canals. Like bone, the hard structure of a tooth is formed by minerals deposited onto a protein matrix. As you'd expect, nutrients important in forming bone are similarly important in forming teeth.

---

*Postmenopausal obese women have a higher risk of endometrial cancer. Their extra body fat results in more estrogen made there—*unopposed estrogen*. Studies are being done now to see if giving progestogen to obese women after menopause will lower their risk of this cancer.

Figure 14-2: The Tooth and Surrounding Structures

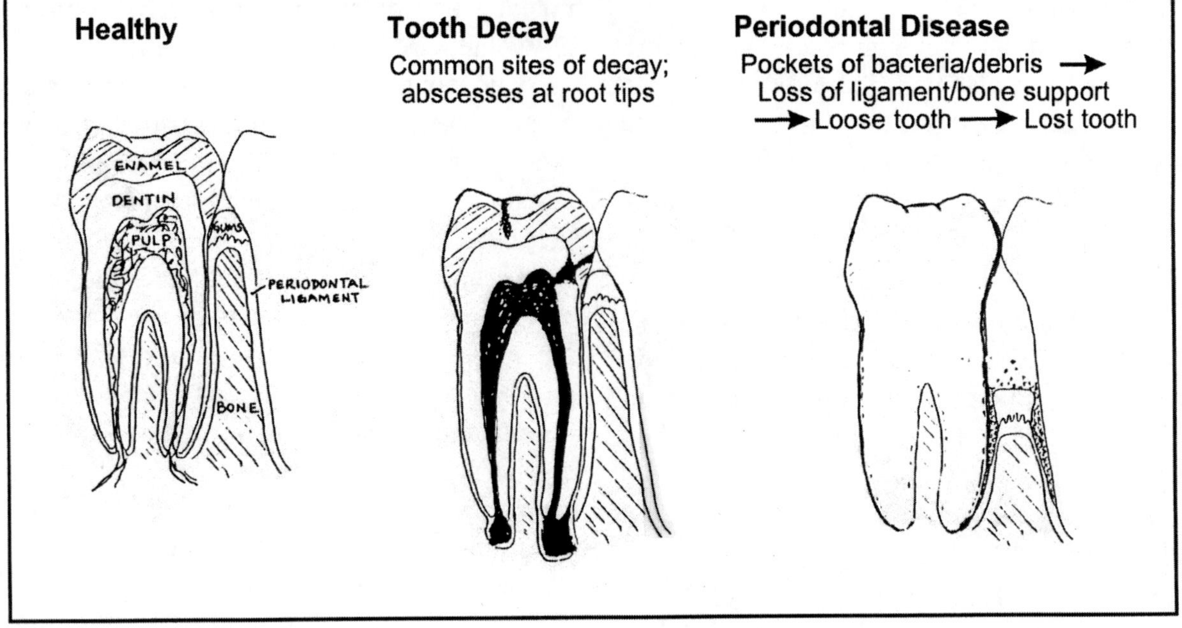

Healthy

Tooth Decay
Common sites of decay;
abscesses at root tips

Periodontal Disease
Pockets of bacteria/debris ➝
Loss of ligament/bone support
➝ Loose tooth ➝ Lost tooth

Periodontal (*around the tooth*) tissues include the gums (gingiva), the periodontal ligament which surrounds the root, and the bone that supports the teeth. The supporting bone can be remodeled—the basis of orthodontics (repositioning teeth into better alignment) and the reason why the upper front teeth can stick out from intense thumb-sucking (any distortion of the supporting bone will usually correct itself if thumb-sucking stops before the permanent front teeth erupt—at about age 6).

Periodontal disease is the main cause of adult tooth loss. The disease begins in the dental plaque that extends into the crevice between the tooth and gums (Fig. 14-2). Bacteria in the plaque release substances that irritate the gums (gingiva), causing redness and swelling—*gingivitis* (inflammation of the gingiva). The plaque calcifies, forming a hard, rough substance called *tartar* that also irritates the gums.

Other conditions can further aggravate the situation. Hormonal changes during the menstrual cycle or pregnancy, for example, can temporarily increase susceptibility to gingivitis. So can diabetes.

Gingivitis can largely be prevented by including the area of the tooth just below the gum-line when brushing and flossing. But despite diligent flossing and brushing with a "tartar-control" toothpaste, we still get some tartar. (Zinc chloride or pyrophosphate is the toothpaste ingredient that lessens tartar—but only above, not below, the gum line.) We're advised to have our teeth cleaned of tartar twice a year by a dental hygienist.

Gingivitis is common, even during childhood. It's so common that some people think swollen or bleeding gums are normal. Some people self-prescribe big doses of vitamin C for bleeding gums. Just because it's a symptom of scurvy (severe C deficiency), this doesn't mean that bleeding gums indicates a deficiency; taking vitamin C in amounts higher than the RDA doesn't help prevent gingivitis.

In most cases, swollen gums or gums that bleed during tooth-brushing indicate gingivitis caused by poor dental hygiene. Gingivitis is reversible, and itself wouldn't be cause for much concern if it weren't for the fact that it can progress to *periodontitis*, the more extensive inflammation of periodontal tissue.

When gingivitis progresses, the crevice between the tooth and gums widens and deepens, forming a pocket that provides a larger and more sequestered place for bacteria and debris to accumulate.* The periodontal ligament and supporting bone can then become infected, causing periodontitis. This can cause loss of surrounding bone, which causes the tooth to loosen.

The extent of periodontitis is measured by the depth of the pocket between the tooth and gums. The tooth is lost when there's not enough periodontal ligament and supporting bone to hold it.

Mild or moderate periodontitis is treated by using fine instruments to reach far down the sides of the tooth to scrape out bacteria and diseased tissue. This helps eliminate pockets by reducing inflammation and swelling in the surrounding gum. Severe periodontitis can require surgery to reach and clean the bottom of the deep pockets around a tooth and reshape the supporting bone.

Bacteria and tartar are the main contributors to periodontal disease, but other factors can hasten the loss of periodontal support once the disease process starts. Clenching and grinding one's teeth increases stress on the surrounding tissue and bone.† Crowded teeth make the gum line harder to clean, and the teeth may have less supporting bone between them.

Periodontal disease may not be entirely preventable, but preventive measures can delay its onset and slow its progression. The loss of even a single tooth can result in the need for an expensive bridge or implant. Unreplaced missing teeth or the wearing of dentures not only can affect what you eat, but can markedly interfere with eating pleasure.

Summary

Muscles make up about 45% of the normal body weight of men and about 35% of women. Muscle is about 70% water and 20% protein; the rest is fat, minerals, and carbohydrate. Muscle cells are also called muscle fibers because they're long and cylindrical; there are two main kinds: *white fibers* (best at anaerobic metabolism) and *red fibers* (best at aerobic metabolism).

The kind and number of cells in a particular muscle seem to be genetically determined. Exercise increases the size of muscle fibers rather than their number, and the muscle becomes thicker and stronger. A muscle's strength is proportional to its size. The size gained through exercise falls fast with disuse. After age 30, we gradually lose muscle protein, and the amount of fat in muscle goes up. This leads to the weaker muscle strength associated with aging.

Anabolic steroids are synthetic substances that are chemically similar to the male sex hormone testosterone. They're used illegally by some athletes to increase muscle size and strength. Anabolic steroids promote increased muscle mass, but also have mild to severe side effects.

Muscles are made to contract by nerves (an exception is heart muscle, which is stimulated by local pacemaker cells). Energy for muscle action comes almost entirely from the ATP generated by the metabolism of glucose and fatty acids.

Bone provides our bodies with physical support, blood cell production, and a mineral reserve. Bone is about 30% protein and about 70% minerals (mainly calcium and phosphorus). Protein in bone gives it flexibility, whereas minerals give it compressional strength.

Bones grow fast through adolescence, reaching peak density by about age 30, although most of the density is acquired by the age of puberty. Bone density stays about the same for about the next 20 years, and then starts to fall beginning at about age 50.

Vitamin D is needed to absorb calcium from the intestine and to properly mineralize bone. With inadequate mineralization during childhood, bones are weak and easily bent. D is made in the skin by the action of ultraviolet light on

---

*Pockets of bacteria/debris are a common cause of bad breath. There are, of course, other causes, e.g., odoriferous substances in garlic are absorbed into blood, and some escape into the breath when blood circulates through the lungs. (The garlicky substances we associate with garlic aren't in the intact clove. Enzymes that make them are released when the clove is crushed or cut.)

†Grinding your teeth also wears down enamel. Thin enamel or a cracked tooth is a common cause of a tooth being extra-sensitive to hot and cold. If you grind your teeth at night, your dentist can make you a nightguard (a piece of plastic molded to fit between the upper and lower teeth) to use at night.

vitamin-D precursors found in the skin. Most people can make enough through normal exposure to sunlight. But certain situations (e.g., being housebound) can lessen sun exposure. Also, the efficiency of D production in the skin falls with age. In these situations, vitamin D is needed in the diet. Sources include eggs, fish, and fortified milk and cereals.

Much of the mineral content of bone is calcium. Calcium is needed for many functions, including blood clotting, muscle contraction, and proper nerve function. Through hormone action, calcium is constantly added to or removed from bone to keep a constant level in the blood. Most of the calcium in the U.S. diet comes from milk and milk products.

Vitamin C is needed to make the collagen portion of bone (it modifies an amino acid in collagen). Our food includes many sources of vitamin C, either as a natural component or as an additive, and the RDA is generous.

Osteoporosis is a bone disease associated with aging. Bone density and flexibility lessen as minerals and protein are lost. Bones become more porous and brittle and are easily fractured. Fractures of the spinal vertebrae cause the familiar stoop of old age.

Osteoporosis is seen on X-rays only after a lot of mineral loss. Commonly, it's diagnosed only after a fracture. The aim of prevention is to achieve a high peak bone density and to slow the bone loss that occurs with aging. Peak density is reached in early adulthood; high peak density delays the onset of osteoporosis.

Women are more at risk than men, mostly due to smaller bones, lower peak bone density, and hormonal changes accompanying menopause. Women can lower their risk by regular exercise, a diet adequate in calcium, not smoking, and hormone-replacement therapy starting at menopause.

Teeth are structurally similar to bone, and their formation is influenced by many of the same factors that affect bone formation. The hard outer surface is the *enamel,* made almost entirely of mineral. Under the enamel is *dentin,* which has a mineral and collagen make-up like bone. The center of the tooth (*pulp*) has nerves and blood vessels. Teeth are surrounded by the gums (*gingiva*), and are attached to the underlying bone by collagen fibers in the periodontal ligament.

Gingivitis is an inflammation of the gums that begins with dental plaque that extends into the crevice between tooth and gums. Gingivitis can progress to where the crevice widens to create a pocket, which in turn becomes the site of a more significant infection.

The spread of infection to the periodontal ligament and surrounding bone is called periodontitis. Periodontal disease is the major cause of tooth loss in adults. Good dental hygiene and regular professional care helps prevent gingivitis and periodontitis.

Chapter 15

Nervous System

Medical science in the 20th century has seen a succession of hunters. The bacteriologists, called "microbe hunters"...occupied the spotlight in the first two decades. They were replaced in the next two by the vitamin hunters. Then the enzyme hunters filled the scene in the 1940s and 1950s, and for the past two decades the gene hunters have been in fashion.... Should the neurobiologists succeed in developing effective new molecular techniques, these hunters—we might call them "head hunters"—may dominate the last part of our century.

From *For the Love of Enzymes*, 1989, by Nobel laureate Arthur Kornberg

Imagine a worldwide network of 5 to 6 billion computers—one for every person in the world. It doesn't come even close to the communication system of the human nervous system.

Our nervous system has about a trillion neurons (nerve cells), with each neuron averaging 1,000 extensions to network within the brain and communicate with cells throughout the body. When we accidentally touch a hot iron, nerve impulses pass the message. We immediately feel the pain, pull our hand back, and say *Ouch!*— or something less civil. Think of the hand-eye coordination needed to hit a baseball closing in at 100 miles an hour. Imagine the fine orchestration of transmissions between neurons that occurs when we feel and respond to the sensations of sitting in the sun while sipping a cold drink and listening to music.

For all its complexity, there are only two basic kinds of cells in the nervous system: *neurons* (meaning *nerves* in Greek), which transmit nerve impulses, and *glial cells,* which play a supporting role. We might think of neurons as royalty, and glial cells as their devoted servants. There are about 50 to 100 times as many glial cells as neurons.

Glial cells appear packed between neurons, and were first thought of as the glue that held neurons together (*glial* means *glue* in Greek). But glial cells are quite complex, and a wide variety of them nurture and protect the neurons. Unlike neurons, glial cells retain the ability to divide (grow). Most brain tumors occur in glial cells.

215

Figure 15.1: The Neuron

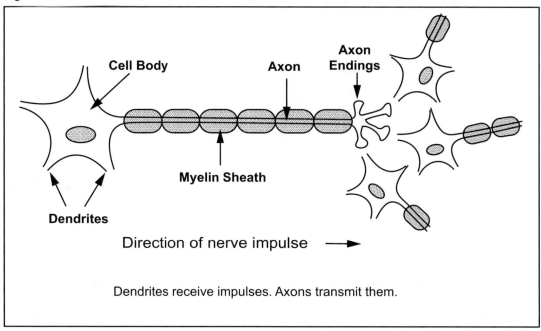

Cell Body   **Axon**   **Axon Endings**

Myelin Sheath

Dendrites

Direction of nerve impulse ⟶

Dendrites receive impulses. Axons transmit them.

Neurons

Neurons have surfaces that bristle with finely branched antennae called *dendrites* (meaning *of a tree* in Greek) (Fig. 15-1). There can be a few or up to more than 10,000 dendrites on one neuron. Dendrites receive nerve impulses.

A neuron has a long extension called an *axon* (meaning *axis* in Greek), which branches at the end and relays impulses to other neurons or tissues. The length of an axon varies from hundredths of an inch to much longer—the axon of a neuron connecting the spinal cord to the toes is more than three feet long in a tall person.

Most axons are wrapped in myelin, a white substance made of fat and protein. Myelin insulates the transmission of nerve impulses, much like insulation around electrical wires. Myelin continues to form around axons during the first year of life. Infants become more coordinated and respond faster to stimuli as this process is completed.

In multiple sclerosis, there's patchy destruction of myelin, resulting in various neurological symptoms, depending on where and how bad the damage is. The cause isn't known, but it is an autoimmune disease—the immune system sees parts of the myelin as foreign and destroys it. Its effects are like the shorting of an electrical system when insulation around the wires is damaged.

Because neurons stop dividing after early infancy, they can't be replaced when lost. But other neurons can help compensate. When a stroke causes speech loss, speech often can be re-learned by training other neurons.

Transmission of Nerve Impulses

A nerve impulse is transmitted along the cell membrane of a neuron. The membrane is polarized: Its outer surface is positively charged and its inner surface negatively charged (Fig. 15-2).* When the neuron is stimulated, positively charged sodium ions enter the neuron, reversing the polarity of the cell membrane at this spot. The impulse ("wave" of reverse polarization) travels down the axon, much as a "wave" in a rope travels

---

*Fluid surrounding the neuron has an excess of positively charged ions (Chap. 3); fluid inside the neuron has an excess of negatively charged ions. Ion channels (membrane proteins) in the neuron cell-membrane control the transport of ions in and out of the neuron. Bert Sakmann and Erwin Neher won a Nobel prize in 1991 for developing a method of studying ion channels in living cells.

Figure 15-2: Transmission of a Nerve Impulse

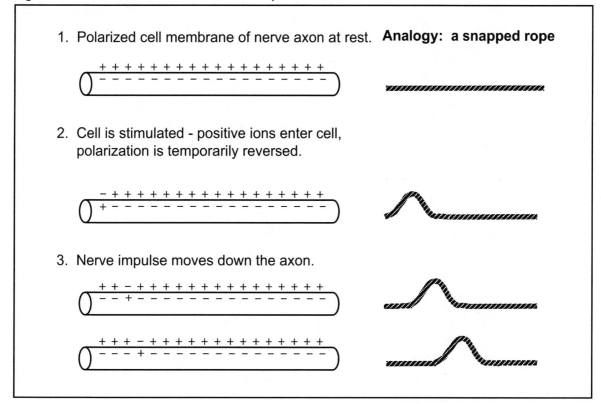

down the rope when it's snapped at one end (Fig. 15-2).*

Sodium ions enter through a membrane protein (Chap. 9) called a sodium channel. Some toxins can block it. For example, parts of the puffer fish (*fugu*) have a potent poison that blocks the channel. Eating *fugu sashimi* (the raw, delicate slices of this fish—a gourmet dish in Japan), is said to give "a pleasant tingling sensation" in the mouth. Too much of the poison leads to respiratory paralysis, a rather unpleasant inability to breathe. How well the chef keeps the poison from contaminating the sashimi can be a matter of life or death to the gourmet. A few people die each year feasting on this delicacy.

Neurotransmitters

A nerve impulse is transmitted from one neuron to another. But the neurons aren't physically connected. The gap between the transmitting end of a neuron and the receiving end of another is bridged by chemicals called neurotransmitters. This gap (and its chemical connection) is called a synapse (Fig. 15-3), meaning *to fasten together* in Greek.

Neurotransmitters are made in the neuron and stored at the end of the axon (the transmitting end; Fig. 15-3, 15-4). When a nerve impulse reaches the end of the axon, the neurotransmitter is released and attaches to receptors on the adjacent neuron. This allows the impulse to resume its course. After the neurotransmitter does its job, it's removed from the receptor so that the cell can return to a resting state.

There are many kinds of neurotransmitters—many more are yet to be discovered. Some of them have other functions, e.g., some are amino acids. They add another complex dimension to the nervous system. Different neurotransmitters have different actions; the amounts released vary; they can be removed at different speeds; and other chemicals can enhance or hamper their action. Drugs used to treat anxiety and mental

*For their discoveries of how an impulse is transmitted in a neuron, Alan Hodgkin and Andrew Huxley won a Nobel prize in 1963.

Figure 15-3: Synapse Between Neurons

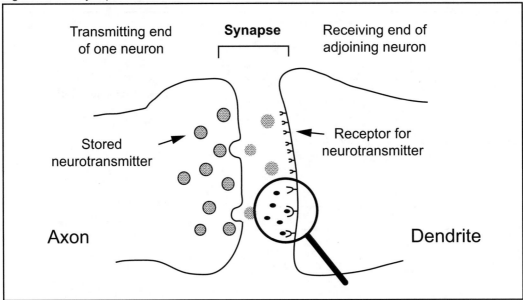

illnesses (e.g., tranquilizers), "recreational" drugs (e.g., cocaine), and even the drug in our coffee (caffeine) act at these synapses. The popular antidepressants Prozac and Zoloft hamper the removal of the neurotransmitter serotonin.

Neurotransmitters also can affect the sensitivity of neurons. Neurotransmitters and drugs that stimulate neurons (or make them more sensitive to stimulation) are called, yes, *stimulants*. Those that make neurons less sensitive are called *inhibitors*. Stimulants lessen the polarization of the cell membrane (Fig. 15-2), making it easier to initiate a nerve impulse. Inhibitors enhance the polarization, making it harder to depolarize.

Neurons average a thousand extensions with which to receive and transmit impulse (in the human forebrain, there are about 40,000 synapses per neuron). So whether a neuron is stimulated enough to transmit an impulse depends on the net effect of the stimulation and inhibition occurring at its many synapses. When we consider the subtlety of our mood, we can appreciate the nervous system's ability to fine-tune its activities—much as we adjust the sound of a musical recording by fiddling with the many controls on a fancy stereo.

Vitamin B_6 is part of the coenzyme needed to make the neurotransmitter GABA (gamma-aminobutyric acid), which makes neurons less sensitive to stimulation. Thus, a severe B_6 deficiency can cause hyperexcitability of neurons and convulsions.*

Chemical transactions that occur at synapses have much to do with memory, mental illness, mood, drug addiction, etc. This is a burgeoning area of research, and there's a bumper crop of startup companies ready to cash in on new developments (annual sales of antidepressant drugs exceed a billion dollars a year in the U.S. alone).

It's said that the center of the nervous system—the brain—is the last frontier of the human body. We know less about its workings than about any other part. We expect that advances in this field will bring about ways to prevent and/or cure such malfunctions as the "storm" of nerve impulses in epilepsy, the severe memory loss of Alzheimer's disease, and the

*In 1951 and again in 1982, a commercial infant formula was accidentally lacking in B_6. Many infants who were exclusively fed this formula developed muscular twitching and convulsions. An FDA (Food and Drug Administration) scientist recalled a study in which young B_6-deficient rats developed similar symptoms, and correctly suspected that B_6 was lacking in the formula. Most of the infants promptly recovered when given B_6; a few seemed to have permanent brain damage. The 1980 Infant Formula Act requires that formulas meet nutrient standards; the FDA adopted quality-control procedures in 1982.

sudden sleep that occurs in narcolepsy. Applications of new findings might be revolutionary. What if we could condense our need for sleep to an hour a night? (It wouldn't be available to children—parents need the peace and quiet!)

Nerve-Muscle Junction

Synapses occur not only between neurons, but also between nerve and muscle, where nerve impulses cause muscles to contract (Fig. 15-4). The neurotransmitter involved here is *acetylcholine,* * the first one discovered. It's released at the nerve ending and attaches to receptors on the muscle cell, causing the muscle to contract. Acetylcholine is then rapidly broken apart by the enzyme acetylcholinesterase, enabling the muscle to return to its relaxed state (Fig. 15-4). Unless acetylcholine—the stimulus—is removed, the muscle becomes hyperactive and can go into a spasm.

For centuries, South American Indians paralyzed their prey—man or animal—by poisoning the tips of their arrows with the curare-containing juice of a native plant. Curare attaches to acetylcholine receptors. This blocks the attachment of acetylcholine, thereby blocking the stimulus needed for the muscle to contract. The resulting paralysis can be "merely" incapacitating, so the victim can be approached and killed by other means. If the dose is high enough, the victim dies of respiratory paralysis. Curare-based drugs are among those used today in surgery as muscle relaxants; breathing is sustained by machine.

During the 1991 Persian Gulf War, it was feared that Iraq would use nerve gases, poisons that bind to acetylcholinesterase, the enzyme that breaks apart acetylcholine,† thereby causing muscle spasm. (Acetylcholine must be removed right after it attaches to its receptor on the muscle cell, so the muscle can relax; Fig. 15-4.) Spasm of the respiratory muscles can be fatal. Allied soldiers carried two kinds of antidotes in autoinjection devices that they were to use within 2 minutes of exposure. One antidote relieves the spasms by attaching to the muscles' acetylcholine receptors. The other breaks apart the nerve-gas-enzyme combination so that the enzyme is freed to do its job.

Although nerve gas wasn't used in this conflict, its use in future wars or in acts of terrorism is still a threat. Better antidotes are being developed. Current ones have side effects, e.g., impaired sweating, impaired muscle coordination—not so good in the heat of battle. One line of research is to make by biotech the part of the acetylcholinesterase enzyme that binds to the nerve gas, to be given as a drug before possible exposure. It would then already be in the blood, ready to attach to the nerve gas as it enters, thereby preventing the nerve gas from attaching to the actual enzyme.**

The disease *myasthenia gravis* (*heavy muscle* in Greek) involves the nerve-muscle synapse. In this autoimmune disease, the body sees acetylcholine receptors on muscle cells as foreign and destroys them. Early symptoms include muscle weakness and, sometimes, the inability to keep the eyelids open. Again, the greatest threat is respiratory paralysis. (Aristotle Onassis died of this disease.)

---

*Acetylcholine is made from acetate (acetyl CoA) and choline; both are abundant and easily made in the body. Acetate can be made from fat, carbohydrate, or protein (Chap. 9), and choline is a part of lecithin (Chap. 5), which makes up the basic structure of our cell membranes.

†A variety of substances can inhibit this enzyme. Some are used as insecticides. Flea powder commonly has such an inhibitor (a big dose for fleas, a small dose for dogs). Some inhibitors are being investigated as drugs for Alzheimer's disease. (Acetylcholine also is a neurotransmitter at neuron-neuron synapses involved in memory.) In Alzheimer's, acetylcholine-making neurons in the brain are damaged, leading to a deficit of acetylcholine—and memory. The drug-design strategy is to raise the level of acetylcholine at the memory-related synapses by hampering the enzyme that breaks it apart.

**This decoy-drug strategy is reminiscent of using biotech-produced CD4 (the attachment site on the cell membrane where the AIDS virus gains entry) as a decoy in hopes of preventing the AIDS virus from attaching to the "real" CD4 (Chap. 9).

Stimulants

Stimulants like cocaine, amphetamines, nicotine, and caffeine generally increase alertness and improve mood. They vary in addictiveness (nicotine is the most addictive) and have different modes of action. Caffeine is a mild stimulant and its mood-enhancing effect, in particular, is much weaker than that of cocaine or amphetamines.

Many stimulants also suppress the appetite. This, combined with other effects that make people feel highly energetic, alert, and euphoric, has been especially useful in getting people to work hard under adverse conditions. When Spain invaded Peru in 1533, the invaders encouraged the Peruvian-Indian workers' use of cocaine-containing coca leaf: *"This herb is so nutritious and invigorating that the Indians labor whole days without anything else ...."*

During World War II, amphetamines were used by both Axis and Allied soldiers, especially pilots. In Japan, they were also given to civilians to raise their wartime productivity. After the war, their use was encouraged in the general population by Japanese drug companies stuck with large stockpiles. The result was a major epidemic of amphetamine addiction. In the late 1940s, about 1 in 20 Japanese between ages 16 and 25 was addicted.

The original Coca-Cola had both cocaine from the coca leaf and the caffeine-containing extract from seeds of the *Cola acuminata* tree. It was first served in Atlanta, Georgia (concocted in 1886 by an Atlanta pharmacist). Early advertisements said that Coca-Cola *"put vim and go into your tired brain and body"* and called it the *"ideal nerve and brain tonic."* In 1903, cocaine was taken out of Coca-Cola, and more caffeine and some flavors from the coca leaf added instead.

Caffeine

We ingest caffeine and caffeine-like substances in coffee, tea, chocolate, and some drinks and medications (Table 15-1).* Caffeine lessens fatigue and increases alertness, urination, and heart rate. Big doses (e.g., 1000 mg) can cause insomnia, nervousness, irritability, tremors, and headache (caffeine withdrawal also causes headache). People vary in sensitivity. Those who don't routinely have caffeine are more sensitive to low doses. Also, caffeine is broken down less quickly as a person ages. Older people often refrain from drinking caffeinated beverages in the evening to avoid insomnia.

Caffeine's health effects are unclear. It's hard to sort out the specific effects of caffeine in population studies. Coffee and tea, for example, have substances besides caffeine that have various effects, and different kinds of coffee and tea as well as brewing methods affect a brew's content.†

Also, certain habits are linked with drinking coffee (our main source of caffeine), making it hard to isolate the health effects of caffeine. People who smoke, for example, tend to drink more alcohol and coffee. The results of studies of coffee-drinking in relation to heart disease, cancer, and pregnancy are inconsistent. But the general consensus is that caffeine in moderate doses (about 200-250 mg/day, equivalent to about 2 cups of coffee) is safe, even during pregnancy.

There's some anecdotal evidence that caffeine causes chronically lumpy breasts.** But controlled studies haven't shown a relationship between caffeine and the frequency of, or the discomfort from, this condition.

Inhibitors

Substances that inhibit nerve transmission include barbiturates, alcohol, and tranquilizers called benzodiazepines, e.g., Librium, Valium,

---

*Caffeine and caffeine-like substances are collectively called methylxanthines. Theophylline is the caffeine-like substance in tea; theobromine is in chocolate. The caffeine-like substances in tea and chocolate are commonly called caffeine.

†Decaffeinated coffee is popular. Some people worry about coffee decaffeinated with methylene chloride, but there's really no basis for worry. Methylene chloride caused cancer when inhaled by lab animals, but didn't when ingested. Also, methylene chloride evaporates quickly, and any residual amount would evaporate when coffee beans are roasted.

**Chronically lumpy breasts is often called fibrocystic breast disease, but isn't really a disease. This condition (and the premenstrual pain and tenderness that may accompany it) is normal and common, especially as women get older.

Figure 15-4: Stimulation of Muscle Contraction

1. Acetylcholine neurotransmitter is released from nerve ending.

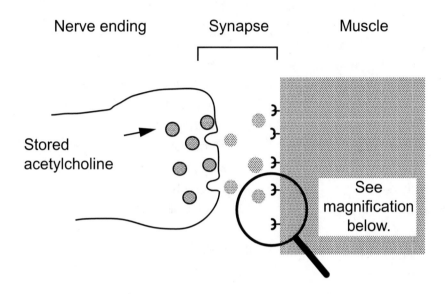

2. Acetylcholine attaches to its receptors, causing the muscle to contract. (Magnified.)

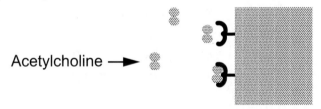

3. Acetylcholinesterase enzyme breaks apart acetylcholine, thereby removing it from its receptors and allowing the muscle to relax.

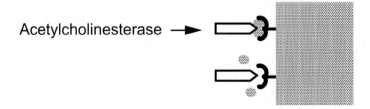

Dalmane. Their general effects are relaxation and reduced anxiety.

Barbiturates were once commonly used to treat anxiety, but they also cause severe drowsiness, and a prescription-container-full is enough to commit suicide. Benzodiazepine tranquilizers are now commonly used instead. Though addictive, they aren't as addictive as barbiturates, and withdrawal symptoms are not as severe. Also, big overdoses are rarely lethal. But combining them with alcohol can be. Judy Garland (of *The Wizard of Oz* fame), died from combining Valium and alcohol.

Alcohol

Although alcohol is absorbed by tissues throughout the body, the nervous system is particularly sensitive (Table 15-2). At low doses, we feel relaxed and cheerful—effects we associate with the pleasures of alcohol. As alcohol levels rise, the effects become those we associate with drunkenness—slurred speech, a staggered walk, and stupor.* Those who chronically drink excessively can develop a tolerance for alcohol. Some develop such a tolerance that they seem sober at normally lethal blood-alcohol levels.

Long-term effects on the nervous system vary a lot, depending on complex interactions between genetic susceptibility, toxic effects of alcohol, and alcohol-related malnutrition.

Withdrawal: Whether it's large amounts over a few days or smaller amounts over a long time, you can get withdrawal symptoms when you stop drinking or drink less (even if that lesser amount is still quite a lot). Symptoms vary in severity and can include tremors, nausea, vomiting, insomnia, confusion, nightmares, hallucinations, and seizures (the nervous system becomes overly sensitive to stimulation). Benzodiazepine tranquilizers (e.g., Valium) are often used to relieve or prevent the symptoms.

Table 15-1: Caffeine Content

	mg caffeine*
Beverages	
6 oz coffee, drip	125-175
6 oz coffee, percolated	70-140
6 oz coffee, instant	45-125
6 oz tea, steeped for 5 minutes	45-115
6 oz tea, steeped for 3 minutes	20-60
1 teaspoon instant powdered tea	25-35
6 oz hot chocolate	2-12
12 oz Mountain Dew	54
12 oz Coca Cola, all caffeinated kinds	46
12 oz Mr Pibb	40
12 oz Pepsi, all caffeinated kinds	36
Desserts	
1 cup Starbuck's coffee ice cream	40-60
1 cup Dannon coffee yogurt	45
1 oz unsweetened baking chocolate	25
1 oz Cadbury milk chocolate	15
¼ cup semi-sweet chocolate chips	14
½ cup Jell-O chocolate pudding	4-12
2 Tablespoons chocolate syrup	5
Medications	
1 tablet Dexatrim ("weight-loss aid")	200
1 tablet NoDoz	100
1 tablet Aqua-Ban (diuretic)	100
1 tablet Excedrin	65
1 stick Stay Alert gum**	50
1 tablet Anacin, Empirin, or Midol	32

* Caffeine content varies most in make-it-yourself items. Similar products tend to be similar in caffeine content.
** Useful in combat; liquid isn't needed to take it.

Wernicke-Korsakoff Syndrome is a degenerative brain disease, caused by a severe deficiency of thiamin (a B-vitamin). There's severe mental confusion and memory loss. Many also walk in an unstable and uncoordinated manner and develop

---

*After a car accident, a driver who's been drinking will sometimes get out to "exercise," hoping to burn off some alcohol before police arrive. Muscle tissue doesn't break down alcohol; the liver metabolizes it at a leisurely pace. The driver might as well stay seated. About half of all traffic fatalities are alcohol-related.

damage to nerves leading to the eyes, causing the eyes to tremor or become fixed into a stare.

In this country, the most common cause is alcoholism. Many alcoholics have diets severely deficient in thiamin (and other nutrients), and chronic drinking impairs the absorption, storage, and use of thiamin. Not all alcoholics with severe thiamin deficiency develop this disease, probably because of genetic differences.

If the disease is caught early, many of the symptoms can be reversed with immediate treatment with thiamin. Considering the cost of hospital treatment and the cost of nursinghome care for the permanently impaired, fortifying alcoholic beverages with thiamin as a means of prevention would be cost-effective.

Fetal Alcohol Effects: Fetal exposure to alcohol affects the developing brain and is thought to be a major cause of mental retardation in the U.S. The full-fledged syndrome (Fetal Alcohol Syndrome) includes mental retardation, a small head, growth retardation, abnormal facial features (e.g., eye-openings that aren't as long as normal), and other deformities. Although the full-fledged syndrome occurs in only about 6% of children of alcoholic mothers, milder forms of brain damage occur in many more.

There's some debate as to whether moderate or low doses of alcohol, especially late in pregnancy, damage the fetus. The controversy exists because of a lack of solid evidence. Unlike deformities of the face or heart, subtle damage to neurons and their synapses isn't easily measured. Even behavior and learning disabilities are hard to assess (it is nearly impossible to distinguish alcohol effects from other environmental or genetic effects).

People sometimes think that if a person does not have the characteristically abnormal facial features of Fetal Alcohol Syndrome, the brain was not affected. But these facial features are formed during only a limited period during the first three months of pregnancy, whereas the brain is formed throughout fetal life and early infancy.

Table 15-2: Alcohol Effect on Nervous System

0.05*	Relaxed, decreased alertness
0.10	Delayed reactions, impaired coordination and peripheral vision, legally drunk in most states (0.08 in Calif.)
0.15	Unsteadiness, slurred speech
0.20	Double vision, staggered walk
0.30	Stupor, marked confusion
0.40+	Loss of consciousness, coma, death

* % alcohol in blood

Illogical behavior is common in alcohol-affected children. They literally act as if they aren't properly "connected," perhaps because alcohol interfered with the development of nerve pathways and synapses. Although animal studies show that fetal alcohol exposure can have such effects as fewer dendrites on neurons (i.e., fewer connection sites), such subtle effects would be hard, if not impossible, to pinpoint in human studies. Given the uncertainties, women who are pregnant or are trying to conceive should not drink <u>any</u> alcohol. Alcohol passes freely across the placenta—blood-alcohol level is the same in mother and fetus.

Diet and the Brain

Although the brain is only about 2% of adult body weight, it uses about 20% of the oxygen and calories used for basal metabolism (Chap. 13). Neurons must constantly make neurotransmitters, pump ions *(not* "pump iron"!) to maintain polarized membranes (Fig. 15-2), etc. The brain is extremely sensitive to lack of oxygen or fuel.

Brain damage occurs in drownings after only a few minutes from a lack of oxygen. An insulin overdose causes blood-glucose to plummet, resulting in a coma from a lack of fuel. (Glucose is the only fuel the brain uses under ordinary circumstances.)

Many vitamins (e.g., niacin, thiamin, B_6, B_{12}) and minerals (e.g., iron, zinc) play a critical role in the making of neurotransmitters and in the chemical reactions that supply the large amounts of ATP-energy needed by the brain. Hampering neurotransmitter production and/or ATP production means hampering brain function. As examples, a severe lack of niacin causes the mental impairment seen in pellagra, and a severe lack of thiamin causes the paralysis and mental confusion seen in beriberi (Chap. 1).

Excesses of these nutrients do not enhance brain function. Large amounts taken as supplements can be toxic, e.g., liver damage and flushing of the face and hands with niacin; headache, irritability, insomnia, and weakness with thiamin; nerve damage with B_6; diarrhea with B_{12}.

The Developing Brain

During infancy, the brain continues to grow. So in addition to oxygen, glucose, vitamins, and minerals, the brain needs a lot of building blocks (the brain is rich in fat and protein). (As a reminder, the advice for a low-fat diet *is not* for children under age 2; Chap. 4.) The dry weight of the brain is about 80% fat, and is very rich in cholesterol. (A 3-oz serving of beef brain or pork brain has about 2000 mg cholesterol. *Scrambled eggs and brain* is—or at least used to be—a popular dish in the Midwest.)

When infants are malnourished, brain growth is a high priority (the head is relatively large on the emaciated body of an infant with severe protein-calorie malnutrition). Severe malnutrition while neurons are dividing (up until about 1 year of age) can permanently retard brain growth, because beyond this crucial period, neurons can no longer divide and the child is permanently left with fewer neurons. For this reason, breast-feeding can be crucial for infants in places where severe malnutrition is common.

If a child is severely malnourished only after neurons have reached their full number, neurons don't grow fully in size. But it appears that neurons can "catch up" in size once an adequate diet is available, although it's unclear if a child is left with subtle effects like moderate learning and behavioral disabilities.

It's hard to isolate the effects of malnutrition. So many, factors (environmental stimuli, infectious diseases, etc.) affect learning and behavior. But it appears that providing an enriched environment along with an adequate diet to children who have been severely malnourished can do much to normalize brain function.

Lead

A child's brain continues to develop rapidly even after the brain has stopped growing. Nutritional deficiencies as well as various toxins affect the developing brain. Lead is particularly toxic. Many children in the U.S. have high blood-levels of lead, indicating substantial exposure to its toxic effects. Lead is toxic to both children and adults, but children are especially vulnerable.

Lead is a potent poison with widespread effects. It can cause kidney damage (which can cause high blood pressure) and damage to red blood cells (which can cause anemia). It can also

"I suppose what bothers me is that it's the one job where you can't say, *Relax— it's not like you're performing brain surgery.*"

damage the nervous system (which can cause mental retardation or derangement) and reproductive system (which can cause infertility).

The atomic structure of lead is similar to calcium, iron, and zinc—each has 2 electrons in its outer electron shell (Chap. 3). This is why lead can displace and disrupt the activities of calcium, iron, and zinc ions in the body. (Calcium, iron, and zinc are essential mineral nutrients; lead isn't.) Essential minerals often act as crucial accessories to enzymes; lead does much of its damage by interfering with the activities of many enzymes throughout the body. In the developing brain, this can have severe consequences.

Lead poisoning was much more common in the past. It has even been theorized that severe lead poisoning caused infertility and mental illness in the ruling class of ancient Rome, and that this was a factor in the fall of the Roman Empire. Lead plumbing contaminated their drinking water, and lead utensils and vessels (used for cooking, drinking, and storage) contaminated their food and drink.

Lead ingestion now is relatively low, but the Environmental Protection Agency states that even low doses are a serious threat to the nervous system of young children. In many studies, lead exposure in fetuses and young children has been linked to delay in mental and physical development.

One study with a particularly long follow-up suggests that effects of low-level lead exposure in early childhood persist into young adulthood. In 1975-1978, all first and second graders from two predominantly white school districts in Massachusetts were asked to provide their lost baby teeth.* Based on the amount of lead in the teeth, 270 children (about 7 years old) were selected and divided into two groups—lower vs. higher lead exposure (no one had symptoms of lead toxicity). Children with the higher levels measured lower in intelligence, speech and language processing, and classroom performance.

In 1988, 132 of these children (at about age 18) were compared again. All of them now had very low blood-lead levels, but the young adults with higher early-exposure (based on the amount of lead in their baby teeth) were more likely to have poorer grades and more absenteeism in high school, reading disabilities, lower test scores in grammatical reasoning and vocabulary, poorer hand-eye coordination, longer reaction times, slower finger-tapping speed, and were 7 times more likely to drop out of high school.

Although studies like this aren't proof of cause-and-effect (their lead exposure might be related to other determining factors), animal studies support the relationship. Monkeys exposed to low levels of lead only during their first three months of life continue to show learning impairments as adults.

There's still much debate about what blood-lead level in pregnancy or childhood is damaging to a child's nervous system. Government agencies use available data to set standards for lead exposure. The maximum allowable levels set by various agencies has steadily gone down as more studies show adverse effects of low doses.

Lead absorption: When the body is growing fast, lead is easily absorbed. Compared to adults, infants and young children absorb 5 to 10 times more lead from a given dose. Dietary deficiencies also have an effect. Lead absorption and/or toxicity is higher when there is a deficiency of iron, calcium, or zinc. Unfortunately, these mineral deficiencies are quite common among young children and women of childbearing age.

Lead exposure: Several changes have greatly reduced our exposure to lead—less use of leaded gasoline, lead-containing house paint, lead-containing plumbing, lead-soldered cans for canned foods, and less lead released by industry. Blood-lead levels in children have shown a parallel decline. But some vehicles still use leaded gas, and much of the lead released earlier (from

---

*Lead tends to go where calcium goes, and calcium is most concentrated in bones and teeth. As mentioned in Chap. 14, taking calcium supplements of ground-up bone (bone meal) or dolomite (a natural rock rich in calcium) isn't advised, since they might be contaminated with lead or other toxic elements.

industrial pollutants and combustion of leaded gasoline) and dust from old leaded house paint still persist in the soil. Lead can be drawn into food grown in this soil.

Food isn't a major source of lead exposure in this country. Our most significant source is drinking water coming through old lead water-mains and service pipes and household plumbing with old lead pipes or newer pipes soldered with lead. We're making progress here. The amount of lead allowable in water is lower, and suppliers are required to notify customers of *any* lead in the water. Also, lead pipes are banned in new plumbing for drinking water (although lead-containing faucets are still sold).

Homes older than 80 years might still have lead pipes, which should be replaced. Lead solder on pipes is less serious (although more widespread), especially if the solder is more than 5 years old (lead solder dissolves more easily during the first 5 years). If your household plumbing is suspect, your local water department or your local health department may offer advice and help. Also, the Environmental Protection Agency provides advice and information (Appendix A-6).

In slum areas, old, peeling, lead-based paint is a major source of exposure. Again, young children are especially vulnerable, since they often eat paint flakes or put things in their mouth that are contaminated with paint dust in the house or yard. Similarly, one must be cautious in removing layers of old lead-based paint when renovating old homes, since lead can be absorbed by inhaling lead fumes or dust.

Canned food from lead-soldered cans can be contaminated with lead. But cans aren't a major source, since about 95% of the cans used for canning foods in this country no longer have lead solder.

Food or drink kept in lead-glazed pottery (typically brightly colored and shiny) can be a source. Lead can leach out if the pottery isn't fired at a sufficiently high temperature. Oven-proof stoneware or porcelain is fired at high enough temperatures, as is most lead-glazed pottery made in the past 25 years in this country. Most lead-glazed pottery coming from Japan and most European countries is also adequately fired.

Lead dissolves easily in acid. So lead contamination occurs more easily when acidic food and drink, such as orange juice, wine, coffee, spaghetti sauce, and vinegar, are put into improperly fired lead-glazed pottery. Drinking orange juice kept [in the refrigerator] in a lead-glazed pitcher has caused severe lead poisoning. Wine, brandy, etc., shouldn't be stored in lead-crystal decanters, and food shouldn't be stored in lead-crystal dishes. Lead foil on wine bottles is being phased out.

The ability of acids to dissolve minerals and metals such as lead is a general chemical principle. Cooking acid foods in cast-iron cookware increases the food's iron content; acid made by bacteria on teeth dissolves calcium in teeth; vinegar softens a chicken bone by dissolving its minerals; acid is used to etch glass and metal; minerals dissolve in stomach acid, allowing us to absorb the minerals; soft water is slightly acidic and picks up more lead from lead pipes and lead solder.

Food and Mood—The Tryptophan Connection

Can what we eat alter our mood? As tantalizing as the question is, the scientific tools and basic knowledge needed to explore it are only now starting to emerge. But what little we do know is intriguing.

The neurotransmitter serotonin has a calming effect and is made from tryptophan, one of the nine amino acids essential in our diet. Although most neurotransmitters are made from substances made easily in the body, the tryptophan needed to make serotonin must come from the diet.

Animals fed tryptophan-deficient diets make less brain serotonin and become irritable, hypersensitive to pain, and develop insomnia. (Alteration of serotonin activity also is a common effect of psychedelic drugs, e.g., LSD, which is structurally similar to serotonin. Ecstasy—popular among college students—is a hybrid of amphetamine and the hallucinogen mescaline that raises serotonin activity. It damages serotonin-producing neurons in rodents and primates; brain-imaging studies show a similar effect in humans.)

Since tryptophan comes from dietary protein, one might expect that a high-protein meal would raise brain tryptophan and serotonin levels. In fact, the opposite occurs, which takes a bit of explaining.

Tryptophan Transport into the Brain

The brain gets its tryptophan from blood, but tryptophan can't enter the brain directly. It is brought in by a special carrier that it shares with some other amino acids. The carrier doesn't discri-minate; it simply carries them in, in proportion to their concentration in the blood. In other words, the amount of tryptophan that gets into the brain depends on the relative amounts of "competing" amino acids in the blood.

Imagine that the only way to get to an island (*the brain*) *is* by a boat (*amino acid carrier*) that holds 8 (Fig. 15-5). If the waiting crowd has 3 times more men (*competing amino acids*) than women (*tryptophan*), the boat picks them up in that proportion (*6 competing amino acids* and *2 tryptophan*) (Fig. 15-5a). But if there are equal numbers of men and women in the crowd, fewer men (*4 competing amino acids)* and more women (*4 tryptophan*) get in (Fig. 15-5b).

Protein has very little tryptophan compared to the competing amino acids. This means that although a high-protein meal puts more tryptophan into the blood, it puts in even more of the competing amino acids. As a result, less tryptophan gets into the brain, and less serotonin is made.

Effect of Insulin on Brain Tryptophan: So far, the only insulin effect discussed has been the effect of causing cells to take in glucose from the blood (Chap. 9). But insulin also causes cells to take in tryptophan's competing amino acids from the blood, allowing more tryptophan to enter the brain (Fig. 15-5b).

A high-carbohydrate meal may change the odds in favor of tryptophan by causing a rise in insulin. The sequence of events would be: (1) more insulin, (2) fewer competing amino acids in the blood, (3) more transport of tryptophan into the brain, (4) more production of brain serotonin, and (5) a calming effect. This sequence may make some people feel sleepy after a high-carbohydrate meal. A calming effect is also theorized to be a reason why people often find comfort ("tranquillity") in carbohydrate-rich foods (e.g., candy).

Tryptophan Supplements

Because of the *typtophan/serotonin/calm* and the *tryptophan-deficiency/insomnia* connections, tryptophan has been sold as a dietary supplement and promoted as nature's

Figure 15-5: Tryptophan Transport into the Brain

a. Tryptophan (*women wearing white T-dresses*) and competing amino acids (*men in black*)
       via a carrier that picks them up in proportion to their number in the blood (*crowd*).

Only 2 tryptophans (and 6 competing amino acids) make it to the brain, because
       the crowd has 3 times more competing amino acids than tryptophan.

b.   Insulin pulls competing amino acids out of the blood and into our cells.

Even though the amount tryptophan in the blood hasn't changed, more gets into
       the brain, because there are now fewer competing amino acids in the blood.

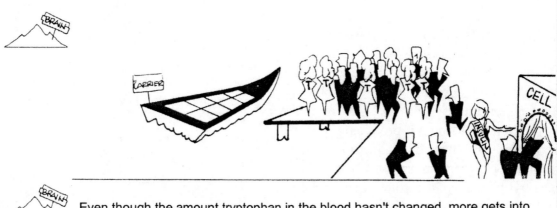

sleeping pill, tranquilizer, etc. Big doses have been self-prescribed for a variety of ills, including insomnia, premenstrual syndrome, and arthritis. (In the Minneapolis-St. Paul metropolitan area alone, an estimated 7400 women took tryptophan in 1988.)

This practice was worrisome for several reasons. One was that the effects of large doses in such uncontrolled circumstances (i.e., people in various states of health taking tryptophan haphazardly) weren't known. When a nutrient is taken in huge amounts, its action is that of a drug rather than a nutrient.

There's no reason to expect that taking tryptophan would affect only brain serotonin. Tryptophan has other functions (e.g., it's used to make protein and niacin), and serotonin is made and used in tissues other than the brain. Also, more tryptophan into the brain means less of the competing amino acids—amino acids which also have important functions in the brain.

We know that nutrients that are essential to the body in small amounts can have toxic effects in large amounts, e.g., liver damage from large doses of vitamin A or niacin, mental retardation from a large accumulation of the essential amino acid phenylalanine in the disease phenylketonuria (PKU; Chap. 3). With very large doses of tryptophan, excessive production of serotonin might possibly occur under certain conditions. Chronic liver disease, for example, reduces the blood-level of many of tryptophan's competing amino acids.

A high level of brain tryptophan and serotonin may play a role in the coma that can result from severe liver disease. One could say that a step beyond calm is sleep, and a step beyond sleep is coma.

Another concern is that tryptophan is classified in this country as a dietary supplement rather than a drug. Supplements don't need to pass the rigorous tests given to drugs (i.e., is it safe, effective, and pure?), and can be purchased freely without the package inserts (listing possible side effects, etc.) that accompany even nonprescription drugs. Calls

for classifying some dietary supplements as drugs are drowned out by loud protests by those who make and sell supplements and those who buy them—transactions worth billions of dollars.

In 1989, tryptophan supplements were linked to a mysterious epidemic of a serious, sometimes fatal, and normally rare disease characterized by severe muscle pain and an abnormal proliferation of certain white blood cells. About 5000 people were struck with this disease. More than 60% were left with severe symptoms, such as painful nerve and muscle damage, and there were at least 38 deaths. The Food and Drug Administration recalled all tryptophan supplements. (The epidemic occurred almost exclusively in the U.S. In Canada, tryptophan is available only by prescription.)

It's unlikely that the connection to tryptophan supplements would have been made, had there not been so many people taking them and had the adverse effect been more subtle, e.g., a vague symptom, such as fatigue, instead of a rare and severe disease. At the time, it wasn't known whether the disease was a toxic effect of the large doses of tryptophan itself, a breakdown product of tryptophan, a contaminant, or a combination of these. It now appears that the toxicant was an inadvertent byproduct of the manufacturing process, and not tryptophan itself. But even without such contamination, a widespread and casual practice of taking tryptophan is still a matter for concern.*

Nutrients and Brain Dysfunction

Because so little is known about how the brain works (what's the brain chemistry of remembering your phone number?), newly proposed relationships between nutrients and brain function are largely speculative, making these wide-open game for the purveyors of dietary supplements (e.g., "smart drinks").

There's no question that nutrient deficiencies can interfere with brain function (e.g., the dementia

---

*The same concern applies to supplements of melatonin, a hormone made by the pineal gland that increases sleepiness. It can help prevent jet lag, but it's unclear what else it does. Claims that melatonin supplements reverse aging are unfounded.

of the niacin-deficiency disease pellagra), and it goes without saying that such deficiencies should be corrected. The problem occurs when this connection is used to support claims that huge doses of certain nutrients can enhance brain function or cure a dysfunction. Depression can result from deficiencies of some B-vitamins, but if a person's depression isn't due to a vitamin deficiency, taking vitamins isn't going to help— except perhaps for a placebo effect.

"Orthomolecular therapy" uses huge doses of vitamins to treat behavior disorders. A task force of the American Psychiatric Association has investigated this therapy and found it to be ineffective (aside from placebo effects).

Alzheimer's Disease

Scientists have tried without much success to use nutrients to correct brain dysfunctions like Alzheimer's. Alzheimer's is a disease of severe memory loss that's fairly common in the elderly. The brain doesn't make enough of the neuro-transmitter acetylcholine, which plays a role in memory. Acetylcholine is made from acetate and choline, both of which are made by the body. Large doses of lecithin* have been tried in patients in hopes of "pushing" acetylcholine production and enhancing memory, but controlled studies haven't found that it helps.† This isn't surprising, since there is a loss of acetylcholine-producing neurons in Alzheimer's.

In 1991, a defective gene was located and identified as a cause of some cases of Alzheimer's (two more were identified in 1995). The gene is for a certain brain protein seen in large amounts in areas where there is a loss of acetyl-choline-producing neurons. It has been unclear whether this protein *causes* the disease or, rather, *results from* the disease. (Like finding soot on a light switch, if you had no idea how light switches

worked, you wouldn't know if the soot caused the switch to go out or came afterwards.)

Finding that a defect in the gene for this protein can cause Alzheimer's suggests that the protein in abnormal form or amount is a cause. The identification of a defective gene that can cause a disease (even if it's not the only cause) is usually a breakthrough. From such a discovery, the protein it makes can be identified, providing a key to understanding the cause of the disease. Once the cause is understood, effective treatments and preventative strategies can be devised.

Diet and Behavior

Despite claims to the contrary, diet as a cause of such behaviors as criminality and hyperactivity isn't supported in double-blind studies. Likewise, double-blind studies haven't found criminal, delinquent, or hyperactive behavior to be helped by "megavitamin therapy" or dietary manipulations such as eliminating sugar. Double-blind studies are essential, since evaluations of behavior are subjective and prone to bias.

Also, dietary changes may improve behavior without the diet itself being directly responsible. Many parents found the Feingold diet (an elimi-nation diet popularized as an effective treatment for hyperactivity in the 1970s by pediatrician Benjamin Feingold) helpful in treating their hyper-active children. But when the substances (a wide variety ranging from certain artificial colorings to substances found naturally in common fruits) were tested in a double-blind fashion, there were no differences in behavior between the experimental and control groups. (In an occasional hyperactive child, behavior seems to be affected by dietary substances; if this is substantiated, of course the substance should be avoided.)

The Feingold diet is so restrictive that it drastically changes the entire family dynamics. This change is what is thought to be the main

---

*Lecithin is the choline-containing fat found in food and in our cell membranes (Chap. 5). Choline itself tastes bitter and mparts a "fishy" body odor when taken in big doses. Acetylcholine isn't given, since it would break apart in digestion; even if it were injected into the blood, it can't get into the brain. The brain makes its own acetylcholine.

†Lecithin has been found to be helpful in treating some patients with another disease—tardive dyskinesia, a neuromuscular disorder caused by long-term use of certain antipsychotic drugs.

reason for the improved behavior. A lot more time is spent shopping for foods, meals are changed and more time is spent preparing them. The child gets more positive attention, and the hyperactivity is blamed on the food rather than the child.

Sugar is popularly believed to cause hyperactivity in children (and delinquent activity in adolescents). But controlled studies in children and adolescents suggest the reverse—that sugar has a calming effect. This finding is in line with the sugar-serotonin connection mentioned earlier.

Summary

The nervous system has two types of cells: neurons, which transmit nerve impulses, and *glial cells*, which support the function of neurons. A neuron has many branched extensions called *dendrites*, which receive impulses from other neurons. The typical neuron also has a long extension called an *axon*, which culminates in another branched structure called the axon endings. The axon acts as the transmission line of the neuron.

A neuron's cell membrane is polarized by positive ions on one side and negative ions on the other. Nerve impulses travel along this membrane. When a neuron is stimulated, the polarity is temporarily reversed at points along the membrane, creating an impulse that travels down the axon like a wave.

Neurons aren't physically connected. The gap between them is called a *synapse*. Impulses are carried across the synapse by chemical substances called *neurotransmitters*. When an impulse reaches an axon ending, it releases a neurotransmitter that travels across the synapse to a receptor on an adjacent neuron. A whole area of research is devoted to studying the interactions at these synapses.

Synapses also occur at the juncture of neurons and muscle. To stimulate a muscle contraction, the neuron releases the neurotransmitter acetylcholine, which attaches to receptors on the muscle to cause contraction. Acetylcholine is quickly cleared from the receptor through enzyme action, allowing the muscle to relax.

Stimulants increase the sensitivity of neurons. They increase alertness, improve mood, and often reduce appetite. Many are addictive, and large amounts can lead to irritability. Caffeine is a commonplace example of a stimulant.

Inhibitors make neurons less sensitive to stimulation and inhibit transmission of nerve impulses. Their general effects are relaxation and reduced anxiety. Examples include barbiturates and alcohol. The developing nervous system is particularly sensitive to alcohol. A collection of symptoms called *Fetal Alcohol Syndrome* includes mental retardation caused by interference with fetal brain development due to alcohol consumption by the mother during pregnancy.

"Because it tends to trigger glands which release euphoria-inducing endocrins, I try not to smile too much."

Neurons are constantly active, requiring constant supplies of oxygen and glucose. They also need vitamins and minerals to make ATP and neurotransmitters. Although it's well established that nutritional deficiencies can cause brain or nerve dysfunction, there is very little indication that large doses of particular nutrients can enhance brain function. The same could be said for altering undesirable behavior through diet.

The brain continues to grow, and neurons continue to divide through infancy. Malnourishment during this period may lead to retardation in brain growth and a permanently reduced number of neurons. If malnourishment occurs only after this period of cell division, the neurons may not grow to full size, but the ill effects appear to be reversible if proper nourishment is restored.

Lead is a toxin with widespread effects. It is chemically similar to the essential minerals calcium, iron, and zinc. Much of its damage comes from its ability to displace these essential minerals, thereby interfering with the function of the many enzymes for which these minerals act as cofactors.

Children absorb lead much more easily than adults. Lead has been shown to delay the mental and physical development of fetuses and young children. High lead levels have been linked to poorer psychomotor skills and lower scores on intelligence tests.

Serotonin is a neurotransmitter made from the essential amino acid tryptophan. It has a calming effect. When lab rats are made deficient in serotonin or tryptophan, they become irritable and develop insomnia. But eating a protein-rich meal doesn't increase serotonin, because protein has relatively more of the amino acids that compete with tryptophan for entry into the brain.

Carbohydrates are more effective in increasing serotonin, since the insulin made in response causes cells throughout the body to take in more of the competing amino acids, making it easier for tryptophan to enter the brain. This may explain the calming effect of carbohydrate-rich foods.

Tryptophan supplements were widely promoted, and many people took them. Because tryptophan is classified as a dietary supplement rather than a drug, it hasn't been rigorously tested for safety, purity, or effectiveness. This lack of testing is good reason to be cautious about supplements. Some are often self-prescribed in large doses, and side effects haven't been determined in controlled studies.

Chapter 16

Food Safety

Everything is poison.
Only the dose makes a thing not a poison.

Paracelsus (1493-1541)

Wash your hands!

Mom

When we look for hazards in food, we see them everywhere. Some toxins are even a natural part of vegetables, some we add to food, and some come into being as food spoils or is cooked. One could even argue that calories are a food hazard—eating too many causes obesity.

We rely on our senses to avoid some hazards (e.g., spoiled food), but even taste can deceive. In drinking water, iron is safe but tastes bad, whereas lead is toxic and tasteless. Even if we could easily spot toxins, we can't avoid them all. They are pervasive in our food supply—most of them natural, and most of them in tiny amounts. Keep in mind that the most toxic substance is safe if the amount is small enough, and the least toxic substance is dangerous if the amount is large enough. The dose makes the poison.

Natural Chemicals in Plants

Many of us think of food hazards as "chemicals"—"unnatural" substances like additives and pesticide residues. We don't give much thought to the fact that even a simple plant is made up of thousands of chemicals, most of them unidentified. As new varieties of plants appear, so do new chemicals. And as plant varieties become extinct, so do some unique and undiscovered chemicals—some of which may have been tomorrow's "miracle drugs."

Drug companies search constantly through this rich and constantly changing array of plant chemicals. Plants have long been sources of drugs. Chewing on the bark of a willow tree was known in ancient civilizations to relieve pain. Based on this willow-bark substance (salicylic acid), aspirin (acetylsalicylic acid) was synthesized in 1853. The heart drug digitalis comes from the leaves of the purple foxglove plant.

Many anti-cancer drugs come from plants, such as taxol (for ovarian cancer) from the bark of the Pacific yew tree, and vinblastine (for breast cancer) and vincristine (for leukemia) from the tropical flower rosy periwinkle. Then there's nicotine in tobacco leaves, caffeine in coffee beans, and cocaine in coca leaves. Some drugs even come into being when a plant spoils, like the blood-thinner dicumarol in spoiled sweet clover (Chap. 7).

People who like to categorize substances into good or bad would have a hard time with plant chemicals (*phytochemicals*). Easiest to categorize might be vitamins—but then again, even too much of these can be toxic. What about caffeine in coffee? It's bad if it makes a surgeon's hand tremble during surgery, but good if it keeps a tired surgeon awake while driving home.

Even if we could identify and test each chemical in a plant before eating it, its chemical content is accurate only for the one part of that one plant at that one moment. Not only do apples on the same tree vary in composition, but one side of a single apple varies from the other. And content changes constantly. How else does fruit ripen, bread become stale, and wine age? How else does the taste of coffee change upon reheating, and cantaloupe give off its fragrance?

Natural Toxins

Our earliest knowledge of natural toxins came about by trial and error. If a caveman got sick from eating a plant, he wasn't likely to eat it again. But many of the same toxins in poisonous plants are found in smaller amounts in edible ones. By eating a variety of foods (Chap. 4), we lessen the chance of eating any one toxin in toxic amounts. Eating a bit of toxin A and a bit of toxin B generally is safer than eating a double dose of either A or B.

In Chapter 13, we saw that goitrogens (substances that can cause goiter) are found in foods like cassava, peanuts, cab-

bage, soybeans, and turnips. Goitrogens are a concern only if these foods make up the bulk of a diet for a long time. Some people don't have much else to eat but cassava. Cassava also has cyanide (yes, the same chemical used in gas chambers for capital punishment), as do some varieties of lima beans and almonds. Much of the cyanide is lost during food processing and preparation. Residual cyanide has been a problem (e.g., caused nerve damage and blindness) only in parts of the world where cassava makes up the bulk of the diet.

Some toxins increase in food during storage. Solanine is a nerve toxin found naturally in potatoes; the amount goes up when stored potatoes are exposed to light. This is evident by a greenish tinge under the potato skin. This green pigment is chlorophyll, which also forms in response to light. In the olden days, potatoes were stored in the dark in a cellar. Today, they're usually sold bagged in colored—rather than clear—plastic to reduce exposure to light.

"They're the natural enemy of roaches."

By peeling off the greenish part, you peel away most of the solanine. Eating it in a modest amount isn't a problem—don't expect any ill effects (e.g., cramps) from eating a green-tinged potato. But now that you know about solanine, you may find yourself needlessly breaking off a green edge on a potato chip!

Some natural plant chemicals (including solanine) are pesticides—they kill pests. Plants can't run from their enemies; they engage in chemical warfare. Natural pesticides are so abundant in edible plants that many scientists think that the amount of residue from farm pesticides is trivial by comparison. Plants don't have nerves like insects do, so natural pesticides that affect neurotransmitters (Chap. 15) are ideal weapons against insects.

Plants typically make more of their pesticides/toxins when injured. Mold damage to celery can cause some varieties to make 100 times more toxin—so much that it can cause a rash on the hands of celery pickers and produce checkers. If organic produce (grown without adding pesticides) is blemished, it can have more pesticides than unblemished non-organic produce. Also, if you're growing plants without using pesticides, you might favor varieties that are more resistant to pests (more "natural pesticides").

Many natural food chemicals can even cause cancer; this can be shown by purifying the substance and feeding it to animals. Safrole is the major component of sassafras oil (from sassafras trees) and causes liver cancer in rats and mice. For this reason, sassafras is no longer allowed to flavor root beer; artificial flavor is used instead. Safrole also is found in much lower concentrations in cinnamon, nutmeg, black pepper, and ginger. Of course, this doesn't mean we should avoid pumpkin pie spiced with cinnamon, nutmeg, and ginger. Remember, the dose matters.

You can buy sassafras root, leaves, and capsules by mail order and in some health food stores.

Because they're sold as dietary supplements, they don't have to be approved by the Food and Drug Administration (FDA) for safety and effectiveness (or even contain what they claim), as they would if they were classified as food additives or drugs.

A mail-order catalog says this about sassafras root, leaf, and capsules: *Has a very useful effect on the blood system. Because it purifies the blood so well, it is excellent for all skin disorders, especially ailments such as acne. It stimulates the action of the liver to clear toxins from the body.**

Claims to cure or prevent a disease are severely restricted on labels of dietary supplements. Marketers get around this by freely making claims in books, brochures, catalogs, on websites, etc. (freedom of speech). Also, the labels themselves are cleverly worded to avoid stating that the product cures or prevents a disease. Using phrases like *promotes prostate health, boosts your immune system, sharpens your memory, perks up your love life*, works just fine in selling such products.

Food Additives

Many substances in food weren't there originally. Some are added intentionally (e.g., food additives), some are residues (e.g., pesticides sprayed on food crops), and some are contaminants (e.g., industrial pollutants in ground water taken up by plants).

People often see packaged food as unhealthful and full of additives. Food-safety experts don't worry much about additives; food additives are very closely scrutinized before being approved. It could be argued that the most unhealthful thing about packaged food is that it's so handy and appealing—so attractively packaged, easily stored, and convenient to eat, that it's easy to overeat. How often would you eat potato chips if you had to make them yourself from a fresh potato? Or ice cream, if you had to start by milking a cow?

---

*Vague terms like *purify blood* and *clear toxins* are commonly used in such claims. Kidneys continually purify blood and clear toxins. If they didn't, we'd soon be poisoned to death, unless we get a kidney transplant, or undergo continual dialysis to clear the blood of toxins. As another example, we can go into a coma and die if the toxin ammonia (from surplus amino groups of amino acids) isn't made into urea by the liver (Chap. 11).

Some additives are listed in Table 16-1: Some are used in the kitchen, e.g., acetic acid (vinegar) and sodium bicarbonate (baking soda). Some make food more nutritious, e.g., vitamin D added to milk, and safer, e.g., mold inhibitors. Some are "gums," e.g., agar, carrageenan, guar, found naturally in plants and often used as stabilizers and thickeners in salad dressings and ice cream.

The most heavily criticized additives are coal tar dyes (named FD&C red no. 40, etc., because they're used to color <u>f</u>ood, <u>d</u>rugs, and <u>c</u>osmetics). They, too, have been scrutinized for safety. We know much less about the safety of the many natural colorants, even though coloring our food isn't new. Ancient Egyptians routinely made food colorants by grinding up colorful plants and insects.

Safety Legislation

Prior to 1958, just about anything could be added to food. It was up to the government to prove it was harmful before disallowing its use. Safety programs of the FDA began with Dr. Harvey Wiley, a chemist with the Dept. of Agriculture from 1883 to 1930. He used a volunteer "poison squad" of 12 men who tested food additives by eating a lot of the additive-containing food to see if it caused them any harm! The 1958 Food Additives Amendment turned things around by requiring that manufacturers do extensive safety tests before asking the FDA for approval.*

For each proposed additive, males and females of at least two species of animals are studied for at least two generations. They're fed a range of doses over their lifetime, to find the highest dose that has no adverse effect (*no-effect dose*). Usually, the highest expected dose must not be more than one-hundredth of the no-effect dose, e.g., a no-effect lifetime dose of 100 mg/day means that the additive can't be added in amounts over 1 mg/day. Getting a new additive approved is a major investment for a manufacturer. Very few additives have been approved since 1958.

GRAS List: At the time of the 1958 amendment, hundreds of additives (including salt, sugar, and some common spices) had already been in use for years without apparent harm, and were widely accepted as safe by scientists at that time. These were put on the GRAS (Generally Regarded As Safe) list, and the safety of each has since been reassessed. Their safety, as well as that of newer additives, continues to be reassessed in light of new scientific information—or when a public outcry to do so arises.

Risk assessments are made for cancer, nerve damage, birth defects, reproductive problems, etc., not only for food additives and processed foods, but for pesticide residues and fresh foods as well. Safety for children receives special emphasis.

Assessing Risk

People worry most about carcinogens (cancer-causing agents). Identification often begins by testing substances in animal tissue cells or bacteria to see if they're capable of causing mutations (see Ames test in Chap. 10). Mutations don't necessarily cause cancer, but if a substance can cause a mutation, it's regarded as a potential carcinogen.

Typically, substances that pass screening tests are then tested in animals using doses that are much larger than what we'd normally eat. Large doses are used because, even if a substance is known to cause cancer, most such substances will cause only a few cancers when fed in small amounts. When cancer rates are low, large numbers of animals must be tested to find a statistically significant difference in the number of cancers between experimental and control groups. Using thousands of rats to test each substance over many years is expensive and impractical. So, high doses are given to fewer animals.

Feeding a large dose (e.g., of an additive proposed for use on apples) is often ridiculed (*it's equivalent to eating a bushel of apples a day*). The question is, if a substance causes cancer at high doses in animals, will it cause cancer at low

---

*In contrast to food additives, dietary supplements don't require FDA approval, and manufacturers aren't required to test for safety. It's up to the government to prove harm before disallowing their use, as they did with tryptophan supplements (Chap. 15)—and with food additives until 1958.

Table 16-1: Some Food Additives

• To thicken:	• To color:	• To retard microbial growth:
Agar	Annato	Benzoic acid
Calcium alginate	Caramel	Calcium lactate
Carob bean gum	Carotene	Calcium propionate
Cellulose	Carrot oil	Calcium sorbate
Gelatin	Citrus red no. 2	Lactic acid
Guar gum	Dehydrated beets	Methylparaben
Gum ghatti	FD&C blue no. 1	Potassium benzoate
Locust bean gum	FD&C red no. 40	Potassium sorbate
Modified food starch	FD&C yellow no. 5	Propionic acid
Pectin		Propylparaben
Potassium alginate	• To emulsify:	
Sodium alginate	Carrageenan	• To prevent oxidation:
Tragacanth gum	Diglycerides	Ascorbic acid (vitamin C)
	Gum arabic	BHA (butylated hydroxyanisole)
• To whiten:	Lecithin	BHT (butylated hydroxytoluene)
Benzoyl peroxide	Monoglycerides	Citric acid
Calcium bromate	Polysorbate	EDTA (ethylenediamine
Hydrogen peroxide		tetraacetic acid)
Potassium bromate	• To prevent caking:	Propyl gallate
	Ammonium citrate	Sulfites
• To control acidity:	Calcium silicate	Tocopherols (vitamin E)
Acetic acid	Magnesium carbonate	
Citric acid	Silicon dioxide	• To enhance flavor:
Lactic acid		Disodium guanylate
Sodium acetate	• To make baked goods rise:	Hydrolyzed vegetable protein
Sodium citrate	Calcium phosphate	Maltol
Tartaric acid	Monocalcium phosphate	Monosodium glutamate (MSG)
	Potassium bitartrate	
• To retain moisture:	(cream of tartar)	• To improve tartness:
Glycerol	Sodium aluminum phosphate	Phosphates
Propylene glycol	Sodium bicarbonate	Phosphoric acid
Sorbitol	(baking soda)	

doses in humans? Of course, this question can't be answered with certainty; testing typical doses on humans isn't a viable option.

What's a typical dose? If a pesticide that causes cancer in animals is used only on apples, should we calculate on the basis of 1 apple eaten daily for a lifetime—or should it be 4? If a substance at a high dose causes 1 cancer per 50 rats, how many human cancers will it cause at 1/1000 of that dose?

Some substances known to cause cancer at low doses in humans can cause cancer at high doses in animal tests. So it's logical to expect the reverse—that substances that cause cancer at high doses in animals can cause cancer at low doses in humans. The problem is that it's also logical to expect that some substances that cause cancer at high doses in animals don't cause cancer at low doses in humans.

Scientific concerns about using a high-dose test to predict a low-dose effect include the fact that DNA-repair systems and immune defenses may take care of minor damage caused by small amounts of a carcinogen. Also, extremely high doses given to animals can cause adverse effects that don't occur with normal doses. These can affect whether test animals develop cancer.

Even with extensive studies, risk estimates have to be made with incomplete knowledge. What's harmful to animals may be harmless to humans, and vice versa. An additive may be harmful only to some people under only certain conditions. Some effects may not be measurable by current technology.

Because it's considered better to err on the high side, estimates typically use worst-case scenarios, e.g., apples, lettuce, spinach, carrots, etc., aren't washed, peeled, or cooked, in estimating ingestion of additives or pesticide residues. Knowing that estimates are based on "soft" numbers, it's easy to see why different organizations with or without biases come up with such different "correct" estimates.

Because such uncertainties can never be completely addressed, risk assessment often is subjective, and scientists themselves argue about it. So industry, consumer and environmental groups, letters to congress, etc., sometimes have more influence than scientific evidence in determining whether a particular food additive is approved.

"Everything tastes so fresh, Mother. Where did you get the potassium benzoate?"

"Macro-Additives"

A food additive, by definition, is something added to food. Should it be called something else if it makes up the bulk of a food? What if it can make up the entire food and has no nutritional value? Is it then neither a food nor an additive?

Olestra (*Olean*®) is such a "macro-additive." It's a non-caloric fat substitute developed by Proctor and Gamble in 1968 and approved in 1996 for use in some snack foods (e.g., crackers, chips). Unlike any fat substitute on the market, it has all the cooking and sensual qualities of regular fat, without the calories. It can be liquid like salad oil, or solid like margarine. It can be used just as fat is used now—to fry french fries or donuts, to make salad dressing, pie crust, or chocolate cake with fudge frosting, though it hasn't yet been approved for these additional uses.

Glycerol is the 3-carbon backbone of regular fat (triglyceride), with a fatty acid attached to each of the carbons (Fig. 5-2). Olestra's backbone is the double-sugar sucrose (Fig. 5-1), which has 12 carbons—more fatty acids can be attached in a variety of positions.

Olestra is completely man-made; it doesn't occur naturally. Chemically, it's a fat, but we don't get any calories from it because we can't digest it—our digestive enzymes can't split the fatty acids from its backbone, so it remains undigested and unabsorbed.*

Fat-soluble vitamins (and other fat-soluble substances such as carotene and some pesticides) that are in foods eaten at the same time can dissolve in olestra. So when olestra leaves the digestive tract, so do any fat-soluble substances that are dissolved in it. Fat-soluble vitamins are added to olestra to offset such losses.

This loss can be useful in some cases—fat-soluble substances like cholesterol and fat-soluble toxins can be carried out of the digestive tract this way. In fact, olestra was found to lower blood cholesterol, initially prompting Proctor and Gamble to seek its approval as a drug. As it turned out, it didn't lower cholesterol enough to be useful as a drug.

An earlier version of olestra had a laxative effect—the same effect people seek when they take mineral oil for constipation. Colon bacteria don't have the enzymes to digest it (or mineral oil), so the oily olestra remained to make stool slippery and easier to pass—fine if that's what you want, not so fine if it's not.†

To overcome this problem, olestra was made more solid—less oily. Some people may still get a laxative effect when they eat a large amount (and we wouldn't expect them to do this again), but, as mentioned in relation to lactose intolerance in Chapter 6, gastrointestinal (GI) upsets are so common that the cause often is hard to pinpoint. In fact, double-blind studies of people fed regular potato chips vs. those fried in olestra show the same number of GI upsets in each group.

It's difficult to get a regular food additive approved by the FDA. It was even more so for olestra, because many of the standard testing protocols weren't applicable. Proctor and Gamble spent about $300 million and about 20 years doing studies on olestra, including extensive studies on rats, mice, pigs, and humans to show safety. The reports totaled more than 100,000 pages—a moving van was needed to take them to the FDA. As an additive, olestra breaks new ground. For this reason, the FDA was extra cautious.

Pesticides Applied to Food Crops

When we grow food, other plants ("weeds") compete for the space, and we provide a tempting buffet for deer, birds, insects, fungi, and other earth creatures. We call these competitors "pests" (to them, we are the pests), and use fences, nets, and scarecrows against big ones, and pesticides (*pest killers*) against small ones.

The FDA monitors pesticides in food, and safe levels are decided by our own experts and by expert committees of the United Nations. They regard the scant amount of pesticide residues in our food supply as safe (accidental overdoses of pesticides among farm workers are another matter). There are, of course, broader concerns. Crop pesticides aren't restricted to pests alone and can upset the natural ecology of the field. Accidental spills and incorrect application of pesticides create hazards to farm workers.

An alternative solution is to use a pest's natural predators. Natural predators can arrive too slowly on their own (it took 3 years for seagulls to come to Utah to rescue crops from the locust plague in the 1850s), so we sometimes import natural enemies, e.g., collecting parasitic wasps in Iran and releasing them on California crops to combat olive scale (a pest to olives, plums, apricots, and other plants).

---

*Recall that enzymes are very specific. Digestive enzymes that remove fatty acids from triglycerides don't work on olestra, just as those that digest starch (i.e., break apart the glucoses) don't break apart the glucoses in the fiber cellulose (Chap. 5). Both cellulose and olestra have calories as measured in a bomb calorimeter (Chap. 3), but not for us.

†Regular fat doesn't normally reach the colon because it's normally digested and asorbed in the small intestine. If it reaches the colon, colon bacteria digest it and make substances that can irritate the colon and cause diarrhea.

Another age-old alternative that's still used is crossbreeding to make crops more pest-resistant. A new alternative is to use biotech to directly transfer into plants specific genes that make natural pesticides (Chap. 10)—a more precise and confined application of pesticide. For example, the pesticide can be localized to the non-edible part of the plant and also wouldn't be dispersed as it would be if sprayed on the plant.

Integrated Pest Management (IPM)

Integrated Pest Management (IPM) is a customized ecological approach to minimize pesticide use by using what's needed in the safest and most effective way possible. IPM integrates strategies based on the biology of the pests and their predators, the specific crop, local soil and weather conditions, etc. IPM includes careful monitoring of pests (to decide if control is needed), using weather information to predict when the pests will be at the most susceptible stage of their life cycle (so less pesticide will do the job), controlling weeds to reduce pest reservoirs, etc.

IPM relies on an extensive base of knowledge. Even if you know that predator mites can control spider mites, you must know how to get the predators to where they're needed (e.g., mix predator mites with corncob grit, then blow the mixture on the crop with a leaf blower). IPM for certain grape crops includes removing leaves around grape clusters, to reduce bunch rot and the number of pesticide applications needed to control powdery mildew.

IPM requires a lot of research, education, and training. Even after databases (e.g., *Database of Alternatives to Targeted Pesticides*) and publications (e.g., *IPM for Apples and Pears*) are used to customize a plan, hands-on workshops for growers and farm workers are needed (e.g., how to distinguish between spider mites and predatory mites). The University of California system has been a leader in IPM research and implementation, supported mainly by state and federal funds.

Environmental Contaminants

Experts don't worry much about residues from food pesticides, but do worry about environmental contaminants. In fact, this is second—right below microbial hazards—on their worry list. Pesticides are used to control mosquitoes, weeds along highways, etc. Some of these pesticides find their way into our food, both plant and animal.

When cars use leaded gas, lead is released into the air and taken up by crops grown along highways. Wines (representing grape crops) from many years and locales are still around and can be used to measure changes in environmental pollution. Another concern is contamination of our food from environmental disasters, such as the Gulf oil spill in 2010 and Japan's radiation leak in 2011 from tsunami-damaged nuclear power plants.

Plants' ability to take up substances in air, soil, and water can be useful. As discussed in Chapter 13, the iodine content of foods—and the distribution of goiter caused by iodine deficiency—varied according to soil iodine content. Plants don't need iodine; they simply take it up if it happens to be there. Plants are used in this way for environmental clean-up, to remove toxic metals from polluted soil and ground water; the plants are then discarded as toxic waste.

Microbial Hazards

Millions of people in the U.S. who get sick each year from microbial contamination of food think they have indigestion, "a bug," or "stomach flu." For most people, it's "only" a short bout of misery, but it can be quite serious for the very young, the very old, and those with impaired immune systems (e.g., AIDS patients or those taking immunosuppressant drugs because of an organ transplant). The Food Safety Modernization Act, passed in 2010, addresses these and other food safety concerns, but budget restrictions may limit its implementation.

Many kinds of microbes can contaminate food and make us sick (a few are listed in Table 16-2).

Again, dose matters. The dose that can cause illness varies according to the microbe and a person's vulnerability.

We can't keep all microbes away. They're everywhere, in soil, air, and water, from the edge of space to the bottom of the sea. In fact, we ingest all kinds of microbes—friend and foe—all the time.* We want to avoid getting too big a dose of the disease-causing ones: **Keep them out. Keep them from growing. Kill them.** This can be hard to do, because a lot of the food we eat is made by someone else. We can't see, smell, or taste most of the microbes or the microbial toxins that make us sick, so it helps to know where these microbes lurk, how they get in food, what conditions favor their growth, and how they and their toxins can be destroyed.

"Salmonella."

Keep Them Out

Knowing how they get in food is key to keeping them out. *Staphylococcus aureus* ("Staph") causes millions of cases of food poisoning in the U.S. each year. Staph itself doesn't makes us sick, but its toxin does. About half the population is thought to carry staph—on skin, in nasal passages, in wounds and skin eruptions. They transmit it to food by direct handling (e.g., via an uncovered cut on the hand), or through the air by a sneeze or cough (a reason for plastic shields—"sneeze guards"—placed over salad bars).†

Hazardous microbes also get in food via fecal contamination. Worldwide, the most common route is sewage-contaminated food or drinking water. We saw this with dramatic effect among the tens of thousands of Rwandans who died of cholera in 1994. In the U.S., a source is food-preparers who don't wash their hands after using the toilet, as required by law. Another source is animal feces; carcasses can be contaminated in slaughterhouses.

In some cases, the animals themselves are infected. Pigs are sometimes infected with the parasite *Trichinella spiralis*. Eating inadequately cooked pork containing larvae-filled cysts can infect us (thorough cooking prevents this). Salmonella is another microbe that can infect animals and taint food by fecal contamination; when laying hens are infected, their eggs can contain salmonella.

Keep Them From Growing

Even when disease-causing microbes get in food, it isn't a problem if they can be kept from multiplying to amounts that make us sick.

---

*We house a lot of bacteria ourselves. In our intestine alone, we have several hundred species of bacteria that vary by the composition of our diet.

†In December, 2010, pastries from a gourmet bakery in Illinois were recalled when they were connected to 100 cases of Staph food poisoning from four separate events—three in Illinois (30 cases) and one in Wisconsin (70 cases). The pastries were sold retail, wholesale (to grocery stores, etc.), and on the Internet, so the recall was publicized nationwide.

Table 16-2: Some Microbes That Can Contaminate Food or Drink

<u>Campylobacter jejuni</u>
Onset of symptoms: about 2 to 5 days after ingestion
Symptoms: diarrhea, stomach cramps, fever, bloody stool
Common source: unpasteurized milk, raw or undercooked meat or poultry

<u>Clostridium botulinum</u>
Onset of symptoms: about 12 to 36 hours after ingestion
Symptoms: trouble swallowing, double vision, progressing paralysis (a medical emergency)
Common source: improperly home-canned foods of low acidity

<u>Escherichia coli O157:H7</u>
Onset of symptoms: usually within 24 hours of ingestion, but can be days
Symptoms: painful bloody diarrhea, can go on to life-threatening blood disorder, kidney failure
Common source: raw or undercooked hamburger, person-to-person via stool

<u>Hepatitis A virus</u>
Onset of symptoms: about 2 to 7 weeks after ingestion
Symptoms: flu-like, jaundice, fatigue, nausea, can be fatal
Common source: shellfish from contaminated waters, infected food handler

<u>Listeria monocytogenes</u>
Onset of symptoms: about 4 to 21 days after ingestion
Symptoms: fever, vomiting, headache, can cause miscarriage of fetus
Common source: unpasteurized milk and soft cheeses

<u>Salmonella</u>
Onset of symptoms: about 5 to 72 hours after ingestion
Symptoms: nausea, fever, vomiting, diarrhea
Common source: raw or undercooked poultry, eggs, beef, or foods contacting them

<u>Shigella</u>
Onset of symptoms: about I to 7 days after ingestion
Symptoms: stomach pains and cramps, nausea, vomiting, diarrhea, fever, bloody stool
Common source: infected food handler (fecal contamination)

<u>Staphylococcus aureus</u>
Onset of symptoms: about 2 to 6 hours after ingestion
Symptoms: vomiting, diarrhea, similar to "stomach flu"
Common source: food handler's cut in skin, infected skin or nasal fluid

<u>Trichinella spiralis</u>
Onset: early symptoms about I to 2 days; later symptoms about 7 to 15 days after ingestion
Symptoms: fever, weakness, similar to "stomach flu;" later, swollen eyelids, muscle pain, fever
Common source: inadequately cooked infected pork or wild game

<u>Vibrio cholera</u>
Onset of symptoms: about I to 3 days after ingestion
Symptoms: diarrhea, stomach pain, can be fatal
Common source: seafood from sewage-contaminated waters

<u>Yersinia enterocolitica</u>
Onset of symptoms: about 2 to 3 days after ingestion
Symptoms: nausea, diarrhea, fever, flu-like
Common source: unpasteurized milk, unchlorinated water

Microbes grow best when they have plenty of nutrients under moderate conditions—not too hot or cold (Fig. 16-1), not too sugary, salty, acid, or dry. We don't get microbial illness from candy (too sugary), pickles (too salty, too acid), or crackers (too dry). We limit microbial growth by drying apricots, sugaring strawberries to make jam, and heavily salting meat (whole grains of salt were known as *corn* in England; hence, *corned beef*).*

Food mixtures that contain mayonnaise, eggs, or milk products, and aren't cooked or reheated after being made (e.g., potato salad, cream or custard-filled pastries, egg salad). are more of a concern. Unless one takes precautions, microbes can get mixed in under conditions that favor microbial growth.

In a classic scenario, you invite friends to a barbecue. You cut the raw chicken while you boil potatoes. Using the same cutting board and knife, you cut up the warm potatoes and mix them with mayonnaise to make a bowl of potato salad. Even if you put it right in the refrigerator, it takes time for the salad to get cold, especially in the middle of the bowl.

You have an ideal growth condition for any microbes that you may have mixed in, whether from raw chicken, a cut on your finger (a place where microbes like to grow), or unwashed hands that just changed a baby's diaper. Potato salad is moist, neither too acid nor too salty; microbes are distributed throughout the salad, surrounded by nutrients to feast on; and the temperature stays cozy long enough for the microbes to grow to a number that can make you and your guests sick.

Some precautions you can take:
- Assume raw meat (including seafood) is contaminated, since you don't know. After cutting it, don't use the cutting board or knife for other foods that won't be well-cooked, unless you thoroughly wash them (and your hands) with soap and hot water. A good habit is to make raw meat the last thing you cut, or have a cutting board used only for raw meat.
- When defrosting, storing, or marinating raw meat in the refrigerator, put it on a bottom shelf (or in a pan or dish) so it can't drip on other food.
- Cool food like potato salad fast. Refrigeration cools from the outside in, so potato salad cools faster in a flat pan. You can transfer the potato salad to a bowl after it's cooled. When you then put the bowl on the table, it will stay cold longer than in a flat pan. Don't leave potato salad out of the refrigerator or picnic cooler for long. People often get sick from contaminated potato or macaroni salad that's left out during a leisurely picnic.

Kill Them

There are many chances to kill germs—disinfectants on food-processing equipment, chlorinated drinking water, pasteurized milk, cooked food. Heat doesn't always have to be so high that it kills all the microbes. Heat used to pasteurize milk kills disease-causing ones, but not the ones that cause spoilage. Ultrahigh heat can sterilize milk (kill all microbes); this "fresh" milk can then be stored for months at room temperature.

Irradiation of food can be used for several purposes, e.g, to kill pests in spices, tea, and other crops (to replace post-harvest use of pesticides); to kill hazardous microbes in meat; to inhibit post-harvest sprouting of potatoes and onions; to delay ripening or spoiling of fruit. Irradiating a food doesn't make it radioactive, as some consumers think.

We eliminate many microbial hazards by cooking, thus killing the microbes or destroying their toxins. People rarely get sick from food that's well-cooked and eaten soon after

Symbol for Irradiated Food

---

*These procedures lessen risk, but don't guarantee safety. Soon after St. Patrick's Day 1993 in Cleveland, 15 people called the local health department about their illness, which was traced to microbial contamination of corned beef from a local deli. When the outbreak was reported in the local paper, 156 people called to report diarrhea and stomach cramps that occurred within 48 hours of eating food from the same deli.

cooking, e.g., a bubbling hot casserole going from oven to table.

Often the problem is "simply" inadequate cooking of contaminated food, as is often the case when people get sick from turkey stuffing. Making stuffing is like making potato salad—meat is often prepared at the same time, and it's easy to cross-contaminate. Furthermore, the cook may stuff the turkey the night before, since it's often a part of a Thanksgiving feast, and there's a lot to be done.

In the refrigerator, the center of the stuffing in a big turkey stays for some time at a cozy temperature for microbial growth. In roasting, the turkey cooks from the outside in, meaning that the center of the stuffing may not get cooked enough. If microbes have flourished there, they won't be killed as they should. If you then leave the stuffing on the table for a long time, the microbes get another good chance to grow. Be cautious—stuff the turkey just before roasting or, better yet, bake the stuffing separately.

Botulism

Most microbial hazards in food are avoided by thorough cooking, but there are exceptions. The microbe that causes botulism isn't destroyed by typical cooking times and temperatures, but its toxin is (it's a protein and is denatured by cooking; Chap. 5). This is why very high heat is used in canning food.

Botulism is caused by a toxin made by *Clostridium botulinum*, a microbe common in soil. The microbe itself isn't toxic. Botulism is uncommon in this country, but it's worth discussing because of some particularly interesting aspects.

The toxin is a nerve poison that affects muscle action, and is one of the most potent poisons known.* An amount as small as a grain of salt is enough to kill several people within an hour.

Symptoms usually appear 12 to 36 hours after ingestion, but can vary from 4 hours to 8 days. Neurological symptoms usually start in the head area, and then move downward. Early symptoms include double vision, dry mouth, drooping eyelids, and speech and swallowing problems.† The toxin can impair breathing and cause death by suffocation.

Early diagnosis is important. Botulism is a medical emergency. Antitoxin is available, and mechanical ventilation can be used when it gets hard to breathe.

Most cases of botulism are from eating home--canned, low-acid food (e.g., green beans, corn, spinach) where the canning temperature was too low and/or the heating time too short. The microbe is left alive in ideal conditions: low in acid, salt, and sugar, and stored at room temperature with oxygen kept out (botulinum is anaerobic—it grows in the absence of oxygen). Because canned food is already cooked, it's often eaten cold (e.g., canned green beans added to a salad) or simply warmed (temperature too low to destroy the toxin).

The microbe or its toxin doesn't necessarily make the food look, smell, or taste unusual. So if contamination is even suspected (haphazard processing, bulging of the canning lid, etc.), discard the food without tasting. "If in doubt, throw it out"—it's not worth the risk.

The toxin (unlike some other toxins and the microbe itself) can be destroyed by thorough cooking, but this isn't advised as a way of making it safe to eat.

Commercially canned foods rarely cause botulism—only four deaths have been reported in the U.S. since 1926. The latest was in 1971 from canned vichyssoise made by a small company. Vichyssoise is a creamy potato soup (non-acidic), usually served cold. Had it been adequately heated, the toxin would have been destroyed, and the death might have been avoided.

---

*Botulinum toxin can be used in biological warfare by sabotaging food supplies or by an aerosol attack. Iraq filled and deployed more than 100 munitions with the toxin before the Gulf War.

†The toxin blocks muscle contraction by interfering with the release of the neurotransmitter acetylcholine (Chap. 15). It's thus used to treat facial tics (injecting a bit of it into the affected muscle keeps it from twitching) and, cosmetically, to relax facial muscles that cause wrinkles.

Concern with botulism in commercially processed food is pretty much confined to processed meats (e.g., frankfurters, sausages, ham), and nitrite is added to hamper the production of the toxin (see nitrosamine section in Chap. 12). The name botulism comes from the Latin word for sausage (*botulus*).

Botulism from sausages used to be quite common. When animals were slaughtered, sausage was a way to use scraps of meat. It wasn't a tidy job; the microbe could easily get mixed in with the ground meat and seasonings stuffed into an animal's cleaned-out intestine (you'll be happy to know that artificial casings are now used instead).

The casing keeps oxygen low (the growth condition for botulinum), and the sausage was then heated enough to cook the meat but not enough to kill the microbe, which could then grow and make toxin during storage. Sausage was often only warmed before eating, or eaten cold.

Infant Botulism

Botulism is usually caused by ingesting the toxin, but in infant botulism, the microbe itself is ingested and the toxin made in the infant's own digestive tract. It's seen most often in infants 2 to 3 months old. An infant's stomach isn't as acid as that of an adult or older child. This aids the growth of the microbe and its production of toxin. It doesn't take much toxin to be a large dose for a small infant.

The only food directly implicated in infant botulism is honey (another source is soil that contains the microbe). It's advised that infants less than a year old not be fed honey. The Center for Disease Control has found the microbe in about 10% of honey samples.

E. Coli O157:H7

E. coli (*Escherichia coli*) is a common microbe normally present in the intestine and feces of all vertebrates, including humans. Most strains are quite harmless; some are even helpful. *E. coli* strain O157:H7 is one of several unusual strains that make a potent toxin that causes serious illness, especially in young children and the elderly.

The first recognized outbreak of *E. coli* O157:H7 was in 1982 when at least 47 people in Oregon and Michigan got sick after eating McDonald's hamburgers. There have been many outbreaks since, including one involving three classes of kindergarten children who drank unpasteurized milk during a trip to a Canadian dairy farm, and another in 1993 traced to fresh apple cider—apples may fall on soil that has animal droppings (feces) or manure fertilizer. The most common route of infection is via fecal contamination, particularly from cows.

A 1993 outbreak in Washington, Idaho, California, and Nevada killed four children and made hundreds of people ill; most cases were traced to Jack-in-the-Box hamburgers.

In a 1996 outbreak in Japan, more than 9,000 people got sick and at least nine died. Most cases were traced to fresh radish sprouts served in school lunches. (Sprouts from contaminated seeds are a problem when eaten raw; seeds won't sprout if heated to kill microbes. Raw alfalfa sprouts in salads and sandwiches are a source of outbreaks in the U.S.) Also in 1996, about 70 people got sick and a 1-year-old girl died from drinking Odwalla juice that contained unpasteurized, contaminated apple juice.

The toxin damages the lining of the colon and its blood vessels, causing severe cramps and bloody diarrhea. In about 5% of the cases, the toxin enters the bloodstream, where it destroys platelets and red blood cells and causes kidney failure. Antibiotics can do more harm than good—they typically work by destroying the bacterial cell wall, releasing the toxin. Vaccines and drugs are being developed for humans and livestock.

In meat, hamburger is more likely to be contaminated because it's usually made by combining meat from many cattle and from many slaughterhouses to get a homogeneous product with a designated fat content. Suppose 1 of a 1,000 pieces of beef is contaminated. If all 1,000 pieces are ground together, all patties made from that batch (and the grinding equipment) will be contaminated.* (If they're not combined, as with a steak or roast, the odds of getting the contaminated piece is 1 in 1000.)

The potential for widespread contamination is even worse when the day's leftover hamburger is added to the next day's batch, as was the case at Hudson Foods. In 1997, more than 16 people in Colorado got sick from tainted hamburger that was traced to this company; federal inspectors found substandard meat-processing procedures, bacterial testing, and bookkeeping (to track the various lots of beef).

The company recalled a record 25 million pounds of hamburger, leaving 1 of every 4 Burger Kings in the U.S. without hamburger for more than a day. Hudson customers also included Safeway, Wal-Mart, and Boston Chicken.

Hamburger chains place huge orders for ground beef (McDonald's buys about 500 million pounds a year). Beef from many sources is combined and the patties shipped to various franchises. If a batch is contaminated, a widespread outbreak can occur (the contaminated Jack-in-the-Box hamburger meat was traced to a single processor).

Contamination won't cause disease if the patties are thoroughly cooked. All parts of the patty must be cooked to 155°F to kill the microbe; 140°F was the standard for Jack-in-the-Box hamburgers. (A contaminated steak would be contaminated only on its surface—only the surface has to be cooked to 155°F.) Consumers should look for a hamburger patty that isn't pink inside.

Fast-food hamburgers are popular among young children, who are particularly vulnerable to the toxin. So it's not surprising that they were the ones who died in the 1993 outbreak. But some of them hadn't eaten the hamburgers.

They probably were infected by person-to-person transmission via an infected child's dirty diaper (also the presumed source of the 1998 outbreak involving 26 children playing in a pool at a water park in Georgia; a 2-year-old boy died). When people ingest the microbe, it's passed in their stool. Person-to-person transmission is a common mode of infection.

Also keep in mind that cattle infected with *E. coli* O157:H7 often don't get sick themselves, and that cows wander—and drop their feces along the way. People have gotten sick from swimming in a lake where an infected cow had wandered to the lake's edge.

Major outbreaks cause a media blitz, but small outbreaks occur regularly. One outbreak in 1994 was traced to raw hamburger bought at a local grocery in Ft. Bragg, California. Ten people got sick; an 85-year-old woman died. In the U.S., about 20,000 people get sick and about 250 die from *E. coli* O157:H7 infection each year. Because contaminated raw beef is a common cause of infection, experts recommend irradiating raw beef to kill the microbe.

There are several variants of *E. coli* that cause disease. A particularly virulent one (O104:H4), traced to fresh sprouts, caused an epidemic in Europe in May-June, 2011, with more than 3900 cases and at least 46 deaths. In July, 2011, the European Food Safety Authority reported that a single lot of fenugreek seeds from an exporter in Egypt was the most likely source of the contaminated sprouts.

Tracking Microbial Contamination

To be effective in preventing illness, epidemics must be stemmed quickly. But an epidemic is hard to avert; it isn't generally recognized—or even considered to be one—until many people get sick. In the typical epidemic, patients are interviewed to look for what they ate in common so as to track the source of contamination. This requires a lot of time, money, and footwork, and is basically detective work that takes place well after the start of an epidemic.

---

*We saw this *combined batch effect* when hemophiliacs were infected with HIV via clotting factor made from blood pooled from thousands of donors (Chap. 7). Likewise, food made in big batches, as in restaurants and school cafeterias, can raise risk. If 1 egg in 10,000 is infected with salmonella, and you scramble 200 eggs together to make scrambled eggs, the risk of getting a contaminated serving is much higher than if you scramble yourself only one egg. But if the eggs are thoroughly cooked, even contaminated eggs aren't a problem. Many restaurants and institutions now use only pasteurized eggs.

If a patient in Ohio and another in Iowa get severe diarrhea, how can we tell if these are just isolated cases? A new method stems from DNA technology. Bacteria mutate fast (Chap. 10). Their DNA sequences match if they came from the same source. So if you culture the stool from the Ohio patient, and the DNA fingerprint of the culprit bacteria matches that from the Iowa patient's stool, you know to act fast on what looks to be the start of a widespread epidemic. Many health departments now use PulseNet, a national molecular subtyping network for food-borne diseases.

Even if an epidemic can't be halted, this new technology can trace back the source. In the summer of 1998, restaurant-associated infections with *Shigella sonnei* occurred in Minnesota, California, Massachusetts, and Canada. DNA fingerprinting of the microbe isolated from stool samples implicated parsley from a farm in Mexico. The municipal water used to chill the parsley and to make ice to pack the parsley for shipping was not chlorinated and was vulnerable to contamination. The restaurants used fresh parsley (sometimes chopped in large batches in the morning and left out all day) in pasta dishes, chicken sandwiches, coleslaw, etc.

Hazard Analysis Critical Control Points

Hazard Analysis Critical Control Points (HACCP) is a systemized food safety procedure used in many food industries, and is regulated by the U.S. Dept. of Agriculture and the Food and Drug Administration. Canada, the European Union, and Japan have also passed HACCP regulations. Foreign companies exporting food to the U.S. must conform to the same standards—they must have an HACCP program and be able to verify that it's working. There are 7 parts to HACCP:

- **Conduct a hazard analysis:** biological (microbe, etc.), chemical (pesticide residue, natural toxin, etc.), physical (chip of glass, walnut shell, etc.)—for each ingredient and process.

- **Identify critical control points**, e.g., heating is where a microbial hazard can be reduced or eliminated; putting lids on jars is where glass might chip and get in the food.
- **Establish criteria that must be met at the critical control points**, e.g., set a time and temperature for heating that will kill hazardous microbes.
- **Monitor the critical control points and keep a record of the data**, e.g., record thermometer readings at regular intervals to show that temperature criteria are being met.
- **Take corrective action** if critical point criteria aren't met.
- **Have an effective record-keeping system** to document the HACCP procedure.
- **Establish ways to verify that HACCP is working.**

HACCP has been used by food manufacturers since the 1980s. It's now mandated for meat processors (including slaughterhouses). Large companies must have an HACCP person on staff; small companies can use an outside service. HACCP is increasingly used by food service establishments such as delicatessens and catering companies.

Consumer Confusion

Scientists know how to make food safer, but a big hurdle is that the public sees hazards very differently than the experts. A disproportionate amount of our food-safety budget is spent on concerns about food additives and residues of crop pesticides, though experts tell us that these are at safe levels and that their benefits far exceed their risks. Allocation of resources on the basis of perceived risks instead of actual risks is not cost-effective.

Life's hazards can't be reduced to zero. We call things *safe* based on their *relative* risk. We say that driving slowly at 10 AM in good weather on a quiet street is safe, but it's still possible that something bad can happen. Relative to other driving situations, the risk of harm is small. And we accept a higher risk in certain situations—we drive to work even when traffic is heavy and it's pouring rain. But emotions often override logic.

Fear of cancer hampers implementation of some very effective food-safety measures. Irradiation of foods can do much to improve safety, by reducing such disease-causing microbes as *Salmonella*, *Shigella*, and *E. coli* O157:H7. Irradiation also can increase shelf life. For strawberries, it staves off mold and preserves freshness, giving the grocer more time to sell them (making them more affordable), and giving us more time to eat them before they spoil.

The word *irradiation* stirs up fears of cancer, and opponents argue, for instance, that it can cause carcinogens benzene and formaldehyde to form in food. But the amounts are trivial, relative to that found naturally. The benzene found naturally in a single egg is more than 100-fold higher than in an irradiated steak; the formaldehyde found naturally in a single apple is more than that made by irradiating a food. Dose matters.*

Another worry is radiation accidents from the machines. We require strong safeguards, just as we do for machines used to treat cancer by radiation or to take X-rays. Another fear is that irradiating a food makes it radioactive. This isn't so, just as you don't become radioactive when you get an X-ray.

Most of these hurdles can be overcome by an informed public. Those in the meat industry know that meat would be safer if irradiated, but are reluctant to do so because they fear losing sales when consumers see this noted on the label.

A real concern about irradiating foods is that it may make consumers complacent. Allowable levels of irradiation kill most, but not all, of the disease-causing microbes. The few that remain can grow to toxic amounts if the food is handled carelessly or prepared improperly.

People fear biotech foods—foods that "had their genes tampered with," though most of what we already eat have had their genes tampered with by traditional crossbreeding. In this sense, biotech foods can be safer, since the gene tampering is more precise and predictable (Chap. 10).

Fear of biotech extends to worrying about the safety of milk from cows given BGH (bovine growth hormone, also known as BST/bovine somatotropin). The injected hormone is identical to that made by cows (its recipe is the cow's gene itself), and is used to increase milk production. It doesn't raise the hormone level in the milk or otherwise change its composition; milk from BGH-injected cows is identical to milk from cows not given BGH.

Of other concerns, ask about relative risk, e.g., cows giving more milk may have a slightly higher risk of mastitis (inflammation of the udder), but the increase is less than the normal variation in mastitis rates between uninjected cows from different dairies. Good farmers aren't going to do anything that jeopardizes the health of their animals. There are other issues, such as BGH's economic impact on small dairy farms, but these shouldn't be confused with safety issues.

Much consumer anxiety and confusion stems from the fact that we like sharp lines between good and bad, vitamins and drugs, natural and unnatural, nutrients and poisons, but the lines are fuzzy. Nicotine is a natural plant substance that just about everyone outside of the tobacco industry agrees is a highly addictive drug. It's a pesticide (Black Leaf 40 garden spray is 40% nicotine sulfate). It's used as medication in smoking cessation programs and in alleviating ulcerative colitis. It's also being studied for use in treating Alzheimer's and Parkinson's disease. Nicotine is a chemical, a natural substance, an addictive drug, a pesticide, and a useful medication.

It's foolhardy to try drawing a sharp line between what's safe and what's hazardous in food, or to focus on only a few aspects of food safety. Only by widening our focus to include what's "natural," can we reasonably assess relative risks and take best advantage of what food science has to offer.

---

*A scare widely circulated via e-mail claimed that the methanol from aspartame (NutraSweet) breakdown causes multiple sclerosis and other maladies. Aspartame breaks down to 2 amino acids and methanol during normal digestion (Chap. 6). Methanol is toxic in large doses, but the amount of methanol from aspartame-sweetened soft drinks is no more than that found naturally in grape or tomato juice. Dose matters!

If a natural carcinogen or a common allergen exists in high concentration in a plant, we might want to use genetic engineering to remove the plant's ability to make the offending substance— or decide against eating the plant. Irradiating produce to kill microbes can lessen the need for post-harvest pesticides. We need to balance one worry against another.

Most of us aren't familiar with what goes on before food reaches a grocery store or fast-food counter. We take our bountiful food supply and its relatively low cost for granted. At home, we routinely discard food when it spoils, but don't think about how much is lost by such natural processes on the farm, or between farm and table. Crop loss, shorter shelf life, etc., mean higher prices. People buy fewer fruits and vegetables when the price is high and/or they worry about getting cancer from residual pesticides (though the risk of cancer can go up from not eating enough fruits and vegetables).

We sometimes need to be reminded that we and food science share the same goals: less need for fertilizers and pesticides, foods that stay fresh from farm to table, more nutritious and tastier foods at an affordable price, and a safer food supply.

Summary

According to our experts, the biggest threat to the safety of our food supply is contamination with disease-causing microbes or the toxins they make. Crop pesticides and food additives are near the bottom of their food-hazards list. For these and any other substance that we might worry about in our food, the most important consideration is dose, e.g., we normally ingest microbial toxins, but they're a problem only when we eat them in amounts large enough to make us sick. The dose makes the poison.

Plants contain a variety of chemicals having a variety of effects. Some could be called poisons, or nutrients, or drugs, or all three.

Food additives are substances added to food for specific purposes, e.g., to enhance flavor or inhibit microbial growth. Until the 1958 Food Additives Amendment, it was relatively easy to get additives approved by the Food and Drug Administration (FDA); the burden of proof of safety was on the FDA. The 1958 amendment shifted the burden of proof to the manufacturer, and relatively few additives have been approved since. The GRAS (Generally Regarded As Safe) list—of additives which had already been in use for years without apparent harm—also came into being at that time.

Food additives are tested extensively for possible hazardous effects, including cancer. Typically, they're first screened in tissue cells or bacteria, and then tested in large doses in animals. The use of huge doses to predict effects of low doses is debated, but there isn't yet a practical alternative. We should keep in mind that there is a lot of uncertainty in the whole process, so the decisions tend to err on the side of safety.

Food additives typically are added in small amounts. Olestra differs—it can make up the bulk of the food. Chemically, it's a fat, but nutritionally it isn't, since we can't digest or absorb it—hence, zero calories. Olestra makes possible fat-free or low-fat versions of foods like french fries, cheese, salad dressings, etc., that taste like the regular high-fat versions. Olestra breaks new ground as a food additive, so the FDA was extra-cautious in giving its approval. For now, it's allowed only in certain snack foods like chips and crackers.

Pesticides used on our food crops are another big consumer concern. Experts regard the scant amount in our food supply as safe but, regardless, the aim is to use as little as possible to get the job done and to find practical alternatives.

One of the best approaches is Integrated Pest Management (IPM), in which pest control is customized for specific pests of specific crops in specific locations. It minimizes pesticide use and uses what is needed in the most effective way possible, taking into account the most vulnerable stage of an insect's life cycle, local weather conditions, etc.

An ancient tool used to give plants natural pest resistance is the exchange of the plants' genes through crossbreeding. A more recent tool is the use of biotech to transfer specific genes from one plant to another.

Microbial food hazards make millions of us sick each year. Young children and the elderly are particularly vulnerable, as are people with an impaired immune system. There are many disease-causing microbes. Three basic rules in prevention are: Keep them out (e.g., sanitation, good personal hygiene), keep them from growing (e.g., keep food cold or hot), and kill them (e.g., thorough cooking, irradiation).

HACCP (Hazard Analysis Critical Control Points) is a systemized food safety procedure used by an increasing segment of the food production and food service industries. When HACCP is mandated for certain foods in this country, it's also mandated for foreign companies that export these foods to the U.S.

Consumer education can vastly improve food safety. The public needs to be able to look objectively at risks, weigh risks vs. benefits, and thereby make best use of the limited resources available for food-safety concerns. The public, government, food industry, and food scientists alike all share a common goal of safe, nutritious, tasty, and plentiful food at affordable prices.

Appendix

Appendix A-1: Measurement Conversion Factors

Metric Prefixes

kilo- = 1000 centi- = $\frac{1}{100}$ milli- = $\frac{1}{1,000}$ micro- = $\frac{1}{1,000,000}$

Weight

1 pound (lb) = 454 grams (g)

1 ounce (oz) = 28.35 g

1 kilogram (kg) = 2.2 lb

1 kg = 1000 g

1 gm = 1000 milligrams (mg)

1 mg = 1000 micrograms (mcg or μg)

1 lb = 16 oz

Length

1 inch (") = 2.54 centimeters (cm)

1 meter (m) = 1.09 yards (yd)

1 m = 100 cm

1 cm = 10 millimeters (mm)

1 mm = 1,000 micrometers (um)

1 mcg = 1 micron (μ)

1 yard = 3 feet

Volume

1 teaspoon (t) = 5 milliliters (ml)

1 liter = 1.06 quarts (qt)

1 liter = 1000 ml

1 cubic centimeter (cc) = 1 ml

1 tablespoon (T) = 3 teaspoons (t)

1 cup (C) = 8 fluid ounces = 16 tablespoons

1 quart (qt) = 2 pints = 4 cups

1 gallon = 4 quarts

Interconversions of Weight and Volume of Water

1 liter = 1 kilogram (kg) 1 gram = 1 milliliter (ml)

Interconversions of Temperature

°Celsius (°C) = (°F - 32) X $\frac{5}{9}$ °Fahrenheit (°F) = (°C X $\frac{9}{5}$) + 32

Freezing point of water = 0 °C (32 °F)
Boiling point of water = 100 °C (212 °F)

Appendix A-2: Periodic Table of Elements

1 Hydrogen								
3 Lithium	4 Berylium							
11 Sodium	12 Magnesium							
19 Potassium	20 Calcium	21 Scandium	22 Titanium	23 Vanadium	24 Chromium	25 Manganese	26 Iron	27 Cobalt
37 Rubidium	38 Strontium	39 Yttrium	40 Zirconium	41 Niobium	42 Molybdenum	43 Technetium	44 Ruthenium	45 Rhodium
55 Cesium	56 Barium	57-71* (see below)	72 Hafnium	73 Tantalum	74 Tungsten	75 Rhenium	76 Osmium	77 Iridium
87 Francium	88 Radium	89-103* (see below)	104 Rutherfordium	105 Dubnium	106 Seaborgium	107 Bohrium	108 Hassium	109 Meitnerium

57* Lanthanum	58* Cerium	59* Praseodymium	60* Neodymium	61* Promethium	62* Samarium	63* Europium

89* Actinium	90* Thorium	91* Protactinium	92* Uranium	93* Neptunium	94* Plutonium	95* Americium

*Elements 57-71 have exceptionally similar characteristics, as do elements 89-103.

When put in order by the element's atomic number (number of protons or electrons), certain characteristics appear periodically. In a periodic table, the elements are lined up by their similar characteristics.

Elements with filled outer electron shells (see Chap. 3) are the least able to combine with other elements and are normally gases. The first electron shell fills with 2 electrons—helium (atomic number 2); the second shell fills with 8—neon (atomic number 10 = 2 in the first shell + 8 in the second); etc. These "noble gases" make up the far right column of the periodic table.

Calcium (atomic number 20) and strontium (38) share some characteristics, as shown by their positions in the periodic table. Radioactive strontium is present in fallout from nuclear explosions. The body handles strontium like calcium, storing it in bone. Blood cells are made in bone marrow, so radioactive strontium in bone raises the risk of leukemia (cancer of the white blood cells).

								2 Helium
			5 Boron	6 Carbon	7 Nitrogen	8 Oxygen	9 Fluorine	10 Neon
			13 Aluminum	14 Silicon	15 Phosphorus	16 Sulfur	17 Chlorine	18 Argon
28 Nickel	29 Copper	30 Zinc	31 Gallium	32 Germanium	33 Arsenic	34 Selenium	35 Bromine	36 Krypton
46 Palladium	47 Silver	48 Cadmium	49 Indium	50 Tin	51 Antimony	52 Tellurium	53 Iodine	54 Xenon
78 Platinum	79 Gold	80 Mercury	81 Thallium	82 Lead	83 Bismuth	84 Polonium	85 Astatine	86 Radon

64* Gadolinium	65* Terbium	66* Dysprosium	67* Holmium	68* Erbium	69* Thulium	70* Ytterbium	71* Lutetium

96* Curium	97* Berkelium	98* Californium	99* Einsteinium	100* Fermium	101* Mendelevium	102* Nobelium	103* Lawrencium

**Elements 110 and higher are extremely short-lived, e.g., element 112 (Copernicum), made in 1996 by fusing zinc (30) and lead (82), lasts only 280 milliseconds.

Jewelry and coins share some characteristics (e.g., shiny, malleable, metallic); copper (29), silver (47), and gold (79) share a column on the periodic table.

Continuing the line of gold and platinum credit cards, Tim Foecke, metallurgist at the National Institute of Standards and Technology says, *"If you want make a statement with a really, really expensive metal, you could go with osmium. My personal favorite is gadolinium. When you say it fast, it sings. On the more fanciful side, californium, for the laid back customer, einsteinium, for the exceptionally wise money manager, neptunium, for stratospheric credit limits, and, for those just starting out, lead."*

Appendix A-3: Elements

*Atomic number	Symbol	Element	†Atomic weight	*Atomic number	Symbol	Element	†Atomic weight
13	Al	Aluminum	27	42	Mo	Molybdenum	96
18	Ar	Argon	40	10	Ne	Neon	20
33	As	Arsenic	75	28	Ni	Nickel	59
56	Ba	Barium	137	41	Nb	Niobium	93
5	B	Boron	11	7	N	Nitrogen	14
35	Br	Bromine	80	76	Os	Osmium	190
48	Cd	Cadmium	112	8	O	Oxygen	16
20	Ca	Calcium	40	15	P	Phosphorus	31
6	C	Carbon	12	78	Pt	Platinum	195
55	Ce	Cesium	133	94	Pu	Plutonium	244
17	Cl	Chlorine	35	19	K	Potassium	39
24	Cr	Chromium	52	88	Ra	Radium	226
27	Co	Cobalt	59	86	Rn	Radon	222
29	Cu	Copper	64	34	Se	Selenium	79
9	F	Fluorine	19	14	Si	Silicon	28
79	Au	Gold	197	47	Ag	Silver	108
2	He	Helium	4	11	Na	Sodium	23
1	H	Hydrogen	1	38	Sr	Strontium	88
53	I	Iodine	127	16	S	Sulfur	32
26	Fe	Iron	56	81	Tl	Thallium	204
82	Pb	Lead	207	50	Sn	Tin	119
3	Li	Lithium	7	74	W	Tungsten	184
12	Mg	Magnesium	24	93	U	Uranium	238
25	Mn	Manganese	55	30	Zn	Zinc	65
80	Hg	Mercury	201	40	Zr	Zirconium	91

* Atomic number = number of protons in the atom
†Atomic weight of the atom relative to carbon = 12.0

Appendix A-4: Adult Recommended Intakes, Daily Values, Upper Levels

Recommended Intake/day

	Women (age)		Men (age)		Daily Value	Upper Level[a]
	19-50	51+	19-50	51+		
Biotin (mcg)	30	30	30	30	300	[b]
Choline (mg)	425	425	550	550	-	3500
Folate (mcg)	400[h]	400	400	400	400	1000
Niacin (mg)	14	14	16	16	20	35
Pantothenic acid (mg)	5	5	5	5	10	[b]
Riboflavin (mg)	1.1	1.1	1.3	1.3	1.7	[b]
Thiamin (mg)	1.1	1.1	1.2	1.2	1.5	[b]
Vitamin A (mcg)[c]	700	700	900	900	1000	3000
Vitamin B_6 (mg)	1.3	1.5	1.3	1.7	2	100
Vitamin B_{12} (mcg)	2.4	2.4[n]	2.4	2.4[n]	6	[b]
Vitamin D (IU)[d]	600	600/800[e]	600	600/800[e]	400	4000
Vitamin C (mg)	75[f]	75[f]	90[f]	90[f]	60	2000
Vitamin E (mg)	15	15	15	15	22	1000
Vitamin K (mcg)	90	90	120	120	-	[b]
Calcium (mg)	1000	1200	1000	1000	1000	2500/2000[g]
Fluoride (mg)	3	3	4	4	-	10
Iodine (mcg)	150	150	150	150	150	1100
Iron (mg)	18	8	8	8	18	45
Magnesium (mg)	310/320[k]	320	400/420[k]	420	400	350[m]
Phosphorus (mg)	700	700	700	700	1000	4000/3000[e]
Selenium (mcg)	55	55	55	55	-	400
Zinc (mg)	8	8	11	11	15	40

[a] Tolerable Upper Intake Level: the maximum intake at which an adverse effect is unlikely

[b] Not determinable due to lack of data; caution advised as to excessive intake

[c] 1 mcg vitamin A (retinol) = 1 Retinol Equivalents (RE) = 5 International Units (IU)

[d] International units (IU). Can get vitamin D via sun exposure

[e] 2nd value is for ages 71+

[f] Recommended amount for smokers is an additional 35 mg vitamin C

[g] 2nd value is for ages 51+

[h] Women capable of pregnancy advised to get 400 mcg from supplements or fortified food

[k] 2nd value is for ages 31-50

[m] Applies to magnesium from pharmaceutical agents only

[n] 10-30% of elderly may malabsorb B_{12}; age 51+ advised to get B_{12} from fortified food or supplements

Appendix A-5: Vitamins and Minerals

Nutrient	Functions	Sources	Deficiency	Possible Toxicity
Vitamin A	Night vision, maintain various tissues	Liver, yellow orange and dark green fruits and vegetables	Night blindness, xerophthalmia	Fatigue, nausea, headache, hair loss
Vitamin D	Absorb calcium, mineralize bone	Fortified milk, sunshine on skin	Rickets, osteomalacia	Fatigue, nausea, calcify soft tissue
Vitamin E	Antioxidant	Plant oils, whole grains almonds	Hemolytic anemia	Cramps, diarrhea, dizziness
Vitamin K	Blood clotting	Intestinal bacteria, green leafy vegetables	Lessened ability for blood to clot	Jaundice in infants
Vitamin C *(ascorbic acid, ascorbate)*	Antioxidant, synthesis of connective tissue	Citrus fruits, berries, potatoes, red and green peppers	Scurvy, loose teeth, bleeding gums	Diarrhea, kidney stones
Thiamin *(vitamin B_1)*	Coenzyme in carbohydrate metabolism	Pork, legumes, whole and enriched grains, liver, nuts	Beriberi, impaired nervous system	Headache, weakness, irritability
Riboflavin *(vitamin B_2)*	Coenzyme in energy and protein metabolism	Liver, meat, dairy products, enriched grains, eggs, broccoli	Sore, red tongue, inflamed skin, eye disorders	None reported
Niacin *(nicotinic acid, niacinamide)*	Coenzyme in energy metabolism	Liver, meat, fish, whole and enriched grains, legumes	Pellagra (diarrhea, inflamed skin, dementia)	Flushing of face and hands, liver damage
Vitamin B_6 *(pyridoxine)*	Coenzyme in amino acid metabolism	Liver, meat, legumes, potatoes, organ meats	Inflamed skin, convulsions in infants	Weak and numb muscles, nerve damage
Folate *(folic acid, folacin)*	Coenzyme in cell division	Liver, legumes, orange juice, dark-green leafy veggies, whole grains	Anemia, risk of neural tube defects in fetus	High folate can May diaqnosis of B_{12} deficiency
Vitamin B_{12}	Coenzyme in carbohydrate, protein metabolism	Animal products (meats, eggs, milk)	Anemia, nerve damage	Diarrhea
Biotin	Coenzyme in carbohydrate and fat metabolism	Liver, yeast, whole grains, egg yolk, fish, nuts, legumes	Dermatitis, depression	None reported
Pantothenic acid	Coenzyme in metabolism	Liver, yeast, eggs, whole grains, legumes	Fatigue, headache, nausea	Diarrhea
Choline	Part of cell membrane, fetal brain development	Eggs, liver peanuts (adults make plenty of choline)	Impaired fetal brain development/ function	None reported

Nutrient	Functions	Sources	Deficiency	Possible Toxicity
Calcium	Bone/teeth structure, muscle and nerve function	Milk/milk products, soft fish bones, leafy dark green veggies	Stunted growth, malformed bones	Kidney stones
Chloride	Fluid balance, stomach acid	Salt (sodium chloride)	Rare; upset acid-base balance	High blood pressure
Chromium	Insulin cofactor	American cheese, liver, whole grains, brewer's yeast, nuts	Impaired insulin action	None reported, except from occupational inhalation
Copper	Cofactor in making hemoglobin collagen	Liver, seafood, nuts, seeds, grains, copper plumbing	Rare; anemia, retarded growth	Vomiting, diarrhea
Fluoride	Stengthen teeth and bone	Fluoride containing drinking water, tea	Increased tooth decay	Mottling of tooth enamel
Iodine	Part of thyroid hormone	Seafood, iodized salt, dairy products	Simple goiter, cretinism, stillbirths	Goiter
Iron	Carries oxygen in hemoglobin	Liver, red meat, fortified cereals	Anemia, fatigue	Hemochromatosis
Magnesium	Cofactor in metabolism	Whole grains, nuts, legumes, dark green leafy vegetables	Weakness, muscle pain, cramps, spasms	Loss of reflexes, respiratory failure
Manganese	Cofactor in metabolism	Whole grains, nuts, organ meats	Rare; nausea, vomiting	None reported, except from occupational inhalation
Molybdenum	Cofactor in metabolism	Milk, legumes, grains	Rare	Gout-like symptoms
Phosphorus	Bone/teeth formation, energy production	Meat, fish, poultry, milk, eggs, legumes, cereals, nuts	Irritablity, weakness, muscleache	Poor bone mineralization if low calcium intake
Potassium	Nerve function	Citrus fruits, bananas, apricots	Weakness, irregular heartbeat	Irregular heartbeat
Selenium	Cofactor in antioxidant	Meat, seafood, milk	Heart muscle disorder	Loss of hair and nails dermatitis
Sodium	Water balance	Salty foods, softened water	Weakness, cramps	High blood pressure
Zinc	Cofactor in metabolism	Oysters, beef, lamb, legumes whole grain	Retarded growth	Nausea, cramps, diarrhea, fever

Appendix A-6: Readings, References, Study Questions

Reading and reference selections touch on some items mentioned in this book and should be fairly easy to find. Many local libraries have *Consumer Reports, Scientific American,* and *Time. Many hospital, county health, and college libraries have The New England Journal of Medicine* (www.nejm.org). You can access many journals online, but full access is often limited to paid subscribers.

Good, reliable, and easy-to-read sources of general health and nutrition information include some monthly newsletters. *Consumer Reports On Health* (1-800-274-7596, www.ConsumerReportsHealth. org) is good, as are those from public health and nutrition departments of accredited universities, e.g., *Univ. of Calif. at Berkeley Wellness Letter* (1-800-829-9170, www.WellnessLetter.com), *Tufts Univ. Diet & Nutrition Letter* (1-800-274-7581, www.TuftsHealthLetter.com).

Our federal government provides a wealth of reliable information online (look for the .gov), e.g., www.nutrition.gov, www.cdc.gov (Center for Disease Control and Prevention), as do many national professional health organizations, e.g., *American Dietetic Association* (www.EatRight.org), *American Cancer Society* (www.cancer.org), *American Heart Association* (www.AmericanHeart.org), *American Diabetes Association* (www.diabetes.org).

It can be hard to distinguish between reliable and unreliable sources. Be suspicious of websites with advertising. It's noteworthy that none of the government (.gov) websites or the national professional organizations mentioned above have advertising on their websites.

Many people offer nutrition advice, but it's hard for consumers to pick out those giving reliable information. Just about anyone can call themselves a nutritionist or diet counselor, or get a Ph.D. in nutrition via correspondence courses from non-accredited colleges. Even some "accredited" schools are accredited by phony agencies. A more consistently reliable credential to look for is the *Registered Dietitian (R.D.),* which requires a bachelor's degree in the field, a year's internship, a passing score on an exam given by the American Dietetic Association (ADA), and continuing education credits. Those with this credential are registered with the ADA, and put *RD.* after their names.

Chapter 1 - Behind the Soundbite

The History of Scurvy and Vitamin C by Kenneth Carpenter, Cambridge Univ. Press, Cambridge, 1986. [Dr. Carpenter has a Ph.D. in nutrition from Cambridge Univ. and was Chairman of the Nutrition Dept. at the Univ. of Calif. at Berkeley. He also wrote the nutrition history books *Protein and Energy* (1994) and *Pellagra* (1981).]

Chapter 2 - Scientific Method

An Evaluation of Internal-mammary-artery Ligation by a Double-blind Technic by L.A. Cobb et al. *New Eng. J. Med.,* volume 260, pages 1115-1118, 1959. [This study was mentioned in discussing the positive results of a "placebo" surgery.]

Final Report on the Aspirin Component of the Ongoing Physicians' Health Study. *New Eng. J. Med., vol.* 321, pp. 129-135, 1989. [This was the example given of a study stopped early by the monitoring committee because the death rate for heart disease was clearly lower in the aspirin group. The study was to see if taking aspirin every other day lowers the risk of death from heart disease, and if taking carotene every other day lowers the risk of cancer. The carotene supplements didn't lower cancer risk.]

Profile of Nancy Wexier, *Time,* 2/10/92. [Dr. Wexler is prominent in research on Huntington's disease, a fatal, hereditary disease. There's a 50:50 chance of getting it if a parent has it; Dr. Wexier's mother died of it. She tells of the effects on her personal life and her research, giving us a feel for the very human aspects of the disease and research.]

www.ncbi.nlm.nih.gov/PubMed [Search this database for peer-reviewed scientific articles on health, medicine, nutrition, etc. From the National Center for Biotechnology Information, National Library of Medicine, National Institutes of Health.]

www.quackwatch.com ["Quackwatch, Inc., a member of Consumer Federation of America, is a non-profit corporation whose purpose is to combat health-related frauds, myths, fads, and fallacies." Information on cellulite removers, chelation therapy, etc.]

www.ncahf.org National Council for Reliable Health Information, Inc. [Organization of scientists and health professionals whose purpose is to combat health fraud; includes links to other such sites.]

Q1 Professor Jones found that students who sit at the front of the classroom get higher grades than those who sit in the back. He concluded that sitting in the front results in better grades. Is this a scientifically valid conclusion?

Q2 Countries whose native diet is a high-fat diet generally have a higher rate of breast and colon cancers than countries whose diet is low in fat. Why is this insufficient proof that a high-fat diet causes breast and colon cancers? What are other possible explanations?

Q3 Human studies which are (a) prospective, (b) randomized, and (c) double-blind are highly valued. What does each of these three terms mean, and why is each important?

Chapter 3 - Chemistry

www.periodicvideos.com [Click on an element in the periodic table for a fun and informative YouTube video on the element. Created by videojournalist Brady Haran, featuring Univ. of Nottingham chemists, including the "wild" and delightful Professor Martyn Poliakoff.]

www.webelements.com [Find out more about the Periodic Table and the elements. Website of Dr. Mark Winter, Dept. of Chemistry, Univ. of Sheffield, England.]

On Food and Cooking. The science and lore of the kitchen. (2004) by Harold McGee. ["Scientific explanations throw light on such mysteries as why you can whip cream but not milk; what makes white meat white; why fruits ripen and vegetables don't—hundreds of unusual questions answered." Mr. McGee has a penchant for science and a Ph.D. in English literature, and is married to a biology professor. He uses this combination well in making delightful what could be dull reading.]

Modernist Cuisine: The Art and Science of Cooking (2011) by Nathan Myhrvold. An incredible 6-volume treatise of culinary history, modern techniques (e.g., sous vide cooking), equipment, recipes, etc. Scientist/chef Myhrvold was formerly chief technology officer at Microsoft Corp.

Q1 McDonald's Big Mac has about: 45 gm carbohydrate, 31 gm fat, 26 gm protein, 3 gm fiber, and 1 gm sodium. How many calories in a Big Mac? What % of the calories comes from fat?

Q2 How are calories in food measured?

Q3 Women often take iron supplements in the form of ferrous sulfate: $FeSO_4$. How many milli-grams of iron is there in a 30 mg tablet? Atomic weights for iron (Fe), sulfur (S), and oxygen (0) are given in Appendix A-3.

Q4 When a sample of granola is burned in a bomb calorimeter, it's found to have 15 calories. Yet, when we eat the same amount, we only get about 13 calories. Why the discrepancy?

Q5 *Ionizing radiation* hasn't been mentioned. But based on what you learned in this chapter, what do you think ionizing radiation does to atoms it encounters?

Chapter 4 - Dietary Requirements and Recommendations

American Dietetics Association [www.eatright.org]

Dietary Reference Intakes (see below) by the Food and Nutrition Board, Institute of Medicine, National Academy of Sciences, and published by National Academy Press (www.nap.edu)

for **Calcium, Phosphorus, Magnesium, Vitamin D, and Fluoride** (1997)

for **Calcium and Vitamin D** (2011)

for **Energy, Carbohydrate, Fiber, Fat, Fatty Acids, Cholesterol, Protein, and Amino Acids** (macronutrients) (2005)

for **Thiamin, Riboflavin, Niacin, Vitamin B$_6$, Folate, Vitamin B$_{12}$, Pantothenic Acid, Biotin, and Choline** (1998)

for **Vitamin C, Vitamin E, Selenium, and Carotenoids** (2000)

for **Vitamin A, Vitamin K, Arsenic, Boron, Chromium, Copper, Iodine, Iron, Manganese, Molybdenum, Nickel, Silicon, Vanadium, and Zinc** (2001)

for **Water, Potassium, Sodium, Chloride, and Sulfate** (2005)

www.nap.edu [National Academy Press publications. [Download PDF versions of their 4,000+ books for free, including the Dietary Reference Intakes volumes listed above.]

http://fnic.nal.usda.gov [Food and Nutrition Information Center, National Agricultural Library, U.S. Dept. of Agriculture]

http://ods.od.nih.gov/databases/ibids.html [International Bibliographic Information on Dietary Supplements: databases of published, scientific literature. Office of Dietary Supplements at the National Institutes of Health]

www.health.gov/dietaryguidelines/dga2010/DietaryGuidelines/ines2010.pdf [PDF version of the booklet explaining the 2010 Dietary Guidelines for Americans.

www.choosemyplate.gov [U.S. Dept. of Agriculture's graphic and information on using food groups to plan and eat a healthy diet.]

Dangerous Supplements. *(Consumer Reports,* September 2010) ["Unsafe products can easily be found online and in retail stores." Tells about 12 to avoid and why (and also gives their alternative names): aconite, bitter orange, chapparal, colloidal silver, coltsfoot, comfrey, country mallow, germanium, greater celandine, kava, lobelia, yohimbe.]

Bowes and Church's Food Values of Portions Commonly Used (2009) by Jean Pennington, Judith Spungen. [An extensive table of foods and their content of standard nutrients (vitamins and minerals given in milligrams, rather than as % Daily Value), plus supplementary tables, listing content of amino acids, caffeine, alcohol, salicylates, etc., of some foods.]

Are You Eating Right? Compare your diet to the official recommendations using the nutrient content of 5,000+ foods. (2003) by Judi Morrill, David Stone, Suzanne Murphy. [Official dietary recommendations; step-by-step instructions for evaluating your diet. Food values given as on food labels: calories; % of calories from fat; gm or mg fiber, carbohydrate, protein, fat, saturated fat, cholesterol, sodium, potassium; % Daily Value for vitamins A, E, C, B6, B12, thiamin, riboflavin, niacin, folate, calcium, phosphorus, magnesium, iron, and zinc]

Q1   What's meant by % Daily Value on a food label?

Chapter 5 - Energy-Providing Nutrients

Q1   How is margarine made?

Q2   As Tim butters his potato, Sue cringes and says, "you just doubled the calories!" The potato weighs 5 ounces. How many ounces of butter did Tim put on his potato? Explain your answer.

Q3   *Simplesse is* a fat substitute made from egg and milk proteins; the proteins are shaped to give the mouth-feel of fat. It has 1/9 the calories of fat. Why is this? Why isn't *Simplesse* used in products that have to be heated?

Q4   What's meant by the statement that cholesterol is essential in the body but not in the diet?

Q5   Dietary fat has been given a bad reputation lately, and we tend to forget that dietary fat also has nutritional value. What are some of these positive aspects of dietary fat?

Q6   What are *partially hydrogenated fats?* Why do food manufacturers use them?

Q7   Explain why an ounce of salad oil has about 10 times more calories than an ounce of cooked, brown rice.

Chapter 6 - Digestive Tract

American Dental Association (www.ada.org) [information on dental health, including use of fluorides to prevent tooth decay.]

Q1   *NutraSweet is* made of *2* amino acids (phenylalanine and aspartate) linked together. Why is it sweet? Is it absorbed from the digestive tract? If so, in what form?

Q2   How might fiber help prevent diverticulosis, constipation, and colon cancer?

Q3   Why do we get flatus (gas) after eating beans?

Q4   There has been a tremendous increase in the use of high-fructose corn syrup in food products. Why might food companies prefer to use this rather than regular table sugar? How is high-fructose corn syrup made from cornstarch?

Q5   What's the cause and symptoms of lactose intolerance? How are the cause & symptoms related?

Q6   Why does a banana get sweeter as it ripens?

Chapter 7 - Circulatory System

Q1   Kim has always been sedentary and starts to become more active. As she becomes more physically fit, she notes that her pulse is now slower at rest. She is concerned that her blood circulation has slowed. Why is this not true despite her lower pulse?

Q2   Why are blood donors asked if they've taken aspirin within the past week?

Q3   Vegetarians who eat only plant foods can have diets that are deficient in vitamin B_{12} and high in folate. What is worrisome about this combination of B_{12} deficiency and high folate?

Q4   What are the three kinds of blood cells, and what is the function of each?

Q5   Maria found from her diet analysis that her iron intake is far below her RDA. What are symptoms of iron deficiency? She would like to get more iron from her diet. What suggestions would you give her?

Q6   Name two proteins dissolved in the plasma portion of blood. What's the function of each?

Q7   What is the meaning of the two numbers (e.g., 120/80) in a blood-pressure measurement?

Chapter 8 - Atherosclerosis

American Heart Association: 1-800-242-8721. **www.americanheart.org** [Extensive information about cardiovascular disease-symptoms, risk factors, dietary advice, etc.]

National Stroke Association: 1-800-STROKES; **www.stroke.org**

www.nhlbi.nih.gov [National Heart, Lung, and Blood Institute of the National Institutes of Health. Lots of information, including guidelines on blood cholesterol, high blood pressure, obesity]

Q1   What is atherosclerosis? Why can it cause more than one disease?

Q2   What's the difference between LDL-cholesterol and HDL-cholesterol?

Q3   What changes in our diet and lifestyle can we make to lower our risk of atherosclerosis? Explain how these changes lower risk.

Q4   Why is it that smoking increases the risk of a heart attack?

Chapter 9 - Cells and Metabolism

http://diabetes.niddk.nih.gov [Diabetes Information, National Institute of Diabetes and Digestive and Kidney Diseases, National Institutes of Health.]

American Diabetes Association (www.diabetes.org)

Juvenile Diabetes Research Foundation (www.jdrf.org)

Q1   There are proteins embedded in the membranes of our cells. Give an example of such a membrane protein and explain its purpose.

Q2   Explain the usefulness of ketone production during starvation.

Q3   What is type 2 diabetes? Explain why it is becoming more common in the U.S.

Chapter 10 - Genes, Protein, Viruses

www.cdc.gov [Center for Disease Control and Prevention, Extensive health info.]

The Blooding (1989) by Joseph Wambaugh. [True story of the first time that genetic fingerprinting was used to solve a murder. Reads like a mystery novel.]

Flu: The story of the Great Influenza Pandemic of 1918 and the Search for the Virus that Caused it. (2001) by Gina Kolata, science reporter fo the New York Times.

And the Band Played On (1987) by Randy Shilts, reporter for the San Francisco Chronicle. [Story of the early years of the AIDS epidemic. A 20th anniversary edition was released in 2007].

My Own Country: A Doctor's Story (1995) by Abraham Verghese, M.D. [A personal account of the author's experience as a physician at the start of the AIDS epidemic in rural Tennessee.]

The Cry and the Covenant (1955) by Morton Thompson. Horrifying look at medicine before "germs" were discovered. Doctors would go from doing autopsies to delivering babies without washing their hands, and many of the women died of "childbed fever." Story centers on Dr. Ignaz Semmelweiss (1818-1865) who was convinced these deaths could be prevented by the doctors washing their hands in an antiseptic solution, but couldn't convince his colleagues.]

Q1   List the steps of protein synthesis, beginning with DNA.

Q2   What are some advantages of producing proteins by biotechnology rather than by extracting the proteins from natural sources?

Q3 Retroviruses have *both* frightening and useful aspects. Explain *this,* using an aspect of HIV as a frightening example, and an aspect of gene therapy as a useful example.

Q4 What's a mutation, and what's meant *by, a mutation doesn't necessarily cause cancer?*

Q5 For the past three years, Val has gotten a flu shot. Why is it necessary for her to get a shot every year for the same disease (influenza)?

Chapter 11 - Dietary Protein

Q1 In developing countries, protein deficiency occurs much more frequently in children than in adults, even when both eat the same diet. Why is this?

Q2 Val takes an amino acid supplement that has 22 amino acids. Kay boasts that her supplement is superior because it has 25 amino acids. Val asks you if Kay's right. What would you say?

Q3 What's meant by *essential* and *nonessential* amino acids?

Q4 Joe's diet has 3 times the amount of protein he needs, plus he takes amino acid supplements. He complains of excessive urination and thirst. What's the most likely explanation?

Q5 Explain why eating 2 sources of plant proteins together can improve the quality of the protein. Include an example of a specific meal or snack in your answer.

Q6 You groaned when I said that eating the person sitting next to you would give you very high quality protein. Why such high quality protein?

Chapter 12 - Cancer

American Cancer Society: 1-800-227-2345. www.cancer.org

National Cancer Institute: 1-800-4-CANCER to find out about clinical trials of cancer therapy.

American Lung Association: www.lungusa.org

www.fda.gov/cder/cancer [Food and Drug Administration, Center for Drug Evaluation and Research, Oncology Tools website. Includes a lot of information on drug therapies for various cancers]

www.cancernet.nci.nih.gov ["Your gateway to the most recent and accurate cancer information" from the National Cancer Institute of the National Institutes of Health]

University of Pennsylvania Cancer Center: www.oncolink.upenn.edu

The Emperor of All Maladies. A biograpy of cancer. by Siddhartha Mukherjee, M.D. (2010). A thrilling and superb telling of the history and biology of cancer. Winner of the 2011 Pulitzer Prize for nonfiction.

Dietary Fat and the Risk of Breast Cancer by Walter Willett et al. *New Eng. J. Med.,* vol. 316, pp 22-28, 1987. [Study of 89,538 nurses mentioned in this chapter; no difference in breast cancer rates when women were grouped by level of fat intake (though all groups had fat intakes of more than 30% of calories as fat)]

Fungus in Corn Crop, a Potent Carcinogen, Invades Food Supplies *(The Wall Street Journal,* 2/23/89) by Scott Kilman. [The heavy contamination of U.S. corn crops by aflatoxin as a result of the 1988 drought.]

Q1 Why are cancer occurrence rates a much less reliable statistic than cancer death rates?

Q2 The occurrence rate of cancer is going up in the U.S., even when lung cancer is excluded. It's popularly believed that this is due to more cancer-causing substances in our food and environment. What are two alternate explanations?

Chapter 13 - Energy Requirements

Q1   Jenny has been off and on "crash" diets since she was 25 years old. Most of these diets have included a drastic reduction in calories, and she typically would put the weight back on soon after the end of the diet. She now finds, 20 years later, that she's having a harder and harder time losing weight. Explain the probable reasons for this.

Q2   Although Scott and Juan are the same in age and weight, Juan has a higher basal metabolism. What are some possible explanations for this?

Q3   Sue would like to know exactly how many calories she uses when working out for 20 minutes on the Stair master. A scientist will use one of two methods to make this measurement. Explain how these two methods work.

Q4   As I sit writing this exam, I feel cold. I can turn on the heat, get on my exercise bike, scrub the bathroom, or eat something. Why would eating something make me warmer?

Q5   What is leptin? In what ways might it cause or prevent obesity?

Chapter 14 - Musculoskeletal System

www.letsmove.gov [The Let's Move initiative was launched by First Lady Michelle Obama to stem the epidemic of obesity in America's children.]

Q1   Lin is 13 years old and has a grandmother with osteoporosis, and wants to know if there's anything she can do now at age 13 to lower her own risk. What recommendations might you give Lin? Explain how each recommendation is expected to lower her risk.

Q2   Besides providing structural support, what are other functions of bone?

Chapter 15 - Nervous System

Alzheimers Association [1-800-272-3900, www.alz.org]

Alzheimer's Disease Education & Referral Center [National Institute of Aging, 1-800-438-4380, www.nia.nih.gov/alzheimers/AlzheimersInformation/GeneralInfo/]

Effects of Diets High in Sucrose or Aspartame on the Behavior and Cognitive Performance of Children by M.L. Wolraich et al. *New Eng. J. Med.,* vol. 330, pp. 301-307, 1994. [It's a common belief that sugar (sucrose) causes hyperactivity in children. This well-controlled double-blind study showed no behavioral or cognitive differences in children (described by their parents as "sugars-sensitive") given diets high in sugar, aspartame (NutraSweet), or saccharin.]

The Tennis Partner (1999) by Abraham Verghese, M.D. [The author's tennis partner was a medical student who was addicted to cocaine. A moving, personal story of cocaine addiction. There are also many tennis tidbits for tennis enthusiasts.]

Beautiful Boy (2008) by David Sheff [The author relates his and his family's harrowing experiences with his son's addiction to crystal meth.]

An Anatomy of Addiction (2011) by Howard Markel, M.D. [In the days before certain drugs were made illegal, cocaine was touted as a "miracle drug," and many people because addicted, including the central characters of this book, Psychoanalyst Sigmund Freud and Surgeon William Halsted.]

The Broken Cord (1990) by Michael Dorris [The author tells the tragic story of his son who was born with Fetal Alcohol Syndrome. Winner of a National Book Critics Circle Award.]

Q1 Describe how a nerve impulse is transmitted across the gap between neurons (nerve cells).

Q2 What are distinguishing characteristics of fetal alcohol syndrome, and why is it that a child can have brain damage from prenatal exposure to alcohol, yet not look like a child with fetal alcohol syndrome?

Q3 It's commonly believed that sugar causes hyperactivity in children. But double-blind studies show that sugar can have a calming effect. How might sugar do this?

Chapter 16 - Food Safety

www.foodsafety.gov [Federal food safety information, including recalls, tips, news. Can chat online with a food safety expert.]

Q1 Why is it that for some minerals, plant content varies according to local soil content?

Q2 What are some alternatives to pesticide use in controlling crop pests and disease?

Q3 What is meant by, "the dose determines the poison"?

Q4 How does the public perception of food hazards differ from that of the experts?

Q5 Do you think we should irradiate food to reduce spoilage or microbes that cause illness? Explain and support your answer.

Final Exam Study Questions

Q1 A study of 6,500 people in China shows that as compared to Americans, their diets are 3X lower in fat, 2X higher in starch, and 30% lower in protein. Suggest explanations for 2 of the findings: (a) Obesity is much more common in the U.S., even though the Chinese eat about 20% more calories. (b) Osteoporosis is much more common in the U.S. (age-adjusted), even though our calcium intake is 2X higher.

Q2 As in most things, moderation is advised. What are problems associated with too little AND too much: (a) salt, (b) sunshine, (c) vitamin A, (d) calories, (e) fat, (f) iron, (g) protein?

Q3 A dietary guideline is to eat a variety of foods. What's the rationale behind this advice in terms of: (a) nutrients and (b) contaminants or toxicants in food?

Q4 If the typical American diet (diet A) could be "mixed with" the diet of those in a less developed country (diet B) to form a composite diet (diet C), would diet C be healthier for both countries? Discuss 3 dietary substances in your answer.

Q5 The Dietary Guidelines for Americans, American Cancer Society, and American Heart Association all have similar advice for a healthy diet. List 3 dietary recommendations that would lower the risk of both cancer and heart disease. Explain your answer.

Q6 Smoking increases the risk of a heart attack, lung cancer, osteoporosis, and a smaller baby at birth. For each of these, give a scientific explanation.

Q7 The soundbite, *people who drink orange juice get fewer cancers,* doesn't tell you if this is a link or a cause-and-effect relationship. Explain why a proven link in this case isn't proof that drinking orange juice helps prevent cancer. Give an alternate explanation for the finding.

Appendix A-7: Glossary

A

Absorption: Process by which nutrients are transferred from the digestive tract into the bloodstream.

Acetylcholine: Neurotransmitter at the nerve-muscle synapse.

Acid: Molecule that releases hydrogen ions into a solution.

Activase: Trade name for the tissue plasminogen activator (TPA) made by biotechnology and used to dissolve blood clots. *See also TPA.*

Adenosine triphosphate (ATP): Main chemical form of energy that is made and used in metabolism. Serves to transfer energy from energy-producing reactions to energy-using reactions.

Adipose cell: "Fat cell," that stores excess calories as body fat.

Aerobic metabolism: Oxygen-requiring reactions occurring in mitochondria which produce energy from the breakdown of acetyl CoA into carbon dioxide and water.

Aflatoxin: Highly toxic substance(s) formed by the growth of a mold (especially *Aspergillus flavus*) on peanuts, corn, etc.

AIDS: Acquired Immunodeficiency Syndrome caused by infection with HIV, characterized by infections stemming from a loss of crucial white blood cells necessary for proper function of the immune system.

AIDS virus (HIV): Common name for HIV (Human Immunodeficiency Virus). AIDS is caused by this virus.

Albumin: Protein found in the plasma portion of blood which helps transport substances, regulates pH of blood, and regulates the amount of fluid held in blood. A deficiency of albumin can lead to edema.

Alcohol: Fermentation product of carbohydrate that has a high caloric content (7 calories per gram) and is essentially devoid of nutrients.

Ames test: Test that uses specially-altered bacteria to identify a substance as a mutagen and, thus, a potential carcinogen.

Amino acid: Structural unit ("building block") of protein; contains an amino ($-NH_2$) and an acid ($-COOH$) group.

Amino acid pattern: Relative proportions of the nine diet-essential amino acids in a protein.

Anabolic steroid: Synthetic hormone that mimics the growth-promoting effects of male sex hormone testosterone.

Anabolism: Energy-requiring metabolic reactions in which larger molecules (e.g., protein, cholesterol) are made from smaller ones (e.g., amino acids, acetyl CoA).

Anemia: Lower-than-normal amount of red blood cells or hemoglobin. Nutritional deficiencies of iron, and folate, and lack of intrinsic factor for B_{12} absorption are common causes.

Anaerobic: Doesn't require oxygen.

Anaerobic metabolism: Energy-producing reactions which break glucose into pyruvate without the need for oxygen. Also known as glycolysis.

Aneurysm: Outpouching of a weakened portion of the arterial wall. Usually caused by a defect in the affected artery and/or high blood pressure.

Anorexia: Loss of appetite.

Anorexia nervosa: Eating disorder characterized by a dramatic reduction of food intake for fear of becoming fat, resulting in extreme weight loss and sometimes death.

Antioxidant: Substance that prevents or retards oxidation. BHA (butylated hydroxyanisole) and BHT (butylated hydroxytoluene) are common antioxidants used in foods. Vitamins C and E can also function as antioxidants in food and in the body.

Appetite: Learned response which causes the desire for food.

Artery: Thick, muscular, blood vessel that carries blood away from the heart. Blood carried in arteries is oxygenated, except for the pulmonary artery which carries blood from the heart to the lungs to be oxygenated.

-ase: Suffix used in forming the name of an enzyme, such as lipase, sucrase, and lactase.

Atherosclerosis: Disease caused by an accumulation of fatty material in the lining of the arterial wall, resulting in the thickening, hardening, and loss of elasticity of the arteries.

Atom: Smallest particle that can no longer be subdivided without losing its characteristic properties. Atoms contain protons, neutrons, and electrons.

ATP: *see* Adenosine triphosphate.

Axon: Extension of a nerve cell that conducts a nerve impulse away from the body of the nerve cell.

B

Basal Metabolic Rate (BMR): Rate at which energy (calories) is used for a person's involuntary functions. Measured under standard conditions, directly by the heat expended, or indirectly by the amount of oxygen consumed.

Base: Molecule that releases hydroxy ions (-OH) into a solution. (It removes hydrogen ions from the solution by combining hydroxy and hydrogen ions to form water.)

Bile: Fluid made by the liver and stored and concentrated in the gallbladder. Released into the upper part of the small intestine (the duodenum) and serves to emulsify fats, aiding fat digestion.

Bile acid: Component of bile made in the liver from cholesterol.

Biotechnology: Use of technology to study or solve problems of living organisms, e.g., production of human proteins (insulin, growth factor, Activase, etc.) by cells/ bacteria that have had the human gene for that protein inserted into their DNA ("recombinant DNA"). *Biotechnology* often used interchangeably with *genetic engineering* and *recombinant DNA*.

BMI: *see* Body Mass Index.

BMR: *see* Basal Metabolic Rate.

Body Mass Index (BMI): Your weight in kilograms divided by the square of your height in meters. Used to assess whether a person is underweight, normal weight, overweight.

Bomb calorimeter: Apparatus used to determine the energy value of food by measuring the amount of heat produced by complete oxidation ("burning") of a food sample.

Buffer: Substance that makes a fluid relatively resistant to changes in pH by taking up or releasing hydrogen ions.

Bulimia: Eating disorder characterized by a compulsion to eat large quantities of food in a short period of time, followed by "purging" the food, typically by inducing vomiting or taking laxatives.

C

Caffeine: Stimulant, found in coffee, energy drinks,etc., which makes the nervous system more excitable.Also refers to related substances found in tea and chocolate which act as stimulants.

Calorie: Amount of heat needed to raise the temperature of one liter of water one degree Celsius. In nutrition, a calorie is 1,000 X the calorie of physics/chemistry and is sometimes called a kilocalorie.

Cancer: Uncontrolled growth of cells which can lead to death.

Capillary: Small, thin-walled blood vessel. Reaching every living cell in the body, capillaries provide the means for exchange of substances between the blood and each cell.

Carbohydrate: One of the three classes of nutrients in food that provide energy to the body; an organic compound made up of carbon, hydrogen, and oxygen atoms. Carbohydrates have an energy value of 4 calories per gram.

Carbohydrate loading: Regimen used by endurance athletes to increase muscle glycogen by emptying the muscle of glycogen by exercise, and then, in the days immediately prior to competition, resting and reloading the muscles with glycogen by eating a high carbohydrate diet. This regimen temporarily increases the muscle's supply of glycogen to higher-than-normal levels.

Carcinogen: Substance that causes cancer.

Catabolism: Energy-generating metabolic reactions that systematically break down energy-providing nutrients (e.g., fatty acids, glucose) into smaller molecules (e.g., acetyl CoA, carbon dioxide).

Catalyst: Substance which increases the rate of a chemical reaction. (Enzymes are biological catalysts.)

Cell: Basic structural unit of an organism.

Cell membrane: The outside layer of a cell.

Cholesterol: A fat found in all cell membranes. Found in animal tissues, but not in plants.

Chromosome: Structures in the cell nucleus that are made of DNA and protein, and contain the cell's genetic information.

Citric acid cycle: Series of chemical reactions occurring in the mitochondria in which molecules are oxidized to produce ATP (energy). Also known as the Krebs cycle or the TCA (tricarboxylic acid) cycle.

Clinical trial: Prospective human study that, for example, tests for the effectiveness of a new drug, or tests to see if a change in diet can lower risk of disease. Because of the magnitude and expense of a clinical trial, preliminary studies in the laboratory and in animals must first show ample evidence of effectiveness and safety before it is approved.

Coenzyme: Non-protein substance which can be required for the activity of an enzyme. Coenzymes often have B-vitamins as part of their structures.

Cofactor: Non-protein substance, often a mineral, that can be required for activity of an enzyme.

Collagen: A protein found in bone, cartilage, and connective tissue.

Compound: Two or more different elements that are combined chemically, e.g., NaCl (sodium chloride, "table salt").

Constipation: Difficult or infrequent passage of stool. Insoluble dietary fiber helps prevent constipation by absorbing water, making stools bulkier and softer.

Covalent bond: Chemical bond in which one or more electrons are shared between two atoms.

Cytoplasm: The fluid in a cell.

D

Delaney clause: Adopted in 1958; prohibited the Food and Drug Administration (FDA) from approving food additives that had been shown, at any dose, to cause cancer in any animal. Repealed/replaced in 1996.

Denaturation: Permanent change in the 3-dimensional shape of a protein molecule, thereby changing its biological activity.

Dendrite: One of the many extensions of a neuron's cell body that receives nerve impulses from other neurons.

Dental plaque: Soft patches, containing bacteria and food debris, that cling to teeth. Involved in tooth decay and gum disease.

Deoxyribonucleic acid: *see* DNA.

Dextrose: *see* Glucose.

Diabetes: Disease characterized by high blood sugar resulting from insulin deficiency, or cell resistance to insulin action.

Diarrhea: Rapid movement of fecal matter through the colon, producing watery stool.

Digestion: Breakdown of foods by digestive enzymes into smaller units that can be absorbed by the body.

Digestive tract: Series of organs responsible for the digestion and absorption of nutrients. Also called the gastrointestinal (GI) tract.

Direct calorimetry: Method for determining the amount of calories expended by an organism by measuring the amount of heat produced.

Disaccharide: *see* Double sugar

Diverticulosis: Outpouching of the colon wall. Fiber is thought to lower risk by providing bulk to contents of the colon.

DNA (Deoxyribonucleic acid): Nucleic acid found in the cell nucleus, that holds genetic information in the form of genes.

DNA fingerprinting: DNA enzymatically broken into pieces of different lengths, depending on its sequence of bases. Pieces are separated by length, giving a "finger-print" that looks like a bar code.

Double-blind study: Study in which neither the subjects nor the investigators actively involved know whether a particular subject is in the experimental group or the control group.

Double sugar: Carbohydrate consisting of two single sugars linked together.

Duodenum: Uppermost region (about the first 12 inches) of the small intestine. Site where pancreatic and liver secretions enter the small intestine through the bile duct to neutralize the acidity of the partially digested food coming from the stomach.

E

Edema: Swelling caused by excess fluids in body tissues. Seen in severe protein deficiency and some other medical conditions.

Electron: Negatively charged particle that orbits the nucleus of an atom.

Element: Substance containing only one kind of atom.

Emulsifier: Substance which finely divides and suspends fat in a water-based solution.

Energy: Ability to do work. The energy value of foods and the energy needs of the body are expressed as calories.

Enrichment: Addition of specific nutrients (thiamin, riboflavin, niacin, folic acid, iron) to refined grains and cereals such as white rice and white flour.

Enzyme: Biological catalyst, usually a protein, that speeds biochemical reactions.

Estrogen: Female sex hormone.

Esophagus: Muscular tube, serving as a passageway for food, that extends from the throat to the stomach.

F

Fast-twitch muscle fiber: *see* White muscle fiber.

Fat: One of the three classes of nutrients in food that provide energy (9 Calories per gram) to the body. Fats dissolve in organic solvents but not in water.

Fat-soluble vitamins: Vitamins that dissolve in fat: vitamins A, D, E, and K.

Fatty acid: Chain of carbon (and hydrogen) atoms with an acid group (-COOH) on one end; the main component of triglycerides.

Fermentation: Anaerobic production of alcohol by the enzyme-catalyzed breakdown of carbohydrates. Fermentation can involve other substances as well.

Fiber: Indigestible substances found in plants. Insoluble fibers might help prevent diverticulosis, constipation, and possibly colon cancer. Soluble fibers may help lower cholesterol levels in the blood.

Fortification: Improvement of nutritional quality by the addition of one or more nutrients not normally found in the food (e.g., vitamin D in milk, vitamin A in margarine, calcium in orange juice).

Fructose: Single-sugar found in such foods as honey and fruit. Makes up half of the double-sugar sucrose and regular high-fructose corn syrup (the other half is glucose).

G

Galactose: Single-sugar that's a part of the double-sugar lactose.

Gastric juice: Acidic (about pH 2) secretion from the stomach lining responsible for such things as killing bacteria ingested along with food, denaturing proteins, and aiding mineral absorption.

Genetic engineering: *see* Biotechnology.

Glial cell: One of the two basic types of nervous system cells. Functions to nurture and protect the less numerous neurons.

Glucose: Most common single-sugar, also known as dextrose. Found in various foods, is the sugar found in the blood, and is a part of the double sugars sucrose, maltose, and lactose.

Glycogen: Complex carbohydrate (a storage form of glucose) found in animal tissue, and stored in muscle and liver.

Glycogen loading: *see* Carbohydrate loading.

Glycolysis: Production of ATP energy from the anaerobic breakdown (metabolism) of glucose in the cytoplasm of the cell.

Goiter: Enlarged thyroid gland. Called simple goiter when caused by a deficiency of dietary iodine.

Goitrogens: Substances found in foods and some drugs which, when eaten in large amounts over a long time, can cause goiter.

H

HDL (high-density lipoprotein) cholesterol: Cholesterol in a plasma lipoprotein that's transporting cholesterol away from cells. Dubbed "good cholesterol" (H for healthy). Low HDL linked to increased risk of cardio-vascular disease.

Heme iron: Iron found mainly in the oxygen-carrying molecules hemoglobin and myoglo-bin; found only in animal tissue.

Hemoglobin: Iron-containing protein in red blood cells that carries oxygen.

HIV (Human Inimunodeficiency Virus): *see* AIDS virus.

Hormone: Chemical messenger, typically secreted by a gland, carried in the blood-stream, and having a specific effect on cer-tain cells.

Hydrogenation: Addition of hydrogen to unsaturated fatty acids to make it more satu-rated. Double bonds are changed to single bonds, resulting in a more solid fat.

Hyperthyroidism: Condition in which an excessive amount of thyroid hormone is produced.

Hypoglycemia: Abnormally low blood-glucose.

I

Indirect calorimetry: Measuring oxygen-use to determine the calories expended by the organism.

Insulin: Hormone made in the pancreas that allows glucose to enter cells.

Integrated Pest Management (IPM): A cus-tomized ecological approach to minimize pesticide use by strategies based on pest biology, local soil conditions, etc.

Intrinsic factor: Protein, secreted by the stomach, that's essential for the absorption of vitamin B_{12}. An insufficient secretion of

intrinsic factor results in pernicious anemia, a B_{12} deficiency.

Ion: Electrically charged atom or molecule.

Ionic bond: Chemical bond resulting from the attraction of oppositely charged ions.

K

Ketone: Chemical formed when acetyl CoA accumulates in metabolism, as can happen in starvation and untreated diabetes.

Kilocalorie: *see* Calorie (Kilocalorie is the technically correct term, but, in nutrition, "calorie" is commonly used.)

Kreb's cycle: *see* Citric acid cycle.

L

Lactase: Digestive enzyme that breaks down lactose to galactose and glucose.

Lactic acid: Acid formed by glycolysis when oxygen is limited (e.g., in sustained, strenu-ous physical activity).

Lactose: Double-sugar (galactose linked to glucose) found in milk.

Lactose intolerance: Reduced ability (insuf-ficient lactase enzyme in small intestine) to digest the milk-sugar, lactose, that can result in symptoms such as diarrhea and gas.

LDL (Low-density lipoprotein)-cholesterol: Cholesterol carried in the plasma lipoprotein that transports cholesterol to cells. Dubbed "bad cholesterol" (L for lousy) because high levels increase risk of cardiovascular disease.

LDL-receptor: Protein in the membrane of cells that serves as an attachment site for LDL, allowing cholesterol to enter the cell.

Lecithin: Phospholipid (a type of fat) found in food and body tissues; used as an emulsifier in food preparation; contains choline; makes up our cell membranes.

Lipoprotein: Spherical particle made of fat and protein; used to transport fat in the plasma portion of blood.

M

Malnutrition: Condition in which the body gets too much or too little of a nutrient, resulting in poor health.

Maltase: Digestive enzyme that breaks down double-sugar maltose into two molecules of glucose.

Maltose: Double-sugar made of two glucoses linked together.

Menopause: Period in the life cycle of women when menstruation ceases permanently.

Menstruation: Monthly flow of blood and cell debris from the uterus during a woman's reproductive years (puberty to menopause).

Messenger RNA (mRNA): Copy of a gene used to make a particular protein.

Metabolism: Sum total of the chemical changes or reactions occurring in the body.

Microvilli: Ruffled portion of the membrane of cells lining of the small intestine; contains digestive enzymes; nutrients are absorbed through the microvilli.

Minerals: Inorganic compounds. Calcium, phosphorous, potassium, and iron are examples of minerals that are important for proper bodily function.

Mitochondria: Structures found in the cell cytoplasm in which all oxygen-requiring reactions occur.

Molecule: Two or more atoms linked together.

Monosaccharide: *see* Single-sugar.

Monounsaturated fatty acid: Fatty acid containing one double bond in its carbon chain. Olive oil is a rich source of monounsaturated fatty acids.

Muscle fiber: Muscle cell, described as a fiber because of its shape. Groups of these cells are held together by connective tissue to form muscle tissue.

Mutagen: Any agent that can change the sequence of bases in DNA.

Mutation: Change in the sequence of bases in DNA.

Myelin: White fatty substance that forms the [myelin] sheath that covers the axon of a nerve cell.

Myoglobin: Iron-containing protein found in muscle; stores oxygen for use during muscle contraction.

N

Natural food: As defined by the Federal Trade Commission, any food that is minimally processed and contains no artificial ingredients.

Neurotransmitter: Chemical substance involved in transferring a nerve impulse from one nerve cell to another, or from a nerve cell to a muscle cell.

Neuron: Nerve cell, consisting of the cell body and its extensions: dendrites and axons.

Neutron: Electrically neutral particle in the nucleus of an atom.

Nitrosamine: Carcinogen formed by the combination of nitrites and amines.

Non-heme iron: Iron not associated with oxygen-carrying molecules. All plant iron is non-heme iron.

Nucleus, atomic: Center of an atom, where protons and neutrons are located.

Nucleus, cell: Structure within a cell that contains the cell's genetic information.

Nutrient: Dietary substance essential for the growth, maintenance, function, or reproduction of a cell.

O

Obesity: Excess accumulation of body fat. Generally defined as a Body Mass Index (BMI) of 30 and above.

Oil: Generally speaking, a fat (triglyceride) that's liquid at room temperature, e.g., corn oil, fish oil. (Exceptions include palm oil.)

Organic compounds: All compounds containing carbon (with a few exceptions, e.g., carbonates, cyanides). Fats, protein, carbohydrate, and vitamins are all organic compounds.

Organic foods: In popular terminology, foods grown without use of chemical pesticides or fertilizers; only fertilizers derived from animals or plants are permitted.

Organism: Any living plant or animal.

-ose: Suffix that is used in forming the name of a carbohydrate, such as cellulose, maltose, and lactose.

Osteomalacia: Vitamin D deficiency in adults, resulting in bone demineralization and easily fractured bones.

Osteoporosis: Loss of bone-calcium in which bones have lost so much density that they are easily fractured. Occurs most frequently in postmenopausal women.

Oxidation: Addition of oxygen atoms to (or the removal of hydrogen atoms from) a substance.

P

Pacemaker cells: Group of cells in the heart that rhythmically stimulate the contraction of the heart muscle, causing it to beat.

PCR (the Polymerase Chain Reaction): Method by which sections of DNA are replicated to amounts large enough for analysis.

Pectin: A dietary fiber which can help lower blood-cholesterol levels. Also used to "gel" jams and jellies.

Peptide: Two or more amino acids linked together. Peptide is also used to describe the linkage (peptide bond) in which the amino group of one combines with the acid group of the other.

Periodontal tissue: Gums, periodontal ligament, and other tissue surrounding the teeth.

pH: Number denoting the hydrogen ion concentration in a solution. A pH value of 7 is neutral; less than 7 is acidic; and greater than 7 is basic. Physiological pH is between 7.35 and 7.45. pH literally means hydrogen power from the French pouvoir *hydrogene.*

Phenylalanine: One of the 9 amino acids required in the diet.

Phospholipid: Phosphorus-containing fat (lipid) made of glycerol, two fatty acids, and one phosphorus-containing compound. Phospholipids are the basic unit in cell membranes and are used as emulsifiers in foods. Lecithin is a common phospholipid.

Photosynthesis: Process whereby plants use light, carbon dioxide, and water to create carbohydrates and oxygen.

Placebo: Inert substance which seems identical to the test substance in studies.

Placebo effect: Effect that results from, but is not caused by, the test-substance or procedure. A psychological effect that occurs because it is expected (e.g., feeling better simply because you expect to).

Plaque: *see* Dental plaque.

Plasma: Fluid portion of blood in which red blood cells, white blood cells, and platelets are suspended.

Platelets: Small blood cells which cluster at the site of injury to a blood vessel, acting immediately to stop the bleeding until a clot of plasma proteins can form.

Polarization: Physical separation of positive and negative charges.

Polymerase Chain Reaction: *see PCR*

Polysaccharide: Carbohydrate of three or more single-sugars linked together. Subdivided into digestible (e.g., starch) and indigestible (e.g., fiber). Digestible polysaccharides are commonly called complex carbohydrates.

Polyunsaturated fatty acid: Fatty acid with two or more double bonds in its carbon chain.

Prospective study: Study that follows the development of, for example, a disease in healthy people who have been grouped according to the presence or absence of the characteristic believed to be involved in the disease (e.g., follows healthy smokers and nonsmokers for the development of lung cancer).

Protein: One of the three classes of nutrients in food that provide energy to the body; an organic compound composed of amino acids linked together by peptide bonds. Protein has a caloric value of 4 calories per gram.

Protein-calorie malnutrition: Severe protein deficiency caused most often by the combination of both calorie and protein deficiencies in the diet.

Protein complementation: Combination of one plant protein low in one or more amino acids with another protein that provides more of the limiting amino acid(s), thus providing a better mixture of amino acids to satisfy the body's amino acid requirements.

Proton: Positively charged particle found in the nucleus of an atom.

Pyruvate: End-product of anaerobic metabolism (glycolysis) that can be made into lactic acid or acetyl CoA.

R

Rancid: Having the disagreeable taste and/or smell of decomposed oils or fats, caused by oxidation of double bonds in unsaturated fats.

Recombinant DNA: *see* Biotechnology.

Red muscle fiber: Muscle cell with a high capacity for aerobic energy production. Important for sustained muscle activity.

Relative Risk: Statistical measure of the risk of developing a disease. Defines the risk of a group with a certain characteristic as compared to the risk of the general population.

Restoration: Addition of nutrients that were originally present in the food but were either lost or destroyed in processing (e.g., vitamin C to instant mashed potatoes).

Retrospective study: Study in which people are grouped according to the presence or absence of a disease or condition. By examining the physical characteristics and earlier habits of each group, scientists try to determine the reason(s) for the disease or condition.

Reverse transcription: Process in which a virus causes a cell to make a DNA copy of the viral RNA. This strand of foreign DNA may then become a part of the cell's own DNA. This occurs with the AIDS virus.

Ribonucleic acid (RNA): *see* RNA.

Ribosome: Structure located in the cytoplasm of a cell that is the site of protein synthesis.

Rickets: Bone deformities due to deficiency of vitamin D and/or calcium in childhood.

Risk factor: Anything that increases one's risk of an adverse effect, e.g., smoking is a risk factor for lung cancer; high LDL-cholesterol is a risk factor for cardiovascular disease.

RNA (Ribonucleic acid): A nucleic acid important in protein synthesis. Messenger RNA carries the directions to make a protein from DNA to ribosomes ("ribosomal RNA") where protein is made. Transfer RNA carries the amino acids needed for protein synthesis. *see* Messenger RNA, Transfer RNA.

S

Satiety: Feeling of fullness or of being satisfied. Fat provides a longer satiety than carbohydrate or protein.

Saturated fatty acid: Fatty acid that doesn't have any double bonds in its carbon chain because it's saturated with hydrogen atoms.

Scientific Method: Collective term for the steps and procedures scientists follow to acquire scientific knowledge. It involves formulation of a hypothesis, experimentation, evaluation, discussion of experimental results, and the discussion of conclusions, all subject to peer review.

Serotonin: Neurotransmitter made from the amino acid tryptophan, has a calming effect.

Single-sugar: Carbohydrate consisting of a single sugar molecule (e.g., glucose, fructose). Also called *monosaccharide.*

Skinfold thickness: A method for determining the amount of body-fat stored under the skin by measuring the thickness of a fold of skin.

Slow-twitch muscle fiber: *see* Red muscle fiber.

Steroid: Synthetic or naturally occurring hormone with a cholesterol-like structure.

Sterol: Type of fat (lipid) which contains a basic four-ring structure (e.g., cholesterol).

Stimulant: As related to the nervous system, a substance that causes a nerve cell to be more easily excited.

Sucrase: Digestive enzyme that breaks down sucrose (a double-sugar) to fructose and glucose (single-sugars).

Sucrose: Double-sugar made of fructose and glucose (single-sugars) linked together. Commonly known as "table sugar."

Sugar: Common name for single sugars (e.g., glucose, fructose, and galactose) and double-sugars (e.g., sucrose, lactose, maltose). "Table sugar" is sucrose.

Synapse: Place where a nerve impulse is transferred between nerve cells or between nerve cell and muscle cell.

T

Thyroxine: Iodine-containing hormone made by the thyroid gland; important in maintaining normal rates of metabolism.

TPA (Tissue plasminogen activator): Substance in blood that triggers the breakdown of clots. Known as Activase when made by biotechnology.

Trans fatty acid: Unsaturated fatty acid that has unusual configuration around the double bond. Most commonly found in partially hydrogenated fat. Like saturated fat, it can raise LDL-cholesterol.

Transcription: Process in which messenger RNA (mRNA) is made by copying ("transcribing") the section of bases in DNA that makes up a gene. (A gene has the instructions to make a protein.)

Transfer RNA (tRNA): Transports amino acids to the ribosome for use in protein synthesis. Each of the 20 amino acids needed to make protein has its own special tRNA.

Translation: Process by which information in messenger RNA (mRNA) is translated and implemented to form protein.

Triglyceride: Fat made up of three fatty acids attached to glycerol; makes up most of the fat in food; the body's storage form of fat.

Tryptophan: One of the nine amino acids required in our diet.

Tumor: Abnormal mass of tissue that results from uncontrolled cell growth; a tumor may be benign or malignant.

U

Unsaturated fatty acid: Fatty acid which has one or more double bonds in its carbon chain.

Urea: Waste product of amino acid breakdown that's excreted in urine.

V

Vegan: Person who eats plant foods only.

Vegetarianism: Consuming a diet entirely of plant foods and plant products. There are modifications of vegetarianism, e.g., a lacto-ovo-vegetarian diet also includes milk and eggs.

Vein: Blood vessel that transports blood to the heart. Veins have valves that direct the blood back to the heart and help prevent pooling of the blood in the veins.

Villus: Small, finger-like projection in the inner lining of the small intestine. Functions in digestion and absorption. (Plural, villi.)

Virus: Infectious agent containing DNA or RNA that can cause disease in both plants and animals. They're smaller than bacteria and, unlike bacteria, can't reproduce unless they infect a cell.

Vitamin: Essential molecule required in the diet. The 13 vitamins are classified into two groups: fat-soluble and water-soluble.

W

Warfarin: Anticoagulant drug that lessens blood clotting by interfering with Vitamin K activity. Also used as a rat poison.

Water-soluble vitamins: Vitamins that dissolve in water: vitamin C and the eight B-vitamins.

White muscle fiber: Muscle cell with a high capacity for anaerobic energy production. Important for bursts of muscle activity.

***

Index

A

Acetaminophen 81
Acetate 125-127, 129-131
Acetic acid 35, 237
Acetylcholine 219, 221, 230-231, 244
Acetylcholinesterase 219, 221
Acetylsalicylic acid 233
Acne 201, 235
Acromegaly 202
Activase 104, 113, 118, 136, 145
Additives see Food Additives
Aerobic metabolism 124-128,
Aflatoxins 174, 175
Agar 237
Agrobacterium tumefaciens 148, 149
AIDS (Acquired Immunodeficiency
    Syndrome; *see also* HIV) 19, 101,
    102, 123, 144, 145, 169
Alanine 129, 140, 153, 154
Albumin 102, 103, 106, 159
Alcohol 18, 38, 39, 49, 55, **59**, 73,
    80, 81, 85, 100, 114, 117, 130,
    169, 172-174, 176, 178, 210, 220,
    222, 223
Alcoholism 100, 132, 208, 210, 223
Alendronate 211
Alternative medicine 22, 23
Aluminum 25, 39, 254
Aluminum hydroxide 208
Alzheimer's 138, 218, 219, 230, 248
Amenorrhea 210
American Cancer Society 6
American Heart Association 6, 49,
    108, 118
American Psychiatric Association 230
American Veterinary Medical Asso-
    ciation. 16
Ames test 151, 152, 174, 181, 236
Amino acids 68-70, 125, 135, 140,
    227 (*see also* specific amino acids)
Ammonia 36, 159, 160, 163, 235
Ammonium citrate 237
Amphetamines 220, 227
Amylase 75, 77, 82
Amylopectin **56-57**, 75
Amylose **56-57**, 58, 75
Anabolic steroids 112, 121, **200-201**
Anaerobic metabolism *see* Glycolysis
Androstenedione 201
Anemia 96-101, 149,-150
Aneurysm 108

Animals in research **14-17**, 23
Angina 13, 108, 149
Angioplasty 112
Animal Studies 14, 15, 16, 17, 19, 23
Anorexia nervosa 96, 192, 210
Annato 237
Antacids 80, 208
Anthrax 17, 102
Antibiotics 41, 79, 81, 85, 86, 90,
    103, 144, 150, 188
Antibodies 70, 91, 100, 102, 106,
    121, 143, 145, 159, 177, 188
Anticoagulants 103
Anus 73, 74, 86, 145
Aorta 93
Appendicitis 87
Appendix 74, 87
Appetite 4, 131, 186, 188, 193, 194,
    196, 220, 231
Arginine 140, 154
Aromatherapy 22
Arteries 93-95, 108, 110
Arteriosclerosis (Chap. 8)
Ascorbate, Ascorbic acid
    see Vitamin C
Asparagine 140, 154
Aspartame (*see also* Equal, Nutra-
    Sweet) 35, 75, 77, 248
Aspartate (aspartic acid) 75, 140, 154
Aspergillus flavus, parasisticus 174
Aspirin 11, 13, 17, 21-23, 66, 81, 85,
    101-103, 113, 119, 233
Association of American Medical
    Colleges 16
Atherosclerosis (Chap. 8)
Athletes 37, 42, 43, 50, 70, 91, 93,
    95, 96, 112, 121, 127, 128, 133,
    158, 183, 200, 201, 202, 213, 183
Atomic fusion 20
Atomic number, weight 26, 29
Atoms **25-29**, 30-34, 37, 39
ATP (adenosine triphosphate) 37,
    125-130, 183, 189, 196, 224,
Autoimmune disease 100, 132, 216,
    219
Avidin 158
Axon 216, 217, 218, 231
AZT (azidothymidine) 144

B

Bacon 60, 82, 172, 173
Bacteria 76-78, 81, 86, 87, 101, 145,
    148, 151, 212, 213, 247
Baking soda *see* Sodium bicarbonate
Bananas 48, 52, 60, 61, 76, 158, 161
Barbiturates 220, 222, 231

Barley 55, 59
Basal metabolism 183-192, 197, 198,
    223
Batch effect 246
Battery acid 36
Beans 52, 57, 60, 86, 97, 99, 115,
    154-157, 161, 162
Beef 64, 89, 97, 161, 245, 246
Beer 18, 44, 49, 55, 59, 114, 126,
    173, 235
Benecol 6
Benzene 248
Benzodiazepine 220, 222
Benzoic acid 237
Benzoyl peroxide 237
Beriberi 3, 4, 5, 16, 224
Beta-blockers 112
Beta-carotene (see also Carotene) 6,
    7, 17
BGH (bovine growth hormone) 248
BHA (butylated hydroxyanisole),
    BHT (butylated hydroxytoluene)
    65, 237
Bile 58, 67, 72, 84, 86, 87, 89, 95,
    102, 105, 110, 115, 116, 119, 170
Bile acids 84, 115
Bile duct 74, 84, 89, 95
Bile pigments 86, 95
Biological weapon 102
Biotechnology 5, 15, 20, 96, 103,
    104, 118, 123, 129, 145, 152, 177,
    201, 202, 204
Biotin 42, 43, 124, 158, 255, 256
Birds 61, 128, 239
Birth defects 53, 100, 236
Bisphosphonates 211
Bitter taste 75, 181, 230
Bladder 6, 10, 169, 173
Bladder cancer 10, 169, 173, 174,
    177
Bleeding 3, 51, 52, 85, 87, 97, 102,
    103, 104, 178, 208, 212
Blood 91-97
Blood clot[ting] 22, 101-104, 107,
    151, 246
Blood donation 97, 99, 145
Blood doping 95
Blood pressure 4, 10, 15, 93, 108,
    110, 111, 113, 114, 117-119, 132,
    211, 224
Blood vessels 91, 93, 95, 101, 103,
    105, 111, 113, 118, 119, 132, 149,
    159, 199, 211, 214, 245
BMI (Body Mass Index) 53
Body fat 6, 36, 40, 43, 121, 128-130,
    134, 176, 184, 186, 192-196, 210

Bomb calorimeter 36-40, 239
Bone 10, 23, 79, 95, 97, 103, 140,
    145, 163, 202-214, 225, 226, 227
Bone marrow 95, 97, 145, 207
Boron 26, 254
Bottle mouth 77
Botulism 172, 244, 245
Bowel movements 87
Brain 66, 70, 130, 194, 196, 215,
    218, 223, 224, 225, 227, 230
Brain tumor 166, 215
Bran 58
Brandy 59
Breast cancer 7, 11, 12, 13, 15, 138,
    151, 165-169, 175, 176, 178, 211,
    233
Breast-feeding 159, 164, 170, 171,
    192, 224
Breast milk 101, 145, 156, 157, 159,
    163, 197, 208
Breath hydrogen 86
Bronchitis 6, 178, 179
Brown fat 189, 190, 196
Brucellosis 17
BST (bovine somatotropin) 248
Buckyball 30
Bulimia 78
Butter 59, 60, 61, 62, 64, 67, 68
B-vitamins (see also specific B-vita-
    mins) 3, 42-44, 52, 53, 99, 100,
    106, 112, 119, 124, 126, 161, 162,
    177, 180, 222, 230

C

Caffeine 128, 129, 183, 218, 220,
    222, 231, 233, 234
Calcitonin 206, 207
Calcium 32, 42, 48, 49, 103, 114,
    162, 163, 170, 203-211, 225, 227,
    237, 255, 257
Calcium alginate, bromate 237
Calcium lactate, phosphate, proprion-
    ate, silicate, sorbate 237
Calcium carbonate, gluconate 32
Calories 36, 37, 38, 39, 40, 41, 42,
    43, 45, 47, 48, 49, 50, 51, 55, 57,
    58, 59, 60, 61, 68, 71, 191
Campylobacter jejuni 242
Cancer (Chap. 12; see specific can-
    cers)
Cancer statistics 7, 109, 165-171
Canola oil 64
Canthaxantin 180
Capillaries 93, 94, 104, 105, 126,
    128, 189
Carbohydrate 38, 42, 49, 55-58, 60,
    76, 128, 130, 192, 227

Carbon 25-30, 32, 34, 37, 39, 43, 44,
    55, 62, 65, 66, 68, 71, 72
Carbon dioxide 4, 27, 29, 30, 31, 34,
    37, 68, 72, 76, 91, 93, 95, 105,
    115, 121, 125-128, 134, 183
Carbon monoxide 95, 111, 113, 119
Carcinogens 81, 82, 88, 89, 111, 151,
    152, 169, 170, 171, 172, 173, 174,
    176, 178, 181, 236, 238, 248, 249
Carob bean gum 237
Carotene 6, 7, 21, 64, 154, 179, 180,
    181, 237, 239
Carotenoids 176, 179, 180
Carrageenan 60, 236, 237
Carrot oil 237
Cassava 57, 161, 188, 234
Cats 16
CD4 123, 145, 219
Cell membrane 34, 67, 72, 82, 105,
    110, 115, 122, 123, 133, 144, 154,
    208, 216, 218, 219, 230, 231
Cell nucleus 122, 123, 130, 137, 139
Cellulose 56, 58, 87, 115, 237, 239
Center for Disease Control and Pre-
    vention (CDC) 5, 171, 245
Cerebrovascular disease 107
Cervical cancer 168, 169, 171, 178
Champagne 126
Chewing gum 80, 87, 113, 171, 222
Chicken 16, 61, 64, 68, 97, 128, 152,
    154, 156, 161, 179, 203, 227, 243,
    247
Chicken pox vaccine 16
Chloride 26, 33, 34, 35, 36, 42, 44,
    78, 114, 147, 212, 220, 257
Chlorine 25, 26, 27, 33, 254
Chlorophyll 179, 234
Chocolate 9, 60, 61, 65, 193, 220,
    222, 238
Cholecalciferol 42
Cholera 70, 241, 242
Cholesterol 17, 34, 43, 63, 67-68,
    122-123, 200, 204, 224, 239
Cholesterol, Blood (see also HDL,
    LDL) 17, 65, 105, 110, 111, 113,
    114-117, 119
Cholesterol, Food 49, 67-68, 116
Cholestyramine 18, 119
Choline 63, 67, 219, 230, 255, 256
ChooseMyPlate.gov 48-50, 52, 54
Chromium 42, 254, 257
Chromosomes 133, 135, 136, 151
Chylomicrons 104, 105
Cigarettes 88, 111, 171, 172
Cimetidine 85
Cirrhosis 81, 99, 117, 160
Citric acid 237

Clinical trials 17, 23, 24
Cloning 147, 148
Clostridium botulinum 242, 244
Cobalamin 42, 44
Cobalt 44, 254
Cocaine 218, 220, 233
Cocoa butter 62
Coconut oil 62, 64, 65
Cod liver oil 4, 205
Coenzymes 123, 124, 126, 130, 218
Coffee 36, 85, 124, 218, 220, 222,
    234
Cold Fusion 20
Cold intolerance 96
Colestipol 119
Collagen 154, 203, 207, 208, 214
Colon 86-88, 116, 239
Colon cancer 9, 18, 88, 89, 166-171
Complex carbohydrates 56-58
Condoms 73, 145
Constipation 58, 85, 87, 88, 90, 98,
    115, 207, 239
Copper 42, 254, 257
Corn 5, 48, 49, 52, 55, 57, 59, 62, 64,
    70, 76, 124, 154, 155, 157, 161,
    174, 179, 207, 243, 244
Corn oil 64
Cornstarch 57, 76
Corn syrup 55, 76
Coronary arteries 93, 95, 104, 107,
    108, 112, 149
Coronary bypass surgery 13, 17, 112
Cotinine 14, 173
Covalent bonds 27, 34, 35, 37, 39
Cowpox 102, 149
Cows 5, 58, 64, 70, 85, 101, 102,
    124, 126, 130, 146, 205, 207, 235,
    245, 246, 248
Cretinism 187
Cross-sectional study 10, 11, 209
Curare 219
Cyanide 126, 181, 234
Cysteine 140, 154
Cystic fibrosis 147, 151
Cytoplasm 122-124, 126, 130, 133,
    134, 137

D

Daily Values (DV) 47, 49-51, 54
Dalmane 222
Death rates 4, 7, 18, 108, 109, 111,
    117, 165, 175, 176, 179
Defecation 87
Dehydration 41, 42, 43, 87, 129, 158
Dementia 4
Dendrites 216, 223, 231
Depression 3

Dept. of Agriculture (USDA) 48, 236, 247
Dept. of Health and Human Services (DHHS) 48
Dermatitis 4, 87
Dexfenfluramine 196
Diabetes 5, 6, 46, 110, 113, 114, 132, 133, 134, 138, 147, 173, 195, 212
Diamonds 26, 29, 30, 35
Diarrhea 4, 42, 73, 86, 87, 90, 129, 159, 224, 239, 242, 243, 245, 247
Dicumarol 103, 113, 119, 234
Dietary guidelines (Chap. 4) 41, 46, 50
Dietary Guidelines Advisory Committee 48
Dietary Guidelines for Americans 38, 46, 48, 49, 54, 114
Dietary Reference Intakes (DRI) 47, 54
Dietary Supplement Health and Education Act 22
Dietary supplements 6, 7, 32, 47, 51, 54, 118, 119, 201, 196, 229, 235, 236
Digestion 2, 67, 72, 73, 80, 82, 84, 89, 105, 110, 115, 183, 198, 230, 248
Digitalis 233
Diglyceride 237
Disodium guanylate 237
Distemper 17
Diuretics 78, 129, 222
Diverticuli 108
Diverticulitis 87
Diverticulosis 87, 90, 115
DNA **135-143**, 145-152, 156, 165, 169, 176, 177, 195, 238, 247
DNA fingerprinting 138, 140, 152, 247
Dogs 16, 17
Dolomite 225
Double-blind studies 11, 12, 13, 22, 23
Double bonds 34, 62, 65, 66, 71, 72
Duodenal ulcers 85, 90
Duodenum 82, 84, 85
DV (*see* Daily values)
Dwarfism 203, 204

E

E. Coli 104:H4 246
E. Coli O157:H7 242, 245, 246, 248
Ecstasy 227
Edema 65, 103, 159
EDTA (ethylenediamine tetraacetic acid) 237

Eggs 49, 52, 61, 68, 97, 116, 124, 153-155, 158, 161, 204, 205, 241
Electrolytes 34, 43, 78
Electrons 25, 26, 29, 32, 33, 34, 39
Elements 26, 28, 29, 32, 39
Embryo 99, 147, 149
Emphysema 6, 179
Emulsification 84
Emulsifier 66, 67, 72, 84
Endurance 37, 42, 43, 53, 54, 70, 91, 93, 95, 126, 127, 128, 133, 200, 202, 183, 197, 198
Endurance events 42, 43, 54, 70, 95, 126, 127, 202, 198
Endurance training 91, 93
Energy 25, 28, 29, 30, 36, 37, 38, 39, 40, 41, 42, 43, 44, 51, 54
Environmental contaminants 240
Environmental Protection Agency (EPA) 225, 226
Enzymes 34, 58, 70, 73, 75, 82-85, 103, 123, 144, 148, 239
Equal (aspartame) 75
Ergocalciferol 42
Erythropoietin 96
Escherichia coli (see *E. Coli*)
Eskimos 118, 206, 192
Esophagus 6, 18, 21, 22, 73, 74, **80**, 85, 89, 169, 171, 172, 173
Essential amino acids 43
Essential fatty acids 43
Estimated Average Requirement (EAR) 47
Estrogen 13, 30, 121, 138, 175, 176, 200, 209, 210, 211
Etidronate 211
Evolution 5, 6, 126, 149, 152, 169, 181
Evolutionary clock 150
Exercise 42, 95, 116, 117, 126-128, 132, 189, **190-191**, 200, 209, 210

F

Familial hypercholesterolemia 110, 111, 115, 129, 138, 197
Famine 131, 210, 188, 189, 192, 193, 196, 198
Fat 34, 36-40, 42, 43, 46-51, 54, 55, 57, **59-68**, 71, 72
Fat-soluble vitamins (*see* specific vitamins) 43
Fatty acids 42, 43, **62-66, 118**, 125, 127, 130, 131, 238, 239, *see also* specific fatty acids
FDA (Food and Drug Administration) 17, 174, 196, 218, 229, 235, 236, 239, 249, 347

FD&C (Food Drugs Cosmetics) coloring 236, 237
Fermentation 55, 59
Fetal Alcohol Effects 223
Fetal Alcohol Syndrome 223, 231
Fetus 96, 99, 197, 223, 242
Fiber 37, 49, **58**, 60, 87, 88, 110, **115-116**, 161, 162, 179
Fibrin, Fibrinogen 103
Fish 62, 64, 65, 66, 82, 97, 98, 101, 115, 118, 128, 143, 148, 156, 160, 172, 217
Fish-oil supplements 118
Flatulence, Flatus 86
Flu (*see* Influenza)
Fluoridation 79
Fluoride 42, **79**, 80, 89, 211, 255, 257
Fluorouracil 177
Folacin, Folic acid *see* Folate
Folate 42, 43, 53, 96, 99, 100, 101, 105, 106, 112, 177, 255, 256
Folate-Deficiency Anemia 99
Food additives 51, 118, 152, 156, 214, 233, 235, 236, 238, 239, 247, 249
Food and Drug Administration (*see* FDA)
Food and Nutrition Board 46
Food Guide Pyramid 48
Food labels 38, 39, 47, 48, 49, 50, 54
Food Safety Modernization Act 240
Formaldehyde 248
Framingham study 11
Frankfurters 38, 39, 52
Fructose **55-56**, 71, 76, 77
Functional foods 6

G

GABA (gamma amino butyric acid) 218
Gag reflex 80
Galactose **55-56**, 58, 71, 77, 86
Gallbladder **74, 84**, 89, 95
Gastritis 81, 87
Gelatin 70, 154, 203
Genes 15, 110, **135-138**, 145-151, 175, 194-196, 209, 230
Gene therapy 2, 146, 147, 151, 152
Genome 138, 152
Gestational diabetes 132
Ghrelin 4
Gigantism 202
Gingivitis 212, 214
Ginkgo 119
Glaucoma 10
Glial cells 215, 231
Glucagon 131, 132, 134

Glucose 42, **55-56**, 57, 58, 59, 67, 71, 75, 76, 77, 86, 121, 123-134, 153, 173, 200, 202, 213, 183, 223, 224, 227, 232, 239
Glucose polymer 42
Glutamate (glutamic acid) 62, 140, 149, 154, 237
Glutamine 140, 154
Glycerol 62, 66, 71, 104, 237, 238
Glycine 68, 140, 143, 154
Glycogen **56-58**, 61, 71, 122, 123, 124, 126, 128, 129, 130, 131, 132, 134, 191, 192, 202
Glycolysis 124-128, 134, 200, 213, 244
Goat's milk 85
Goiter 187, 188, 197, 234, 240
Goitrogens 188, 234
Gold 26, 254
Gout 11, 160
Grains 57
Grape Nuts 52
Graphene 29
Graphite 29, 35
GRAS (Generally Regarded As Safe list of food additives) 236, 249
Greenhouse effect, gases 29
Growth hormone 186, 201, 202, 203, 204, 248
Guide to Daily Food Choices 46
Guinea pigs 30
Gums 3, 51, 52, 78, 79, 207, 208, 212, 213, 214, 236, 237

H

HACCP (Hazard Analysis Critical Control Points) 247, 250
Hamburger 49, 52, 60, 68, 97, 128, 161, 242, 245, 246
HDL (High Density Lipoprotein) 104, 105, 110, 112, 114, 116, 117, 120, 150, 196, 197, 201
Heart 91-94
Heart attack, disease 7, 8, 10-14, 17, 22, 41, 46, 23, 103, 104, 107-119
Heart beat 94, 108, 112, 119, 188, 197
Heart burn 80, 85
Helicobacter pylori 81
Helium 20, 27, 28, 32, 33, 39, 254
Hematocrit 96
Heme 95, 97, 98, 128, 162

Hemicellulose 58
Hemochromatosis 98, 99
Hemoglobin 95, 96, 97, 105, 106, 128, 129, 135, 149, 159

Hemophilia 103, 146, 151, 246
Hemorrhage 103, 118
Hemorrhagic stroke 22, 108, 114, 117, 118, 119
Heparin 113
Hepatitis 17, 144, 160, 175, 242
Herbal medicine 22
Hernia 87
High-Density Lipoprotein *see* HDL
High-fructose corn syrup 55, 76
Histidine 42, 140, 151, 154, 155
HIV (Human Immunodeficiency Virus; *see also* AIDS) 11, 102, 103, 123, 143, 144, 145, 146, 151, 152, 169, 246
Homeopathy 22
Homocysteine 100, 112
Homocysteinuria 112
Homogenization 84
Honey 55, 61, 76, 245
Hormone replacement therapy 7, 175, 176, 178, 179, 202, 211
Horses 17
H. pylori 81, 82, 85, 90, 171, 173
Human Genome Project 19, 138, 151, 152
Hydrochloric acid 27, 35, 80, 81
Hydrogen 20, 25-30, 32-36, 39, 44, 55, 62, 68, 71, 72
Hydrogen peroxide 32
Hydrogenated fat 62, 64-65
Hydrolyzed vegetable protein 237
Hydroxyapatite 206, 208
Hydroxyproline 154, 207
Hyperactivity 13, 230, 231
Hyperthyroidism 188
Hypoglycemia 133, 134

I

Ibuprofen 81
Immunizations 17
Immunodeficiency 77, 144, 147
Infant botulism 245
Infections 82, 101, 102, 106, 143, 147, 247
Influenza ("flu") 143, 240, 242
Inositol 77
Insomnia 220, 222, 224, 227, 229, 232
Integrated Pest Management *see* IPM
International Olympic Committee 96
International Thermonuclear Experimental Reactor 29
Insulin 68, 70, 121, 123, 131, 132, 133, 134, 135, 136, 145, 146, 147, 152, 195, 223, 227, 232
Intrinsic factor 80, 81, 84, 100, 101

Iodine 42, 187, 188, 197, 240, 254, 255, 257
Ionic bonds 27, 32, **33**, 39
Ions **33-34**, 35, 36, 39, 78, 147, 202, 216, 217, 223, 225, 231
IPM (Integrated Pest Management) 240, 249
Iron 5, 25, 32, 42, 44-47, 51, 53, 95-99, 103, 105, 106, 128, 154, 162, 163, 207, 215, 223, 225-227, 255, 257
Iron deficiency 96, 97, 105
Irradiation 243, 248-250
Isoleucine 42, 140, 154, 155
Isotopes 26, 39

J

Jaundice 95, 242

K

Kaposi's sarcoma 101
Ketones 131, 132, 134, 196
Kidney 11, 14, 15, 91, 113, 114, 119, 132, 150, 155, 160, 173, 189, 204, 205, 224, 235, 242, 245
Kidney cancer 169
Kilocalorie (Calorie) 36
Knockout mouse 15

L

Lactase 75, 82, 85, 86, 90, 123, 133, 148
Lactic acid 70, 77, 89, 125, 126, 128, 129, 237
Lactobacillus acidophilus 86
Lactose 32, **55-56**, 71, 75, 77, 82, 85, 86, 87, 89, 90, 123, 129, 144, 176, 205, 206, 239
Lactose intolerance 85, 86, 87, 89, 90, 123, 129, 176, 205, 239
Laetrile 44
Lamb 64, 68, 89, 97, 147
Lard 64
Large intestine *see* Colon
Lauric acid 115
Laxatives 78
LDL (Low Density Lipoprotein) 105, 110, 111, 113-117, 119, 120, 123, 133, 197
LDL-receptors 110, 123
Lead 26, 34, 42, 53, 68, 80, 85, 117, 123, 132, 168, 207, 194, 224-227, 231-233, 240
Lean body mass 163, 186, 197
Lecithin 61, 63, 66, 67, 71, 72, 123, 133, 208, 219, 230, 237

Legumes 57, 101, 155, 156, 159, 161, 162, 163
Lemon juice 36
Leptin 4, 195, 196, 198
Leucine 42, 140, 149, 143, 154, 155
Leukemia 17, 101, 144, 145, 147, 169, 177, 207, 233
Librium 220
Life expectancy 6, 7, 110, 150
Lignin 58
Limestone 206
Limewater 207
Linoleic acid 2, 42, 62, 64, 66, 71
Linolenic acid 42
Lipoproteins (see also HDL, LDL) 1, 18, 104, 105, 106, 110, 133
Listeria monocytogenes 242
Liver 57, 68, **74**, 84, 97, 100, 104, 105, 110, 115, 116, 132, 151, 201
Liver cancer 18, 167, 169, **174**
Longitudinal study 11, 209
Low-carbohydrate diet 131
LSD (lysergic acid diethylamide) 227
Lung cancer 6, 17, 22, 88, 111, 165-172, 174, 175, 178, 181
Lungs 6, 14, 22, 88, 91, 93, 104, 111, 143, 147, 165-167, 171, 172, 174, 175, 178, 180-182, 199, 205, 213
Lycopene 176
Lymphoma 169
Lysine 42, 140, 154, 155, 156

M

Magnesium 25, 39, 42, 114, 203, 255, 257
Magnesium carbonate 237
Maize 57
Malaria 150
Maltase 82
Maltol 237
Maltose **55-56**, 59, 71, 75-77, 82
Manganese 42, 254, 257
Mannitol 77, 87
Marathon 127, 128, 202, 189, 192
Margarine 1, 6, 59, 61, 64, 65, 68, 116, 179, 205, 238
Marijuana 111, 171, 172
Masa harina 207
Mayonnaise 59, 60, 61, 66
McDonald's 60, 157, 161, 175, 193, 245, 246
Meat 48, 52, 60, 61, 68, 97, 98, 124, 128, 153, 154, 156, 157, 160, 161, 172, 199, 200, 208, 243, 245, 246
Melanin 159, 169, 176, 178, 182, 205, 206
Melanoma 147, 166, 169, 177, 178

Melatonin 6, 229
Membrane protein 121, 123, 133, 135, 147, 195, 216, 217
Menadione, Menaquinones 42
Menopause 7, 23, 112, 160, 176, 178, 179, 209, 210, 211, 214
Menstruation 47, 96, 99, 175, 176, 178, 186, 210, 212
Mescaline 227
Messenger RNA (mRNA) 137, 138, 139, 140, 144, 152
Meta-analysis 12
Metabolism 4, 30, 31, 121, 123, 124, 126, 127, 128, 131, 133, 183, 184, 186, 187, 188, 189, 190, 191, 192, 197, 198, 200, 202, 213, 223
Methane 86
Methanol 248
Methionine 42, 112, 140, 154, 155, 156
Methotrexate 177
Methylene chloride 220
Methylparaben 237
Methyltestosterone 201
Methylxanthines 220
Metric conversions 251
Mice 14, 15, 16, 23
Microbes 59, 101, 102, 124, 126, 150, 240, 241, 243, 244, 245, 247, 248, 249, 250
Microvilli 73, 82, 83
Milk 38, 48-52, 53, 55, 68, 78, 84, 85, 86, 115, 124, 145, 158, 159, 161, 162, 164, 174, 176, 205, 206, 208, 243, 248
Mineral supplements 32
Mitochondria 122, 123, 126, 127, 128, 134, 200, 189
Modified food startch 237
Molasses 59
Molecules 29-32
Molybdenum 21, 42, 254, 257
Monkeys 16
Monoglycerides 237
Monounsaturated fat 49, 62, 64, 65, 71, 72
Mouth 58, 60, 61, 64, **75-76**, 77-80, 89, 171, 173, 217, 226, 244
Mouth Bacteria 76
mRNA (see Messenger RNA)
MSG (monosodium glutamate) 62, 237
Mucus 88, 147
Multiple sclerosis 15, 216, 248
Muscle 57, 73, 91, **127-129**, 158, 186, **199-202**, 206, 219, 244
Muscle contration 202, 221

Muscle size 200
Mutations 86, 145, 149, 150, 151, 152, 168, 169, 181, 195, 236
Myasthenia gravis 219
Myelin 100, 216
Myoglobin 97, 128, 172, 200
Myristic acid 115

N

National Academy of Sciences 46, 47
National Cholesterol Education Program 114
National Institutes of Health 12, 146
Nausea 98, 108, 131, 174, 222, 242
Neon 27, 32, 33, 39, 254
Nerve cells 100, 206, 215
Nerve damage 53, 100, 101, 106, 163, 224, 234, 236
Nervous system (Chap. 15)
Neural tube defects 99
Neurons 215, 216, 217, 218, 219, 223, 224, 227, 230, 231, 232
Neurotransmitters 157, 217, 218, 219, 223, 224, 227, 230, 231, 232, 235, 244
Neutrons 25, 26, 29, 39
New England Journal of Medicine 6, 19
Niacin 4, 5, 21, 42-44, 52, 119, 124, 126, 223, 224, 229, 230, 255. 256
Niacinamide, Nicotinamide see Niacin
Nicotine 14, 111, 113, 119, 171, 173, 190, 220, 233, 248
Nicotinic acid 42, 52, 119
Nitrate 43
Nitrite 81, 82, 172, 173, 245
Nitrogen 25, 26, 34, 39, 44, 68, 72, 127, 158, 254
Nitroglycerin pills 13, 14
Nitrosamines 82, 172, 173
Nitrosomyoglobin 172
Nobel prize 4, 5, 19, 28, 29, 30, 37, 68, 70, 100, 101, 103, 111, 118, 126, 127, 132, 137, 138, 140, 144, 145, 150, 169, 216, 217
Non-steroidal anti-inflammatory (NSAID) drugs 81
Normal curve 45
Nosebleeds 118
Nuclear fission 28, 29
Nuclear fusion 26, 28
Nucleus 25, 32, 39, 123, 133, 137, 147
Nutraceuticals 6
NutraSweet (aspartame) 35, 75, 76, 77, 248

O

Oat bran 88
Oats 49
Obesity 2, 5, 6, 15, 53, 84, 110, 113, 116, 132, 134, 173, 175, 189, **193-197**, 233
Obestatin 4
Oil 59, 60, 61, 62, 64, 65, 66, 67, 68, 72
Oleic acid 62, 64
Olestra 238, 239, 249
Olive oil 51, 62, 64, 72
Omega-3 fatty acids 42, 66, 118, 119
Omega-6 fatty acids 42, 118
Oral contraceptives 96
Orange juice 36, 48
Orthodontics 212
Osteomalacia 204, 205
Osteoporosis 6, 10, 22, 23, 48, 79, 179, 197, 203, 208, 209, 210, 211, 214
Ovarian cancer 169
Ovulation 186
Oxalic acid 97, 103, 162, 207
Oxygen 4, 13, 19, 25, 27, 28, 29, 30, 31, 32, 34, 36, 37, 39, 40, 44, 55, 65, 68, 91, 93, 95, 96, 105, 108, 111, 112, 113, 119, 123, 124, 126, 127, 128, 133, 134, 149, 158, 200, 183, 184, 223, 224, 232, 244, 245

P

Pacemaker 202, 213
Palmitic acid 62, 64, 115
Palm oil 62, 64
Pancreas 6, **74**, 82, **84**, 89, 123, 129, 131, 134, 146
Pancreatic cancer 10, 169
Pangamic acid 44
Pantothenic acid 42, 43, 124, 126, 255, 256
Papillomavirus 169, 178
Pap test 178
Parathormone 206, 207
Parkinson's disease 13, 248
Partially hydrogenated oils 64, 115
PCR (polymerase chain reaction) 138, 142, 152
Peanut oil 64
Peanuts 58, 64
Pectin 58, 59, 116, 237
Pellagra 3, 4, 5, 16, 124, 224, 230
Penicillin 144
Pepcid 85
Periodic Table of Elements 252-253

Periodontal disease 78, 79, 208, 211, 212, 213, 214
Periodontitis 212, 213, 214
Peristalsis 73
Pernicious anemia 4, 81, 100
Perspiration 41, 53, 54, 93
Pesticides 181, 233, 235, 236, 237, 238, 239, 240, 243, 247, 248, 249
pH 35, 36, 39, 70, 75, 78, 79, 102, 103, 106
Phenylalanine 34, 35, 42, 75, 112, 140, 154, 155, 229
Phenylketone 34, 112
Phenylketonuria *see* PKU
Phosphates, Phosphoric acid 237
Phospholipids (*see also* Lecithin) 122
Phosphorus 25, 42, 66, 72, 77, 89, 203, 208, 210, 213, 255, 257
Photosynthesis 30, 31, 103
Phylloquinone 42
Phytic acid 97, 162
Phytochemicals 234
Pineal gland 6, 229
Pituitary gland 203
PKU (phenylketonuria) 34, 35, 44, 112, 129, 138, 229
Placebo 11, 12, 13, 23, 53
Plant Genetics 148
Plaque 77, 78, 79, 80, 107, 112, 212, 214
Plaques 68, 77, 89, 107, 112
Plasma 95, 102, 103, 104, 105, 106, 123, 146, 159
Plasma Proteins 102
Platelets 95, 101, 103, 105, 118, 203, 245
Pneumocystis carnii 101
Pneumonia 101, 178, 209
Poisons 75
Polio vaccine 16
Polymerase Chain Reaction *see* PCR
Polysorbate 237
Polyunsaturated fat 1, 49, 62, 64, 65, 71, 72, 115, 118
Postmenopausal women 12, 51, 96, 97, 99, 105, 117, 176, 211
Potassium 25, 26, 33, 34, 42, 49, 78, 114
Potassium alginate, benzoate, bitartrate, bromate, sorbate 237
Potatoes 57, 60
Poultry 49, 52, 62, 115, 179, 204, 242
Pregnancy 23, 44, 53, 79, 96, 99, 100, 158, 207, 212, 184, 190, 192, 193, 197, 220, 223, 225, 231
Progestogen 211

Proprionic acid 237
Propyl galate, paraben 237
Propylene glycol 237
Proline 140, 154, 207
Prostaglandins 66, 118
Prostate cancer 12, 166-171, 173, 176, 179, 181, 235
Protein, Dietary (Chap. 11)
Protein deficiency 57, 157, 159, 163
Protein synthesis 129, 138
Prothrombin 103
Protons 25, 26, 28, 29, 32, 33, 34, 39
PSA (Prostate-Specific Antigen) 166
Pulmonary embolism 104
Pulse 91, 93
PulseNet 247
Purdah 205
Pyridoxal, Pyridoxamine, Pyridoxine (see also Vitamin B$_6$) 42
Pyruvate 124-127, 129, 130, 134, 153

Q

Questran 119

R

Rabies 17
Rats 14, 15, 16, 79, 103, 114, 147, 158, 174, 194, 197, 218, 232, 235, 236, 237, 239
RDA (Recommended Dietary Allowance) 46, 47, 51, 52, 53, 54, 97, 98, 99, 101, 119, 157, 158, 161, 162, 163, 179, 180, 184, 204, 205, 208, 212, 214
Recessive gene 194, 195, 196
Recessive trait 194
Recommended Dietary Allowance *see* RDA
Rectal cancer 166, 168, 169
Rectum 74, 86, 89, 90, 145, 166, 169
Red blood cells 94, 95, 96, 97, 99, 100, 105, 106, 119, 128, 149, 150, 203, 224, 245
Red muscle fibers 127, 128, 133, 200, 213
Rennin 145, 146
Retinal, Retinoic acid, Retinol 42 (*see also* Vitamin A)
Retrovirus 144, 147, 148, 152, 169
Riboflavin (Vitamin B$_2$) 5, 21, 42, 43, 48, 124, 162, 163, 255, 256
Ribosomes 123, 133, 137, 138, 143, 152
Rice 3, 4, 16, 42, 49, 52, 57, 60, 61, 70

Rickets 4, 205, 206
Risk factors 11, 18, 21, 22
RNA 70, 137, 138, 140, 143, 144, 152, 208
Rose hips 31, 51
Rotary International 102
Rum 59
Rumen 58, 64, 65, 101, 124
Ruminants 58

S

Saccharin 37, 38, 77, 174
Safflower oil 64
Safrole 235
Salicylic acid 233
Saliva 59, 75, 76, **77-78**, 80, 82, 89, 138, 140, 143, 173
Salmon 48, 64, 68, 97, 118, 128, 207
Salmonella 241, 242, 246, 247, 248
Salt 6, 12, 26, 33, 34, 42, 44, 46, 49, 51, 67, 75, 81, 82, 87, 94, 114, 120, 132, 173, 187, 236, 243, 244
Sardine oil 64
Sassafras 235
Satiety 61, 194
Saturated fat 47, 49, 50, 62, 64, 65, 71, 72, 108, 115, 116, 120, 153, 160
Scurvy 3, 4, 6, 154, 180, 181, 196, 208, 212
Seaweed 60, 188
Selenium 21, 22, 42, 52, 53, 255, 257
Serine 140, 154
Serotonin 157, 196, 218, 227, 229, 231, 232
Serum 103
Sesame seeds 61, 162, 207
Sewage 70, 87, 241, 242
Sham surgery 13
Shigella 242, 246, 247, 248
Sickle cell anemia 129, 149, 150
Silicon 25, 254
Silicon dioxide 237
Simplesse 60
Single bond 34
Skin 41, 50
Sleeping sickness 150
Small intestine 31, 39, 44, 58, 73, **74**, 81, **82-85**, 86, 88, 89, 97-100, 103-105, 110, 115, 116, 119, 123, 124, 204, 207, 208, 210, 213, 239, 245
Smallpox 102, 149
Smoke 10, 20, 21, 81, 82, 95, 108, 111, 113, 119, 120, 171, 172, 173, 178, 180, 210, 211, 220

Smoking 6, 10, 17, 21, 22, 88, 95, 108, 110, 111, 113, 116, 117, 119, 171, 172, 173, 174, 178, 179, 181, 182, 190, 193, 197, 210, 214, 248
SNP (Single Nucleotide Polymorphism) 149
Soda-loading 129
Sodium 25, 26, 27, 33, 34, 36, 42, 43, 44, 47, 48, 49, 50, 62, 84, 89, 114, 129, 144, 211, 216, 217, 236, 257
Sodium acetate. alginate, citrate 237
Sodium aluminum phosphate 237
Sodium bicarbonate ("baking soda") 36, 84, 89, 129, 236, 237
Sodium chloride 26, 27, 33, 34
Soft drinks 222
Solanine 234, 235
Soluble fiber 60, 115
Sorbitol 49, 77, 80, 87
Sour taste 68, 70, 75, 158
Soybean oil 64
Soybeans 52, 57, 64, 154, 156, 161, 162, 175, 179, 188, 234
Soy milk 52, 85, 101, 162
Soy products 51
Sphincter 80, 82
Spinal cord 99, 100, 216
Sports drink 42, 54
Stanozolol 201
Staphylococcus aureus ("Staph") 241, 242
Starch 30, 39, 55, **56-57**, 58, 59, 61, 70, 71, 73, 75, 76, 77, 82, 84, 86, 87, 89, 124, 237, 239
Starch blockers 82, 86
Starvation 5, 15, 127, 130, 131, 134, 192, 194, 196
Statin drugs 119
Stearic acid 62, 64
Stent 112
Stimulants 218, 220
Stomach 22, 35, 36, 58, **74**, 78, **80-82**, 84, 85, 86, 87, 88, 89, 90, 98, 100, 106, 118, 129, 133, 134, 145, 165, 166, 171, 172, 173, 174, 175, 193, 207, 227, 240, 242, 243, 245
Stomach Cancer 81-82
Stool 58, 84, 85, 86, 87, 90, 110, 115, 116, 177, 178, 239, 242, 246, 247
Streptokinase 113
Stroke 11, 21, 22, 42, 104, 107-111, 113, 114, 117-120, 132, 166, 216
Strontium 207, 254
Sucrase 75, 82
Sucrose 32, 42, **55-56**, 61, 71, 75, 76, 77, 82, 85, 239
Sucrose intolerance 85

Sugar 12, 13, 30, 32, 39, 42, 48, 49, **55-56**, 57-61, 67, 70, 71, 75, 76, 77, 78, 79, 80, 82, 87, 88, 89, 124, 126, 133, 134, 137, 160, 193, 230, 231, 236, 239, 244
Sugar alcohol 49
Sugarless gum 80, 87
Sulfites 237
Sulfur 25, 44, 254
Sunlight 30
Sunshine 41
Supplements 6, 17, 23, 32, 47, **51-53**, 62, 97-99, 118, 158, 174, 180, 205, 207, 227, 229, 235, 236
Survival Curve 8
Swallowing 80
Sweat 42, 43, 158, 189
Sweet taste 48, 51, 55, 59, 75, 76, 103, 133, 180, 222, 234
Sweetbread 84
Sweet clover 103, 234
Sweetness 9, 70, **75-77**

T

Table salt (sodium chloride) 42, 44
Table sugar (sucrose) 32, 42
Tagamet 80, 85
Tallow 64
Tamoxifen 138
Tannins 97
Tardive dyskinesia 230
Tartaric acid 237
Taste buds 75
Taxol 233
Tea 97, 220, 222, 243
Teeth 21, 76-80, 89, 90, 116, 144, 208, 211-214, 225, 227
Termites 58
Testicular cancer 176
Testosterone 30, 112, 121, 176, 186, 199, 201, 209, 213
Tetanus 17
Tetracycline 79, 188
Thalassemia 150
Thaumatin 75, 77
Theobromine, Theophylline 220
Thiamin (Vitamin B$_1$) 3, 4, 5, 16, 42, 43, 124, 222, 223, 224, 255, 256
Thirst 42
Threonine 42, 140, 154, 155
Throat 36, 75, 171, 173
Thrombin 103
Thymus 84
Thyroid gland 6, 187, 188, 197
Thyroid hormone 6, 187, 188, 197
Tissue plasminogen activator *see* TPA

Tobacco 21, 111, 119, 171, 172, 173, 174, 178, 179, 233, 248

Tocopherol, Tocotrienol *see* Vit. A

Tolerable Upper Intake Level *see* UL

Tongue 75, 78, 80, 194

Tooth decay 76, 77, 78, 79, 80, 89, 90, 211

TPA (tissue plasminogen activator) 104, 118, 136

Tragacanth gum 237

Tranquilizers 218, 220, 222

Transcription 144

Trans fat 49, 65, 115

Transfer RNA (tRNA) 137, 139, 143, 152

Trichinella spiralis 241, 242

Triglycerides 61, **62-63**, 66, 68, 71, 72, 73, 89, 104, 115, 121, 123, 127, 189, 238, 239

Tripe 84

Tropical oils 62

Trypanosomiasis 150

Tryptophan 42, 44, 77, 124, 140, 153, 154, 155, 157, 227-229, 232, 236

Tyrosine 140, 154

Tuberculosis 17, 210

Tubers 57

U

UL (Tolerable Upper Intake Level) 47

Ulcer 11, 21, 22, 81, 85, 87, 90, 97, 119, 178

Ultraviolet light 41

Umami 75

Uncoupler 196

Underweight 53

Uranium 29, 254

Urea 125, 160, 163, 235

Uric acid 160

Urine 5, 14, 34, 37, 38, 42, 43, 44, 53, 54, 129, 128, 131, 132, 158, 160, 163, 173, 174, 177, 178, 187, 210, 211

U.S. Dept. of Agriculture (USDA) 48, 236, 247

Uterine cancer 166, 169

V

Vaccination 102, 175

Vaccines 14, 16, 23, 102, 143, 145, 149, 168, 177, 178, 245

Valine 42, 140, 149, 154, 155

Valium 220, 222

Valves 94, 105

Vegans 101, 106, 162, 163

Vegetable Food Group 52

Vegetarian 21, 45, 57, 88, 101, 116, 153, 155, 158, 161, 162, 163

Veins 93, 94, 95, 104, 105, 145

Velveeta 52

Viagra 10, 175

Vibrio cholera 237

Villi 73, 82, 83, 84, 86, 88

Vinblastine, Vincristine 233

Vinegar 3, 35, 36, 59, 66, 70, 78, 81, 98, 203, 226, 227, 236

Viruses 102, 123, 129, 135, 143, 144, 145, 147, 149, 152, 160, 168, 169, 175, 219, 242

Vitamin A 4, 5, 21, 42, 49-51, 62, 64, 154, 174, 179, 180, 229, 255, 256

Vitamin B$_1$ *see* Thiamin

Vitamin B$_2$ *see* Riboflavin

Vitamin B$_6$ 42, 43, 47, 124, 130, 218, 255, 256

Vitamin B$_{12}$ 4, 5, 42-44, 53, 81, 84, 96, 100, 101, 105, 106, 124, 161, 162, 163, 223, 255, 256

Vitamin C (ascorbate, ascorbic acid) 3, 4, 21, 30, 31, 42, 43, 49, 51, 62, 78, 97, 98, 162, 173, 180, 181, 196, 208, 212, 214, 237, 255, 256

Vitamin D 41, 42, 50, 162, 163, 176, 204-207, 214, 236, 255, 256

Vitamin E 12, 21, 42, 237, 255, 256

Vitamin K 41, 42, 86, 103, 255, 256

VLDL (Very Low Density Lipoprotein 104, 105

Vomiting 42, 78, 222, 242

W

Warfarin 79, 103, 113, 119

Water 29-32, **41-43**, 87, 159, 160

Watermelon 48, 61

Water-soluble vitamins 43, 46, 54

Weight-lifting 126, 127, 200

Weight-loss diet 60, 127, 131

Wernicke-Korsakoff Syndrome 222

Wheat bran 88, 97

Whiskey 59

White blood cells 95, 101, 105, 123, 143, 145, 146, 147, 203, 207, 229

White muscle fibers 127, 128, 200, 213

Whole grains 48, 51, 52

Whole wheat 48, 52

Windpipe 80

Wine 49, 59, 98, 114, 126, 173, 226, 234

Women's Health Initiative 12, 13

World Health Organization (WHO) 45, 79, 102, 187

X

Xeroderma pigmentosum 169

Y

Yams 57

Yeast 59, 101, 126, 146

Yersinia enterocolitica 242

Yogurt 86

Z

Zinc 21, 42, 47, 49, 162, 163, 223, 225, 232, 255, 257